THOSE RAGGED BLOODY HEROES

From the Kokoda Trail to
Gona Beach 1942

Peter Brune

ALLEN&UNWIN

To Brigadier Arnold Potts, DSO, MC and the soldiers of Maroubra Force, who defended the Kokoda Trail and fought on to desperate victory at Gona . . . 'Those Ragged Bloody Heroes'.

First published in 1991
This edition published in 2005

Allen & Unwin
83 Alexander Street
Crows Nest NSW 2065
Australia
Phone: (61 2) 8425 0100
Fax: (61 2) 9906 2218
Email: info@allenandunwin.com
Web: www.allenandunwin.com

National Library of Australia
Cataloguing-in-Publication entry:

Brune, Peter. 1951- .
    Those ragged bloody heroes : from the Kokoda Trail to Gona
    Beach 1942.

    Bibliography.
    Includes index.
    ISBN 978 1 74114 559 5

    1. World War, 1939–1945 – Campaigns – New Guinea.
    2. Kokoda Trail (Papua New Guinea). I. Title

940.5246

Set in 11/13 pt Bembo by Midland Typesetters, Victoria, Australia
Printed by South Wind Production, Singapore

10 9 8 7 6 5 4 3 2

Contents

Note: Owing to the age and circumstances under which some of the photos used in this volume were taken, reproduction quality may vary throughout.

Foreword

Lieutenant-Colonel Ralph Honner DSO, MC, (RL), formerly commander of the 39th Battalion, Maroubra Force, Honner Force and the 2/14th Battalion.

They fought their brief day in a too-forgotten war but Peter Brune's truly historical work deepens our understanding that 'Those Ragged Bloody Heroes' belong to all time. Over the years we have been presented with episodic reproductions of their struggles against a rapacious foe to save their grateful country from invasion. However, the dramatic figures of the protagonists have tended to obscure the background from which they emerged. How crucial was their achievement? How grateful was their country? How committed was it to repelling invasion? And how considerate was it of its young sons whom it was willing to plunge, ill-prepared and ill-supported, into the most desperate plight—or, perhaps, even to abandon? Such questions are for the historian to stir and to strive to answer, shedding light amongst the shadows so that, from the illumined picture of the past, lessons and warnings for the future may be drawn. We may need to call on heroes again; we need not again leave them so ragged and so bloody.

Peter Brune has stirred the questions and striven for the answers in his challenging study of one of the most controversial phases of the war that neared our shores. Born after that war, he has the non-participant's objectivity as well as the historian's dedication to the discovery of truth. He has, of course, explored the archives; but he has also sought out survivors of the events he examines, recording and weighing their experiences and assessments, to build his conclusions on broader premises. In the process he has brought into fresh focus the politico-military setting of the war, he has provided a keen insight into the strategic and tactical significance of the Papuan campaigns and their critical engagements and, out of valorous defence and desperate victory, he has unrolled an enthralling chronicle. It is a story of Homeric conflict on faraway frontiers—Kokoda and Isurava, Abuari and Eora Creek, Mission Ridge and Brigade Hill. It does not end at Ioribaiwa in the mountains where Maroubra Force completed its Herculean task but follows its rallied remnants to tragedy and triumph at distant Gona on the shore of the Solomon Sea.

That resonant saga sounds one clarion call that rings out above all others—Kokoda! With their land wide open to invasion, Australians were uplifted in spirit and fired with admiration by the tonic tidings that an isolated band of their young fellow-countrymen had faced overwhelming odds at far Kokoda and had acquitted themselves with honour; and the kindling spark of Kokoda, flaming to a fiercer conflagration, was to blaze into a symbol of national pride.

The fate of the nation did not hang on the outcome of two forlorn forays at Kokoda, audacious and courageous though they were. In each of them only a few score of our troops confronted a tenfold enemy—with no realistic hope of holding on to the vital airstrip. That strategic prize had already been conceded by the lack of planning to protect it; and no tardy token resistance could reverse the foregone consequence of that neglect.

But Kokoda came to signify much more than an outpost and its airstrip. The Kokoda track, up from the northern beaches and over the Owen Stanley Range, was chosen by the Japanese South Seas Force for its push to Port Moresby, the final stepping-stone for the invasion of Australia. That primitive path was to become a soldiers' Calvary; and, along its grim Golgotha, the decisive action was not some valiant, fruitless venture at Kokoda but the grinding four-day Battle of Isurava. If Isurava's defenders had wavered in the face of the first onslaughts, or had fought less tigerishly through the succeeding days and nights, the ensuing course of the campaign must inevitably have been radically changed.

Attacking in unending waves, crashing with the thunder of their overpowering fire, the massed invaders eventually won that violent encounter; but in their costly victory were sown the seeds of their defeat. Their greatly superior force was grievously depleted by mounting casualties and increasingly eroded by four extra days' exposure to the supply shortfalls and the health hazards of the hostile mountains; and they had failed to cut off the withdrawal of their reduced but resolute foe, their desperately delaying foe, exhausted, emaciated, decimated but undaunted, pugnaciously mauling every assault and savaging every encirclement, and tenaciously contesting command of the track, creek by creek and ridge by ridge, all the way back to Ioribaiwa. The all-conquering samurai spirit was broken by that indomitable defiance; and the once-proud South Seas Force turned away, bowed and beaten.

Kokoda's auroral glory glows from the brave battalions that sustained the shock of battle along all the Kokoda track, to be shattered and dismembered and disintegrated in the cruel mountains, the strangling jungles and the fetid swamps, never vanquished and, in the end, triumphant, but at a mortal cost— the life-blood of their loved brothers, poured out across those fearful killing-fields. That glory is not of the exultation of war but of the exaltation of man, the nobility of man sublimated in the fiery crucible of war, shining faithfulness and fortitude and gentleness and compassion elevated from all dross.

Hence, a deeper theme of the epic of Kokoda is surely the noble conduct, the towering stature of the selfless, courageous young warriors who created it. How do we now see them? One author[1] has dubbed them 'Knights of Kokoda'. Ragged bloody heroes might have seemed incongruous in Camelot; and they sought no mystic Holy Grail. Yet they may, themselves, sense some transcendent aura attending the later legend of the Kokoda Trail, burgeoning from the mud and blood of the Kokoda track they knew and flourishing from unforgetting hearts and hands and voices:

> Time and rain and the jungle will obliterate this little native pad; but for evermore will live the memory of weary men who have passed this way, ghosts of glorious men that have gone, gone far beyond the Kokoda Trail.[2]

The legend grows as veterans of the Trail forgather each Kokoda Day much in the spirit in which Henry the Fifth envisaged his outnumbered liegemen keeping their future Crispian's Days should they survive their Armageddon of Agincourt:

> He that outlives this day, and comes safe home,
> Will stand a tip-toe when this day is nam'd,
> And rouse him at the name of Crispian.
> He that shall live this day, and see old age,
> Will yearly on the vigil feast his neighbours,
> And say 'Tomorrow is Saint Crispian'.
> Then will he strip his sleeve and show his scars,
> And say 'These wounds I had on Crispian's day'.
> Old men forget; yet all shall be forgot,
> But he'll remember, with advantages,

What feats he did that day. Then shall our names,
Familiar in his mouth as household words . . .
Be in their flowing cups freshly rememb'red.
This story shall the good man teach his son;
And Crispin Crispian shall ne'er go by,
From this day to the ending of the world,
But we in it shall be remembered–

So may it be with our own Armageddon, the cataclysmic conflict along the Kokoda Trail; its story, too, shall the good man teach his son—and the caring chronicler recount for the son's sons and the generations yet unborn. But a vanished host of the heroes of Kokoda were to sire no sons. Their legacy of pride and of sorrow passed to those enriched by their living and bereft by their dying; and it is the treasuring memory of their brief brave lives that provides the most moving motive for the commemoration of Kokoda Day.

How, then, do we remember them? Survivors of the bomb-loud battles of the ragged and the bloody might muse where sleep the brave whose gathered bones rest in the hushed, unsan-guined beauty of Bomana.[3] There they might review long lines of mute memorials immaculately dressed for that ultimate parade, seeing again the familiar names of the fallen—and almost their once-familiar faces. And they might scan again the sundered years of their severed lives—'19', '18', '17'—and ponder the ravished promise of their perished youth. They died so young. They missed so much. They gave up so much—their hopes, their dreams, their loved ones. They laid down their lives that their friends might live. Greater love hath no man than this.

No less reverently, and perhaps even more poignantly, their thoughts might reach out, across the Goldie River and beyond the distant mountains from which it springs, to the desolate wilderness where their undiscovered dead repose, clasped in the cold embrace of the battleground that sealed their savage doom, far from the light and laughter and peace and love of home. There no garlands fade, no yew-trees weep, no sad sacrificial cross sanctifies the unknown sepulchre; their supernal cenotaph is shaped elsewhere.

Wherever their bones may lie, the courage of heroes is consecrated in the hearts and engraved in the history of the free. Across twenty-five centuries the paean of Pericles rings clear:

> For this offering of their lives made in common by them all they each of them individually received that renown which never grows old, and for a sepulchre, not so much that in which their bones have been deposited, but that noblest of shrines wherein their glory is laid up to be eternally remembered upon every occasion on which deed or story shall call for its commemoration. For heroes have the whole earth for their tomb; and in lands far from their own, where the column with their epitaph declares it, there is enshrined in every breast a record unwritten with no tablet to preserve it, except that of the heart. These take as your model, and judging happiness to be the fruit of freedom, and freedom of valour, never decline the dangers of war.

After the timeless universality of that eulogy, a fresher, more intimate tribute may touch us more closely. One typical impetuous volunteer[4]—on active service overseas at the age of seventeen and fighting in the first lone company to face the enemy on the Kokoda Trail—records the pride in their proud battalion of the 'half-trained . . . beardless youths' who were his companions in arms; and he recalls:

> Now on Kokoda Day when the names are read out of those killed in action, I know them all and *still* see them as they were. They will never become old or embittered. Just laughing kids forever.

They have joined the immortals; and of their immortality this searching and revealing history is both faithful testimony and enlightening testament. Time may dull even the untarnished gold of their emblazoned battle honours; but the loom of ages cannot blur the pure oblation of their lives. At the going down of the sun and in the morning we *will* remember them.

Ralph Honner
Kokoda Day, 1990

Acknowledgements

The research for this book was made possible by the generous support given the author by many Maroubra Force veterans who granted interviews, answered questionnaires, sent diaries, files and photographs. Their names are recorded in the bibliography.

I am indebted to Mr John Stirling, 2/14th Battalion Association; Mr Ken Murdoch and Mr Keith Goldsmith, 2/16th Battalion Association; Mr Glen Williss, 2/27th Battalion Association; Mr Noel Hall, 39th Battalion Association; Mr Kevin Barry, 55th/53rd Battalion Association; and Mr Fred Cranston, 49th Battalion Association for continued liaison with their members on my behalf.

I would like to record my appreciation to the following veterans of Maroubra Force for their time, wisdom and patience, who read the work and offered, on behalf of their battalions, astute advice; Major Max Bidstrup and Captain Hugh Dalby 39th Battalion; Lieutenant-Colonel Frank Sublet, Lieutenant-Colonel Ken Murdoch and Major John Hearman, 2/16th Battalion; Captain Stan Bisset, Lieutenant-Colonel P.E. Rhoden, Mr Jim McAllester and Mr H.W. Fielding, 2/14th Battalion;

Acknowledgements

Lieutenant-Colonel Geoff Cooper, Brigadier C.A.W. Sims, Private Bert Ward, Warrant Officer Alain Thomson and Sergeant John Burns, 2/27th Battalion.

I should like to express my gratitude to Mr Bill Fogarty of the Australian War Memorial for his assistance with the selection of photographs taken from the legendary Damien Parer's film footage shot on the Kokoda Trail; to the staff of the Australian War Memorial and the Australian Archives for their patience and guidance; to Major M. Hurford, of the United Services Institute Library, Adelaide, for his assistance; to Mr Trevor Gill, for his encouragement and astute advice; to the Melbourne University Press for permission to use extracts from a number of their books; to Mr Peter Stanley, Australian War Memorial for permission to use extracts from the official histories and various articles; to Heinemann Publishers for permission to use extracts; and to Mark Tredinnick of Allen and Unwin Pty Ltd.

I desire to tender my thanks to Mr Trevor Lamshed, for his untiring work and enthusiasm towards the illustrations for the book and to my sister, Mrs Chris Burke, for her hard work and patience with the typing of the manuscript.

Through much of the five years spent on this project I am indebted to two men who have made extraordinary sacrifices of time and energy to offer expert criticism and great encouragement: Major Harry Katekar, 2/27th Battalion, has been a constant source of inspiration and guidance at all times—I thank him sincerely; to Lieutenant-Colonel Ralph Honner, 39th Battalion, I owe a debt I shall never be able to repay—his proofreading of the manuscript, his most astute advice, unflagging enthusiasm for the work, his moving foreword and his assistance with my expression are most sincerely acknowledged and appreciated.

Last, to my daughter, Kylie, who remains the inspiration for all that I do, I say thank you.

PB
Adelaide
January 1991

Abbreviations

AAMC Australian Army Medical Corps
AA & QMG Assistant Adjutant and Quartermaster General
ADC Aide-de-Camp
ADS Advanced Dressing Station
ADV. HQNG Advanced Headquarters New Guinea
AGH Army General Hospital
AIF Australian Imperial Force
AQ Army Quartermaster
AMF Australian Military Forces
ANGAU Australia and New Guinea Administrative Unit
Arty Artillery
Bde Brigade
BEM British Empire Medal
BGS Brigadier General Staff
Bn Battalion
Brig Brigadier
Capt Captain
CB Commander of the Order of the Bath
CBE Commander of the Order of the British Empire
CCS Casualty Clearing Station
CO Commanding Officer
Coy Company

Cpl Corporal
CRA Commander of Royal Artillery
DAQMG Deputy Assistant Quartermaster General
DCM Distinguished Conduct Medal
Div Division
DSO Distinguished Service Order
ED Efficiency Decoration
EM Efficiency Medal
Fd Coy Field Company
FDL Forward Defended Localities
Gen General
GHQ General Headquarters
GOC General Officer Commanding
Gp Group
GSOI General Staff Officer Grade I
HQ Headquarters
I/C In command
Indep Independent
Inf Infantry
IO Intelligence Officer
KBE Knight Commander of the Order of the British Empire
KCMG Knight Commander of the Order of St Michael and
    St George
KIA Killed in action
L-Cpl Lance Corporal
LHQ Allied Land Forces Headquarters
LMG Light Machine Gun
LO Liaison Officer
LOC Line of Communication
Lt Lieutenant
Lt-Col Lieutenant-Colonel
L-Sgt Lance Sergeant
Maj Major
Maj-Gen Major-General
MBE Member of the Order of the British Empire

MC Military Cross
MD Military District
ME Middle East
MG Machine Gun
MMG Medium Machine Gun
MM Military Medal
NCO Non-Commissioned Officer
NG New Guinea
NGF New Guinea Force
OBE Officer of the Order of the British Empire
OC Officer Commanding
Ops Operations
PIB Papuan Infantry Battalion
Pl Platoon
Pnr Pioneer
Pte Private
POW Prisoner of War
RAAF Royal Australian Air Force
RAP Regimental Aid Post
Recce Reconnaissance
Regt Regiment
RMO Regiment Medical Officer
Sect Section
Sgt Sergeant
Sig Signal
Sqn Squadron
SWPA South-West Pacific Area
Trg Training
Tps Troops
UK United Kingdom
USA United States of America
VC Victoria Cross
VDC Volunteer Defence Corps
WIA Wounded in action
WO Warrant Officer

1

Peace in our time

Our God and Souldiers we alike adore,
Ev'n at the Brink of danger; not before:
After deliverance, both alike requited;
Our God's forgotten, and our Souldiers slighted.

Francis Quarles, 1592–1644

This is a story essentially of the involvement of two Australian infantry brigades in two equally desperate but markedly different campaigns in Papua in 1942. The 39th and 53rd Battalions of the 30th (militia) Brigade were early components of Maroubra Force opposing the Japanese thrust, from the northern landings near Gona, along the Kokoda Trail over the Owen Stanley Range towards Port Moresby. The 2/14th, 2/16th and 2/27th Battalions of the 21st (AIF) Brigade brought such resolution to the still far-outnumbered Maroubra Force that it completed its task—and its history—by halting the Japanese advance at Ioribaiwa.

From there the Japanese could only retreat before fresh forces to a defiant last stand at their northern beach-heads, including their first foothold, Gona. Into that extremity of their broken war along the Kokoda Trail were flung the depleted battalions of the 21st Brigade; and there, too, to fight beside them once more, trudged the hastily reinforced 39th Battalion. But the roots of their being thrown together in adversity, in the steamy swamps as in the chilling mountains, go back much deeper than their first association in Maroubra Force.

When British Prime Minister, Neville Chamberlain, returned to England after the Munich Conference in September 1938, much of the western world was lulled by the vaunted but spurious triumph of the diplomacy of appeasement into an expectation of a world peace that could last for generations. Nazi Germany, having already digested the Rhineland, Austria and the Danzig Corridor, was presented with the prize of Czechoslovakia on the assurance that this bloodless victory marked the end of her territorial ambitions. Such conquests seemed of little consequence; except of course to the conquered. The idealism and hope of Munich was in reality the death knell of a European peace which had lasted a mere 21 years.

If its achievement in the Great War of 1914–18 was a proclamation of the nationhood of Australia, then the war of 1939–45 was to be a harsh and exacting test for its survival. Before that test had been endured and surmounted, the young nation was to learn that it could no longer look exclusively to the Empire for defence and indeed leadership. Involved with a rapidly changing Asian community of nations, Australia would realise that the defence of its shores was to be increasingly dependent upon a fresh appraisal of its own region and a new and powerful ally, rather than upon a distant and less urgent view of European affairs and Britain's role in them.

Between Federation and the onset of the Second World War, Australia underwent two experiences that changed the

Long-distance thinking (Mahoney, *Daily Telegraph*, 1942)

character and structure of the nation and its people. The first was the Great War (1914–18) and the second, the Great Depression of 1929–35. While the Great War had forged and tested Australia's new-found nationalism, and while the boom years of the 1920s had given it expression and pride through the surge from the country's expanded immigration, the growth of its iron and steel industry, the wholesale development of its land and the exploitation of its natural resources, the Great Depression brought into critical analysis the very foundations—social, moral and political—of that nationalism. Such changes and experiences before the Second World War very significantly affected Australia's defence policy between the wars with regard to the army.

Amidst the material wealth amassed from the rapid technological and communications explosion of the 1920s came the idealistic crusade amongst western nations for world pacificism and, as a consequence, disarmament. The result was a massive dilution of the military strength of the western powers and a consequent closing of the armament gap between them and their would-be antagonists. Prime Minister Hughes put nearly half of the ships in the Australian Navy out of commission, reduced the militia to approximately 25 per cent of its former strength and, tragically, diminished the permanent army by discharging 72 officers. To so restrict the trained and professional core of an already small army was an act of extreme folly.

Reflecting the contemporary Empire emphasis upon sea and air power in the period 1923–29, Australia gave its army not even the only slightly increased budget support accorded to its navy and air force.

From 1924 until the onset of the Great Depression the ailing army relied upon a small but devoted core of officers whose experience and knowledge were enhanced by very effective exchange duty with the British Army in England and India. This period also saw the militia grow to some 45 000 men through compulsory training—training by committed regular and militia officers and staff imbued with a high and realistic sense of public duty and service.

If the preoccupation of Britain and the dominions with air and naval power as the keystone of their defence was misplaced during the interwar period then their Pacific strategy during that time was a calamitous blunder that would degenerate into the biggest British capitulation in history. On account of a massive 40 per cent cut in military funding in the 1920s, a marked diminution of British naval power in the Pacific, a vulnerability to a main attack from its landward side and a population who were neither trained nor adequately skilled to furnish a prime base, Singapore became a strategic focal point for disaster.

As German expansionism threatened security in Europe and Japanese ambitions for a wider empire escalated in Asia during the 1930s, successive Australian governments continued to place their faith in naval and air power and the hope that the British diplomacy of appeasement would at least prolong a tenuous European peace. Yet the warnings of impending disaster were many and unmistakably clear.

The fall of Singapore (Mahoney, *Daily Telegraph*, 1942)

Most Australians took comfort in the belief that future forces committed in a European conflict could be recovered, in time, behind the security screen of the Singapore fortress. Japan's undeclared war upon China, the merciless rape of Nanking and the incredible breaking in 1940 of the Japanese Naval Code through which the Allies were given stark evidence of Japanese intentions, all served to vividly convey both the tactics and the ruthlessness of the Japanese. By September 1939, the proverbial chickens incubated by two decades of politico-military ineptitude, were coming home to roost—and they looked ominously like vultures.

It is my melancholy duty to inform you officially that in consequence of a persistence by Germany in her invasion of Poland, Great Britain has declared war upon her, and that as a result, Australia is also at war . . .

With these words, on 3 September 1939, Prime Minister Menzies declared Australia to be at war with Nazi Germany.

As was the case prior to the Great War, there were three types of armies to be found in the world in September 1939. The first was the longstanding volunteer army which was usually very efficient, as it had the advantages of being staffed and trained by full-time soldiers and of having a large proportion of trained troops who provided a long-term stability to its ranks. The British Army at this time was an excellent example of such an army.

The second type of army was the large conscript army of which Germany provided a classic example. When given conscripts for a period of two to three years, such an army was able to quickly raise, in time of need, a very formidable force.

The last of the three alternatives was a militia army which was considered inferior to the first two options because it was raised out of a need, or desire, for an economical army which was trained for an initial period, to enable its troops to receive a very basic training, and then given once weekly sessions and an annual camp of some seven to sixteen days' duration. The two primary criticisms of the militia army were related to the fragmentary nature of its training and to the insufficiency of the allotment of time for that training. Thus, the Australian Army in the period leading up to Prime Minister Menzies's declaration of war, was essentially a threadbare defensive force, rather than a highly trained army capable of either overseas service or offensive action at home.

The majority of Australians favoured an Empire defence entailing possible service by Australian forces anywhere in the world. However, a very large section of the populace had an abhorrence of conscription as a means of raising such forces for overseas service or 'unrestricted service'. Lieutenant-General Rowell:

> The government was faced with two alternatives: either to introduce legislation requiring the Army as then constituted to serve overseas, or to raise a special force for that service. It chose the latter, a decision which was to bedevil the Army until the end of the war with its division of the service into what was, in effect two armies.[1]

For men of military age in 1939 there were many options available as to their involvement in the Second World War. In order to understand this two-army system and therefore more fully come to terms with the Papuan campaigns, it is important to examine those options and their consequences.

Many of the initial volunteers for the second AIF were, no doubt, imbued with a sense of duty towards the Empire; but they were also spurred by other promptings—the perception of the duty of a citizen, the attraction of the experience and adventure of service with a large overseas force and, not least, a desire to follow in the footsteps of the first AIF.

The 7th Division raised in May 1940 were dubbed 'the deep thinkers' by the originals of the 6th Division, because of their eight-month delay in joining. While their reasons for enlistment were broadly the same as those of the earlier volunteers, they had tended to wait for the 'phoney war' to conclude before joining. Hitler's invasion of the Low Countries was the motivating factor.

However there is strong evidence to suggest that some of the volunteers joined the expeditionary force because of far less romantic ideals. The Labor politician Eddie Ward is credited with being one of the first people to coin the term 'economic conscripts' when describing many such men. At the time of the raising of the second AIF an unemployed single man received eight shillings and sixpence per week from the government. That same young man could join the AIF and receive five shillings per day in addition to his food and lodging.

Just as there were a multitude of reasons for the enlistment of many young men into the AIF, so too were there a number of reasons why many young men chose not to join that force, or were prohibited from doing so.

Whilst the bitterness, frustration and despair born of the depression years caused some young Australians to join the AIF, these very same reasons caused others to reject enlistment in that force. Allied to such an attitude was often the political opinion that the defence of Australia was a matter of her troops defending her own shores, rather than becoming involved in another bloodbath such as had been experienced in 1914–18. Many thousands of young men were also precluded from enlistment because of skills they possessed in industry and commerce.

Thus, while nearly 100 per cent of the nation's young men were quite prepared to fight to defend her, there were some

"Cripes, I wonder if the jockey was hurt!"

Lock in the *Bulletin* (Sydney, 12 Feb 1941)

very strong and conflicting points of view as to what was the most effective or appropriate way to do it.

An army which had formerly been composed of citizen soldiers and permanent soldiers, was now to be divided into militia and AIF. To thousands of ex-servicemen in Australia today such a division is more commonly remembered under the terms 'choco' (chocolate soldier) and AIF. The term 'choco'[2] is hardly one of endearment, and was used by the AIF to describe the militia in 1939 and later as being men who possessed the so-called 'trappings' of soldiers, but because of the conscription law of service for the militia in Australia and her territories only, were not going to fight, and whose rates of pay were initially higher than those of the AIF. In addition, if the crucial test of the so-called 'heat of battle', ie action, ever came, the chocolate soldier, according to many of the AIF, would 'melt' under the pressure. For their part, the militia often perceived the AIF to be arrogant in their dealings with them. Because of this ill-feeling between the two forces many militiamen refused outright to join the AIF during the Papuan Campaign.

This two-army problem was made more obvious by some readily identifiable differences between the two forces. A militiaman was identified by an army number preceded by a letter denoting his state, eg N for NSW, V for Victoria. An AIF enlistment had the same letter with the letter X to distinguish it from a militia enlistment.

Each militia unit maintained its links with the original AIF, retaining the same unit number and colour patch as those borne by its corresponding unit in the original AIF. Second AIF units adopted corresponding unit numbers preceded by a figure 2; thus there was an original AIF 11th Battalion, a continuing militia 11th Battalion and a second AIF 2/11th Battalion. Second AIF units also adopted corresponding colour patches (sometimes varying miniatures fitting inside grey backgrounds in the distinctive shapes of the colour patches of the higher formations to which they were allotted). Finally

"*They tell me things are not too good in Europe, Dave.*"
"*What's wrong? Drought?*"

Unk White in the *Bulletin* (Sydney, 26 July 1939)

AIF soldiers wore unmistakable identifying badges, with the word 'Australia', on their shoulder straps.

Prior to the Japanese attack on Pearl Harbor, Australia had created a two-army system in the belief that it could accommodate its dual obligation to Empire defence and to defence of the homeland. Such a policy no doubt seemed a sensible one to many politicians and army leaders at that time. An elite, well-officered and well-trained AIF with an enormous tradition to uphold was embarking upon Australia's commitment to assist in the defence of the Empire. A long-running and bitter controversy over conscription as a means of maintaining an expeditionary force, such as had been experienced during the Great War years was, in early 1940, perceived to have been avoided.

2

The threshold of fear

The year 1941 saw immense political and military change in Australia as both the government and the army were forced to ponder the Japanese potential to bring them to war in the Pacific. In February, the Chiefs of Staff provided their political masters with an appreciation of possible Japanese ambitions and military options and of how Australia might best react to the apprehended threats.

Firstly, it was perceived that an invading force would be likely to attack an area essential to Australia's economic ability to wage war—the region Newcastle–Sydney–Port Kembla. Secondly, Melbourne, Brisbane, Fremantle, Albany and Adelaide were identified as additional defensive focal points. The Northern Territory and Papua and New Guinea, although strategically important, were seen as areas that could deplete and therefore dilute the army's ability to protect the more important centres. It was believed that the Japanese would be forced to conquer the Malayan Peninsula and the Dutch East Indies and to neutralise the American Pacific Fleet as a prerequisite to an invasion of Australia.

To react to the needs of a South-East Asian and home defence, the forces in Australia at this time consisted of the AIF 8th Division, and the militia—the 1st and 2nd Cavalry Divisions, four infantry divisions and components of a fifth division and corps troops. On paper, this seemed a formidable force. However severe deficiencies in strength, training, equipment and, above all, leadership, due to the priority given to the AIF 6th, 7th and 9th Divisions in the Middle East, caused this paper assessment to represent not much more than a military paper tiger.

To compound an already disastrous state of affairs, the 8th Division was dispersed in token gestures to the threatened north—a battalion to Rabaul to hold forward airfields; another portion of the division to Timor and Ambon; and the remainder to participate in the not-too-distant disaster at Singapore.

As a result of the preliminary appreciation, it was decided to raise a militia battalion to garrison Port Moresby. The role was allotted to the 49th Battalion from Queensland. Its personnel were volunteers for tropical service, and, after a commendable degree of enthusiasm towards preparation for embarkation, the battalion left Brisbane on 15 March 1941, on the SS *Katoomba* and the SS *Zealandia*.

The staff work, dealing with the logistics for the arrival and care of this battalion in Port Moresby was abysmal. It might be justifiably claimed that such a state of affairs would never have been tolerated had an AIF battalion been involved. 'They had no mess tins, plates, pannikins or mosquito nets (all of which had to be purchased locally) and a number had no waterproof sheets.'[1]

Until the outbreak of war with Japan, in December 1941, the degree of effort given to the training, equipping and morale of the 49th Battalion was a disgrace which was to place it at a severe disadvantage when the time later came to commit it to battle. It was given the laborious tasks of building roads, unloading ships, and constructing buildings as well as the expected duties of siting and preparing defensive positions. All such tasks were necessary but the battalion was essentially intended for a defensive role and the emphasis should have been upon ensuring more advanced training than the minimum platoon-level instruction it received.

Three other points are worthy of consideration. Firstly, in early May 1941, after many men of the battalion had repeatedly attempted to join the AIF but were refused because sufficient reinforcements had already been acquired, the Army, in a dramatic change of heart, actively sought enlistments for the AIF. The men's reaction was one of frustration and anger—and a poor enlistment response. Later, when the AIF supplied a leavening of young veterans from the 7th Division to the 30th Brigade in June 1942, further requests were made for enlistment into the AIF from these officers. The men's reactions were once again varied. The second point of interest is that Brigadier, later Major-General, Morris[2] assumed command of the 8th Military District on 26 May 1941. The next twelve months provided a sorry reflection upon his command in that absolutely no reconnaissance of the Owen Stanley Range was undertaken and the standard of training of the increasing garrison was not improved to any significant degree. Thirdly, the Chief of the General Staff, Lieutenant-General Sturdee, visited Port Moresby on 11 July 1941 and, after an inspection, described the 49th as 'quite the worst battalion in Australia'[3].

Towards the latter part of 1941, as war clouds loomed larger on the South-East Asian horizon, it was decided to increase the Port Moresby garrison to brigade strength; the 53rd Battalion from New South Wales and the 39th Battalion from Victoria were chosen to implement that decision.

In the long, proud history of Australia at arms, there can be no more tragic and damning story than that of the raising, deployment, equipping and training of the 53rd Battalion. Originally raised for service in Darwin, the battalion came into being around 1 November 1941, after eighteen militia battalions were

Close to Home

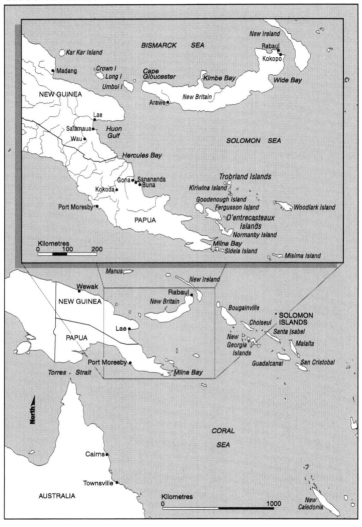

each ordered to supply a quota of 62 men for the new unit. To bring the battalion to full strength, an additional 100 personnel were recruited in a manner that reflects the appalling staff work of the time. Sergeant Keith Irwin, 53rd Battalion:

> Even at this stage we received a draft of soldiers, mostly eighteen years of age. These poor devils had no idea what was happening to them. They had not been told where they were going, what unit they were destined for, or any information at all. They had received no final leave, were given no chance to let their families know what was happening to them. They were just taken down to the *Aquitania* and put on board. Most of them had never seen or handled a rifle. This was a disgrace because many of these youngsters, who had literally been shanghaied, later paid the supreme sacrifice during the battles in the mountains and at Sanananda. Once the *Aquitania* put to sea, we were told that we would be heading for Port Moresby, not Darwin. A training programme was implemented so that we NCOs could give the new recruits some elementary training in the use and handling of the .303 rifle.[4]

This battalion, under the command of Lieutenant-Colonel Ward[5], had obviously no chance in its initial training to build an esprit de corps, so vital to any unit's morale and pride, but rather, because of the conditions of its formation, was to develop a bitterness and anger within its ranks that would work directly against the very qualities needed for success. And the sorry tale of woe did not end there. After making the journey from Sydney in company with the 39th Battalion on the *Aquitania*, the 53rd arrived at Port Moresby on 3 January 1942, to be confronted with a logistics nightmare. The Barry Commission Report:

> Making every allowance for the state of affairs existing in Australia at the time of the outbreak of the Japanese war, the

condition which manifested itself immediately after the arrival of [the *Aquitania*] convoy calls for severe censure of the persons responsible for the loading of the troops' camp equipment. The troops were of the average age of eighteen and a half years, and had received no proper training. They were in the charge of inexperienced officers who appear to have had little or no control over them. They were inadequately equipped in every way; in particular, they were without much of the equipment necessary to give them any reasonable prospect of maintaining health in an area such as Port Moresby. In [the] general state of unpreparedness, that may have been inevitable, but no excuse is apparent . . . for the gross carelessness and incompetence which resulted in the stowing of camp equipment at the bottom of the holds, so that when the troops were disembarked, there were no facilities to enable them to be fed and encamped.[6]

The period between the battalion's arrival in Port Moresby, and its deployment on the Kokoda Trail in August 1942, would see only a worsening of the 53rd Battalion's tragic plight.

The 39th Battalion was raised in Victoria in October 1941 from elements of the 3rd and 4th Infantry Divisions, and the 2nd Cavalry Division. The circumstances of its formation were far less trying than those of the 53rd's. Its original commander was Lieutenant-Colonel Conran,[7] a veteran of the first AIF. Although 52 years of age, and later destined to suffer a decline in health from the demands of tropical service, Conran, along with some of his officers, can be given high praise for the esprit de corps that they instilled into their new battalion. In their role as a garrison brigade the 39th, 49th and 53rd Battalions had the 13th Field Regiment and the 23rd Heavy Anti-Aircraft Battery as support. Major-General Morris could also look to assistance from two other sources. The Papuan Infantry Battalion (PIB) consisted of Papuan natives led by Australian officers and NCOs. Emphasis was placed upon having in its ranks men with knowledge of local conditions and, above all, of the terrain. The second territorial unit was the New Guinea Volunteer Rifles. This force was predominantly manned by returned soldiers settled in New Guinea and their enthusiastic neighbours.

Barely six weeks after the arrival of the 53rd and 39th Battalions to complete the strength of the 30th Brigade, the Japanese had attacked and captured Rabaul, bombed Port Moresby, and captured Singapore (15 February 1942). Further, before the end of that month, they had landed on Timor and invaded Java. From that time on, the utter vulnerability of the Australian mainland could not be concealed from an Asian conqueror exploiting his success.

The Australian Army leaders were fully aware that in the event of Singapore's loss, the forward outposts to the north of Australia would be totally inadequate, and that defence of the mainland would be the key concern. The evidence to support this is overwhelming. The fate of the garrison of Rabaul in New Britain is a strong case in point. Attacked by a division, its gallant but grossly outnumbered garrison was doomed to defeat, surrender, and barbaric slaughter.

An examination of the events leading up to the eventual deployment of the veteran 7th Division in New Guinea can leave little doubt that the 30th Brigade was going to be sacrificed, if need be, in much the same manner. This splendid 7th Division, confident from its success in Syria and from its 18th Brigade's efforts in Tobruk, had arrived back in Adelaide by the end of March 1942. Between the beginning of April and its eventual deployment in New Guinea on 12 August 1942, only the Coral Sea and Midway battles were to justify its deployment. When these events are taken into account it is understood why the Army reinforced Port Moresby with a poorly trained and ill-led 14th Brigade rather than the 7th Division. The Army was certainly not under any illusion as to the standard of training and efficiency of the Port Moresby garrison.

In early April 1942, Major-General Vasey[8] wrote to subordinate army commanders requesting monthly reports concerning the combat efficiency of brigades in the army. There were six guidelines, or ratings:

A Efficient and experienced for mobile offensive operations.
B Efficient as a formation for mobile offensive operations but not experienced.
C Individual brigades are efficient for mobile offensive operations, but higher training has not been completed.
D Individual brigades are efficient in a static role. Additional brigade and higher training is required.
E Units have completed training. A considerable amount of brigade and higher training is required.
F Unit training is not yet complete.

Barely five weeks before the 30th Brigade was committed to action in the Owen Stanley Range its grading given by its General Officer Commanding, was a F, ie the 39th and 53rd Battalions were, along with the 49th, given the lowest possible grading. It is important to note that most formations in Australia at this time were being rated at standard C or higher. The garrison of Port Moresby was thus given the lowest rating whilst being stationed in the most threatened area. A very tragic toll was to be paid by the 30th Brigade for its lack of training and leadership.

With the commencement of the Japanese bombing of Port Moresby on 3 February, followed on the 5th by a far greater bombardment, natives fled, desertions from coastal ships became high and general chaos reigned in Port Moresby itself. After Zeros had sunk three Catalina Flying Boats off the coast on 28 February, there remained just two Catalinas and a Hudson for the defence of the garrison. The only reinforcement for a period of some three weeks was a final, if somewhat belated, arrival of the promised Kittyhawk squadron, which because of the endless delaying of its arrival had been dubbed, amongst other things, 'Tomorrow Hawks' and 'Neverhawks'.

As the situation in the South-West Pacific deteriorated further, the Army had decided to act in a more positive way. On 17 April, it sent the garrison a new brigade commander in Brigadier S.H.W.C. Porter[9]. Porter brought with him an impressive Middle East record. He had, as commanding officer of the 2/31st Battalion, captured Jezzine during the bloody, but largely unpublicised, campaign in Syria. His organisation of the billeting of the 7th Division in Adelaide in March 1942 and his subsequent work in Townsville deploying and structuring its defence displayed the professionalism and high ability of this young commander.

Porter was faced immediately with four important problems. The first was the deficiency of the defence strategy of Port Moresby itself. He noted that defensive positions were static and dispersed, and thus deprived of potential for mobility. In addition, the positions were in many cases readily identifiable to an invading force's naval batteries.

The second problem lay with leadership. It must have been painfully obvious to Porter that the brigade's troops were very poorly officered because of two factors. Firstly, many officers were far too old for tropical service. Secondly, the standard of training of the officers in Australia was not good. Major M.L. Bidstrup MC, 39th Battalion:

> I came back in 1944 teaching tactics at the officer cadet unit at Woodside and I was appalled at the instructors; absolutely appalled at the standard of instruction. Most of these blokes had the rank of captain and they had never been in action in their lives.[10]

As a consequence of poor leadership, Porter's third problem was the lack of training and discipline of the garrison's troops. Lieutenant Harry Mortimore, 39th Battalion:

It was one of those things where the troops weren't trained, but later did a hell of a good job. Most of the officers weren't fully trained either. They'd done a certain amount of training in the militia, like in peace time. I was in the militia before the war, but the training there was nowhere near what we got with the AIF. So that meant that the troops were poorly trained . . . [11]

Porter's fourth problem was the abominable standard of the troops' equipment. Not only were the garrison troops in Port Moresby performing as labourers on the docks, roads and defensive positions, but the limited amount of training given them was done with equipment that was outdated and in poor condition.

In consultation with Major-General Morris, Porter reasoned that an immediate, if partial, solution to the dual problems of leadership and training might best be achieved by applying for a quota of young AIF officers from the 7th Division.

Porter and Morris used the militia officers' age and/or physical condition as a guide in selecting those officers to be replaced. Many of the officers were First World War veterans who were handicapped by age and poor health. It is interesting to note that in rare cases, if an officer was seen as worth keeping, age was not a barrier to his retention. The classic example was the retention of Captain Sam Templeton[12], who was to command B Company 39th Battalion. Each of Templeton's platoon commanders during the Owen Stanley Campaign is adamant that Templeton was at least 50 years of age.[13]

Having generally assessed the situation, and requested his quota of AIF officers, Porter proceeded to examine his brigade more closely. Training had been taken to no greater extent than platoon level; it bore no relationship to the type of warfare that the men might face; and, most importantly, it was being undertaken by officers who were, in the main, inexperienced. The result was that many soldiers were not proficient even in their most basic requirement: knowledge of the use of their weapons. The health of the garrison was also a matter of deep concern. Many men were contracting malaria, particularly in the 49th Battalion which had served longer in Port Moresby than any other battalion.

When Porter and his men, knowing the 7th Division was still stationed in Australia, became aware of the massacre of the Australian force at Rabaul, they must have perceived themselves to be a meagre and threatened force indeed, particularly with the realisation that the enemy was at liberty to employ two divisions against them—an enemy which had not as yet known defeat. Another Rabaul with the prospect of further slaughter and its military and political consequences was the only realistic appraisal to be made in the circumstances.

There can never have been, before or since, a more crucial naval engagement, as far as our young nation is concerned, than the Battle of the Coral Sea[14]. At the beginning of May 1942, Japanese naval forces were driving south towards the Coral Sea. By 5 May, the Allied fleets deploying to intercept them knew that a strong force of troop-transports was moving from Rabaul towards Port Moresby with a naval escort. On the morning of 7 May, each force knew where its antagonists were, and the transports turned and went back to Rabaul. The battle, which ended the next day, checked the Japanese Navy for the first time during the war, and suspended, for the time being, the seaborne threat to Port Moresby. There, from 6–9 May, the garrison had been apprehensively awaiting heavy bombing attacks to be followed by the landing of troops from enemy transports. Porter and his brigade had been accorded a brief reprieve. In the next month they were to receive critical reinforcement.

On 21 June, 36 AIF officers were posted to the 30th Brigade. The manner in which these young sergeants, subalterns and captains were allocated to the three militia battalions of the 30th Brigade, and the resulting conclusions since reached by historians concerning the consequent standards of the battalions, has led to some widespread misconceptions. Of the 36 officers allocated, sixteen were posted to the 39th Battalion, the breakdown being one lieutenant-colonel, one major, six captains and eight lieutenants. The 49th Battalion received twelve; one major, five captains and six lieutenants. Significantly, the 53rd Battalion received but eight of these young officers; two captains and six lieutenants. The popular conclusion reached is that Porter believed that the 53rd Battalion was the pick of the battalions in his 30th Brigade. It would seem that Raymond Paull[15] (1958), is the instigator of this school of thought: 'In spite of its early problems, he considered that the 53rd Battalion made a better showing than the other two, and he judged Ward to be as good as any A.I.F. commanding officer of his acquaintance.'[16]

Paull gives absolutely no evidence to substantiate his claim. Indeed his theory defies all logic and very persuasive evidence to the contrary. Porter had spent considerable time in the Middle East mixing with soldiers of the calibre of Brigadier (then Lieutenant-Colonel) Arnold Potts, Eather, and Caro. These officers were battle tested and tried commanders who had worked their way up through their respective battalions during the bloody Syrian Campaign. It is ludicrous to suggest, as Paull does, that after two days[17] in Port Moresby, Porter could have rated Lieutenant-Colonel Ward in this way. Captain Noel Symington MC, 39th Battalion:

> As the 53rd Battalion performed so badly, the reflection upon Lieutenant Colonel Ward must be poor. By no stretch of my imagination could his command performance be equal to that of any AIF CO. And I think that's a fair statement.[18]

The question does remain as to why the three battalions received such an imbalance of these AIF officers. Captain M. L. Bidstrup, MC, 39th Battalion:

> I think this was the way it happened. He [Porter] was told to, or asked for, a certain number of experienced officers, which he

got. Now he would have said to the CO's 'How many do you want?' Because when we were allocated to the 39th, I remember a bloke who was acting in command, Finlay; he personally posted these officers. So I think it was up to the CO's 'You want so many officers? You post them!'[19]

This procedure, in combination with the circumstances of its formation, was at the root of much of the tragedy and ridicule that was later to be the lot of the 53rd.

Three of the captains posted to the 39th Battalion received company commands. The two remaining company commanders, Merritt[20] and Templeton, were capable commanders who, newly promoted, were to provide, with the AIF officers, sound leadership for the battalion. Lieutenant-Colonel Conran was replaced by Lieutenant-Colonel Owen[21] on 7 July. Owen had escaped from Rabaul after its fall and while his influence upon his new command was only of a three-week duration, he led his battalion in action in a positive and brave manner. The important point here is that it was basically only the 39th Battalion which gave its AIF arrivals company commands. It is at both battalion and company officer level that the greatest effect on training can be achieved, ie capable battalion commanding officers and company commanders have the greatest effect on discipline and training.

Initially, the arrival of these AIF officers was met with a degree of resentment from many militia officers and men alike. For their part, the AIF officers were given the onerous task of attempting to instill standards of discipline and training into their new troops they had taken completely for granted in their original AIF battalions. Lieutenant Hugh Dalby posted from the 2/27th Battalion to the 39th has vivid recollections of that important period. He had first-hand experience of the men's resentment:

Of course it was so. All you have to do ever is put yourself in the other fellow's situation. Number one; we monitored their correspondence. So one of the words I was cutting out mostly was AIF. In other words, 'We've got some new AIF officers, they're bastards!' I left 'they're bastards!' in. I can take this a step further. When we went there these men were unshaven, they wore dirty clothes; they were hang-dog if you like. We started in on training. They had to get rifle drill; rifle practice . . . But after a few weeks, they started to feel like soldiers . . . They became good troops. Although they resented us their resentment was understandable. Me, I could understand it. I knew what they were telling me in their correspondence. They knew I was going to get the message from them. There was a very deep distrust when I went to New Guinea between the AIF and the militia. It was something that had to be broken down. The officers had to make the effort.[22]

Such a state of affairs is, in hindsight, quite understandable. The militia were poorly led and poorly trained and had to contend with substandard equipment. The resentment at this time was also aggravated by the fact that the AIF officers were instructed to request militia applications to join the AIF. Unbeknown to these officers, many of the militia had applied for and been refused admission to that force, at a time when it needed no additional enlistments. Private Les Armitage, 39th Battalion:

We would have gone anywhere anyway. It was just the way it was done. If I'm going to join the AIF I'll do it under my own steam, when I want to. I had every intention of doing it, but because someone tells you 'You're bloody doing it!' then it gets your back up and you say 'Well that's what you think!' It caused a lot of resentment.[23]

This was yet another manifestation of the very real rift that existed between the AIF and the militia. This gulf had its genesis as far back as the First World War, when Prime Minister William Morris Hughes had fought two extremely bitter referendum campaigns which effectively split the nation over the issue of conscription for service overseas. Lieutenant A. G. Garland, a young militia officer in the 39th Battalion, concludes that this resentment only really ever subsided as a result of action against the Japanese:

> Well there was resentment amongst the troops. I felt this. I was a lieutenant. I went over in action as such. And when I came back I was put in for promotion that I didn't get because of reinforcement AIF officers. I'd been given a VX number but we were still militia. There was resentment from most of the militia officers, and I think it probably always existed. But it didn't mean that we weren't friendly with them. We got on well with them in the end once we got to know them. Once the troops had been in action with the particular officer and had seen his capabilities, then they got to know him on a better level. The tide definitely turned, there's no doubt about that.[24]

Thus, the 39th Battalion, manned by volunteers for tropical service, and led in June 1942 by a very capable leavening of AIF and enthusiastic young militia officers, was a battalion in change. With these factors came a sharp improvement in physical fitness, a drastic injection of discipline and military demeanour and some basic training. In comparison, the 53rd Battalion and, to a lesser degree, the 49th Battalion, were not experiencing similar changes. Many of the 53rd Battalion young men still harboured a very understandable and bitter resentment against an army which had shanghaied many of their number on the Sydney docks prior to embarkation. The fact that none of the AIF officers newly arrived to the 53rd Battalion received a company command meant that companies were led by inexperienced officers; and the potential influence of the experienced AIF was restricted not only by the subordinate nature of their postings but also by the smallness of their number. Porter could not have been under any illusion as to the relative merits of his battalions, contrary to Raymond Paull's assertions. Over 40 years after the event Major Bidstrup was in no doubt as to Porter's knowledge of the 53rd Battalion:

> I've got a very great admiration for Porter. I can remember what he did mainly in training was to try and find out what the officers knew in tactics and sand-table exercises particularly. We had a brigade exercise and I was an umpire, one of the umpires of the 53rd, and I can remember being appalled. Porter said that we were a bit hard, but he agreed with us afterwards. He said we were quite right.[25]

Porter had thus achieved much in the short time at his disposal with the 30th Brigade. He had been able to strengthen his brigade with some experienced officers and had attempted through them to influence the training and discipline of his troops. The Battle of Midway from 4–6 of June, further lengthened his reprieve.

The Australian Government and Army began to view New Guinea in a different light. In the dark weeks between the fall of Singapore and the Battle of the Coral Sea, it seemed that Japan would repeat the tragedy of Rabaul at Port Moresby. The only well-trained and battle-hardened division in Australia, the 7th, was, understandably, preserved for a possible attack upon mainland Australia. The Battle of Midway redressed the balance of naval power in the Pacific.

The Australians and their American Commander-in-Chief, South-West Pacific Area, General Douglas MacArthur, perceived that it might be time to change from the defensive to the offensive; and they turned their attention to the north coast of Papua. Their investigation of that coast raised two important factors. A small party of American and Australian officers had conducted an examination of the ground between Buna and Dobodura. An area north-east of Dobodura was regarded as

'If War Came' (Cross, *Smith's Weekly*, 1938)

'The Hope of his Side' (Jac, *Smith's Weekly*, 1943)

being an ideal location for an advanced air base whence the Allied air forces could attack Rabaul as a prelude to future invasion. In addition, a small force could guard against any attempts by the Japanese to assist other forces elsewhere in an attack on Port Moresby, for instance from Milne Bay or by journeying over the Owen Stanley Range—though that was considered a natural barrier to any force, other than a minor one.

As a consequence of such thinking, Blamey instructed Morris, on 29 June, to secure Kokoda, north of the range, envisaging that the occupying force could later protect a proposed Allied air base planned for Dobodura. It is fascinating to note that the Allied command in Australia had no conception whatsoever of the Kokoda Trail in terms of the number of troops that it could accommodate, the possible manner of their supply or the nature of the terrain itself. It was believed that the Japanese would not make a major thrust across the Own Stanley Range. Yet the Japanese had shown from Sunday morning 7 December 1941, a very real propensity for attempting and succeeding in 'impossible' missions. Pearl Harbor, the jungle campaign in Malaya, and the fall of Singapore should have provided ample evidence of this Japanese capacity.

To implement Blamey's instruction, Porter was ordered to send a rifle company over the Kokoda Trail. Captain S.V. Templeton and his B Company 39th Battalion were entrusted with the bold enterprise. Into an unknown environment, to await the best jungle troops on earth was to be plunged one company of a raw militia battalion. It is more than a little ironic that the direct defence of the last fortress before the Australian mainland was to be initially undertaken by a small detachment of so-called 'chocolate soldiers' from a brigade which, judging particularly by its very recent official 'F' grading on combat efficiency, was apparently amongst the least trained, worst equipped and most inexpertly led forces in the entire Australian Army.

3

The devil's design

Take a large number of fit, healthy young men flushed with the mental enthusiasm and the physical determination that the prime of life can accommodate. Burden them with anywhere between 50 and 70 pounds of equipment, much of which will be found to be unsuitable. Clothe them in a uniform which will not blend them into their environment but instead offer them as an easy target to their foe—and expose them also to constant wetness and the chill of the night. Give them a half-blanket, if they are to be amongst the lucky ones, for a token gesture of warmth. Feed them sparsely, so much so that they will lose two to three stone in weight over a period of six to eight weeks. Take them far into the recesses of a jungle that even today is mysterious, dark, wet, cold and yet, at times, steamy—a jungle virtually unknown. Isolate them, by making communication almost impossible over any significant distance. Isolate them further by creating a situation where they can be resupplied only by air or by overtaxed native porters, and never to a degree whereby they can gain sufficient strength to perform at their optimum level. Through all this expose them, without protection or remedy, to the worst tropical diseases, and fevers such as malaria, hookworm, dysentery and scrub typhus.

Deprive them even of a sure, safe and speedy passage out if they are to be wounded. Instead, submit them to a humble blanket-and-tree-bough litter and a treacherous muddy evacuation that they will endure for six days, left to the care of native porters—the legendary Fuzzy-Wuzzy Angels. Captain H. J. Katekar, 2/27th Battalion:

> Half way down where the path was cut precariously out of the side of a cliff, I stopped to allow some native boys to manoeuvre a stretcher around a difficult corner. My heart filled with admiration for those stalwart natives; they took one quarter of an hour to get around that cliff edge, handling the stretcher tenderly. I went down the hill thinking how sincere and humane these simple folk were; how superior to those Jap savages, and to a lot of smug and complacent people in Australia.[1]

If they can survive, treatment will await them only when this nightmare can be escaped. But beyond all, test them, try to break them with endless ascents that will induce utter exhaustion and at times vomiting. Strain their knees and their backs and save a special agony for the descents, where a fall will incur a muddy, slimy penalty and very often a desperate need for an unavailable change of clothes.

Incredibly, when they have survived the worst, deprive them of sleep and of relief of their force, when to endure another day will almost certainly bring annihilation, pitting them against soldiers trained and equipped for jungle warfare and flushed with the morale-boosting subjugation of Asia.

Reward them with the condemnation of their commander-in-chief, an American ignorant of them and of their totally unique plight. In later years they will show the physical scars of arthritis, back complaints, heart disease, and a host of other physical disabilities. Many will not come to terms with weeks in their lives that seemed an eternity, and will suffer war neurosis.

The Kokoda Trail was the devil's design—the ultimate military obstacle course. That the soldiers of Maroubra Force endured and surmounted the ordeal to bring their mighty foe to a standstill will stand forever as their memorial.

Warfare is an ancient form of conflict. Over thousands of years nations have observed its basic principles. The chapters of history bear tragic testimony to the ruin of nations and their armies which have neglected one or more of these principles, and suffered deprivation and defeat as a consequence. Unity of command, concentration of force and above all administration, ie supply and logistics, were but some of the areas in which mistakes were made by American, Australian and Japanese leaders on the Kokoda Trail because of the tremendous obstacles presented by the unique terrain.

The Kokoda Campaign was to test the amazing fortitude of both poorly trained and, as yet, unblooded young militiamen and veteran AIF battalions who were to be strained far beyond what human flesh and blood could have been expected to withstand. Opposing them were Japanese troops trained on their mandated island possessions prior to the outbreak of war in the Pacific in December 1941. Such fundamental considerations as jungle uniforms, lightweight packs, and light, efficient weapons enabled the Japanese to move efficiently and, above all, quickly through the jungle. They also had a completely different military–moral code of behaviour which, in battle, was exemplified by a fanaticism that the young Australian soldiers found hard to understand.

Prior to the outbreak of hostilities in New Guinea in 1942, travellers from Port Moresby to the area beyond the Owen Stanley Range could either sail to the northern coast or fly to an inland outpost 1200 feet up in the northern foothills of the mountains. This was Kokoda, a Papuan Administration Post with officers' houses, police house, native hospital, station garden, a rubber plantation and the only landing strip in the region. The natives had their own routes including the hazardous one over the Owen Stanley Range—a primitive track, often three to four feet wide, restricting movement in most places to single file. Only scant knowledge of that track had reached the outside world through occasional reports of patrol officers, plantation owners and missionaries.

The 25-mile journey from Port Moresby to Ilolo and thence to Owers' Corner had given the young Australian soldier facing the great mountain-crossing little insight into exactly what he was to experience; but he received his first inkling as he slithered, out of control, down steep muddy slopes on his way to the village of Uberi, the first on the Kokoda Trail.

From Uberi lay an extremely hard day's march to Ioribaiwa. Distance, so the soldier would quickly learn, was to be measured not in miles but by the number of gruelling hours' marching with, of course, usually a 65-pound pack and a weapon to carry. Many men quickly acquired a body-length stick to assist them in their labours. Such a stick was to become a trade mark of the appearance of troops on the Kokoda Trail. This first day's march across the mountains began with a mile's rough journey beside the Goldie River, and then a steep and daunting climb up a razorback spur on the Imita Ridge. The soldier was confronted by the first, but by no means the last, excruciating ascent on the Trail—the Golden Stairs.

The Golden Stairs consisted of several thousand logs of wood pushed into the ascent and held in place by wooden pegs. Filthy, putrid mud constituted the rest of the 'step'. At some points the exposed roots of trees formed the steps, thereby making them irregular in distance and shape and often harder to climb, especially for shorter men. The stairs became permanently sodden and slippery because of the daily rains that soaked and saturated the jungle. Men fell, banged knees, shins and ankles on the exposed log steps, gave vent to their anger and struggled agonisingly to their feet; and orderly progress became impossible. Lieutenant Hugh Dalby, 39th Battalion:

> They were so steep . . . We soon had it worked out that instead of trying to walk over the mountain range in sections as we started off doing, and nearly killed ourselves, the next day we set off at intervals . . . So you might be five minutes getting rid of your men. But instead of getting to the next staging place at five o'clock at night when it was dark and have people out looking for you, you'd get there at two in the afternoon because you weren't hampered by this stop start, stop start.[2]

Periodically the soldier would catch and clutch at a glimmer of hope through the foliage—sky. The top of the ascent was near; extra strength was summoned; the ultimate exhausting effort was put forth; the Golden Stairs were beaten. But the beguiling point of success was repeatedly found to be a false crest and the daunting reality that there were many hundreds of steps still to climb became evident. When the summit was eventually reached, to reveal that the distant horizon bounded a succession of ridges and valleys all of which appeared as formidable as the one just conquered, the true proportion of the torture of the Kokoda Trail began to appall even the toughest soldier.

From Imita Ridge the Trail swung steeply down through dense forest to a fast-flowing stream, whose course it followed for a few miles before climbing up to traverse a stretch of kunai grass and continue the long and ever-steeper ascent to Ioribaiwa Ridge and its village. Little distinguished one village on the Trail from another save its location. Each consisted basically of a collection of native huts built to accommodate small groups and never able to cope with a daily military influx or occupation, usually in at least company strength. Some of these villages were to be found clustered below abrupt excruciating descents while others were seemingly precariously perched

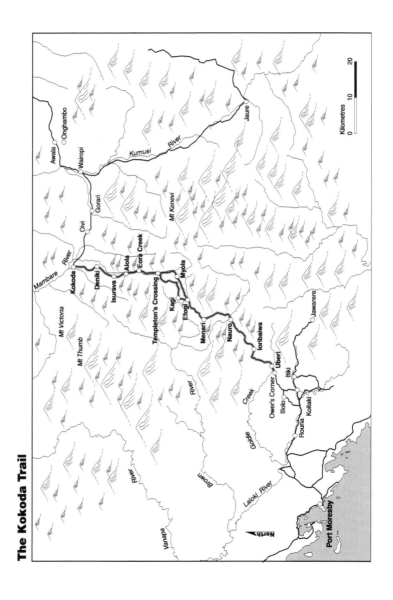

The Kokoda Trail

upon knolls above steep and depressingly gloomy, thick, jungle ascents. However, whether the overburdened soldier travelled up or down, he experienced the unending aching of strained knees and a suffering back never designed to carry a load of 60–70 pounds over the Owen Stanley Range.

After his last sporadic spurts of desperate, joint-wrenching, lung-bursting scaling of the Golden Stairs, many a sweat-sodden campaigner reached Ioribaiwa utterly worn out. Accustomed to a more open countryside he was hopelessly disorientated as the strange pitch-black darkness of the enveloping jungle closed in with the descending evening; and, huddled in the chill of the night nearly 3000 feet above sea-level, he was hardly warmed by his Moresby-ordained issue of half a blanket or comforted by the prospect of another 100 miles of clawing up and catapulting down mountains two or three times as high as Ioribaiwa.

The second day in the mountains began with a series of descents and ascents until the village of Ioribaiwa could be seen again from the direction of Nauro. Nauro was situated at the end of a slippery slope down to a pleasant valley on the edge of the Brown River. This river was approximately twenty feet deep, had a fast-flowing current and afforded the soldier a refreshing stop before he headed on to Menari. He was then faced with about half a day's journey consisting of a march through a river valley, followed by a very steep and exhausting climb over a high mountain and an equally sheer descent to an open area where Menari lay at the junction of two creeks with precipitous banks. The Trail negotiated one of these by means of a long, large log—the standard creek crossing. Yet another steep and tiresome ascent saw the soldier on the summit of what came to be known as Brigade Hill, or Butcher's Hill, later the scene of some very savage fighting and the birthplace of bitter controversy.

Just out of Brigade Hill, the Trail left the jungle and over-looked a small kunai patch and thence a staggering and yet depressing view of numerous summits and spurs; seemingly an endless characteristic of the Owen Stanley Range. This scene was dominated by Mount Victoria, some 13 000 feet high, its summit wreathed by swirling cloud. The kunai patch was yet another feature that the soldier would frequently encounter. Private Bert Ward, 2/27th Battalion:

> Kunai grass . . . grows six, seven, eight feet high and the track at times would go through this . . . and you wouldn't have the faintest clue what was twelve inches off into the kunai grass. Those were the areas I used to find stifling; and for some reason or other, we always seemed to strike the kunai patches at the hottest time of the day—early afternoon.[3]

From the kunai, the Trail swung down approximately 1700 feet into a valley where yet another fast-flowing river with a log-crossing awaited the weary men. Many veterans today regard Efogi as the most soul-destroying segment of the Trail. The day's exertions to reach Efogi culminated in the final gruelling scaling of a lofty height, towering up some 700 feet, whose sharp gradient had to be renegotiated next morning as a descent. An extremely steep ascent of 1800 feet was then to be faced which led to a ridge where the village of Kagi, seem-ingly perched on the hillside, awaited the soldier. From Kagi the track ran east, rising some 3000 feet in about five miles before turning steeply north to the watershed at 9000 feet that formed the western rampart of the deep seven-mile-wide Eora Creek Valley.

'The Gap' was the name sometimes given to the upper reaches of that valley but more specifically to the lowest point—below 6900 feet—in the summit-line of the Owen Stanley Range crossed by aircraft to enter the top of the valley. It was fancied in high headquarters that a few well-trained troops, with explosives, could defend or demolish this 'Gap' to deny its passage by a vastly superior enemy force.

But the soldier on the Kokoda Trail did not see the Gap—away to the south-east—as he marched north along the summit at close to 9000 feet for almost another five miles before swinging east for the steep descent of 3000 feet in a few miles down the side of the valley. The track plunged so dramatically to the raging torrent below that the hapless soldier was forced to cling to saplings and vines to minimise the frequency and severity of falls before slithering over the log-crossing of Eora Creek which was to become known as Templeton's Crossing. Some three hours later, after a difficult zigzagging scramble north above the eastern bank, he was confronted by the now familiar cluster of huts; he had arrived at Eora Creek village on a steep, timbered height some 200 feet above the rushing waters.

From that crossing the Trail was constricted by the very thick jungle to its narrowest form until near Alola where it emerged into clearings with cultivated native gardens. Alola stood about 500 feet above Eora Creek on an open spur on the western side of the valley. Some two hours ahead, along a track hugging the hillside between jungled slopes, on the east falling away to Eora Creek and on the west rising to dominating heights, lay Isurava, where one of the most epic battles in Australian military history would later be fought.

From Isurava, the Trail, whilst running generally downhill, taxed the soldier with a series of rises over substantial spurs lifting its path, to be followed in turn by slippery descents down their farther slopes. The rough hillside going also offered a variety of huge rocks, swift creeks, sudden waterfalls and tangled roots as additional obstacles to progress on the winding way to the village of Deniki whence the Yodda Valley lay exposed below with the Kokoda airstrip clearly visible.

The Trail quickly descended into the green Yodda Valley and after some three hours' walking, the soldier had journeyed out of the mountains and into the oppressive heat of Kokoda.

Leaving Kokoda, the Trail wound its way much more gently down to the coast for three full and extremely tiring and hot days' marching. The soldier still faced the crossing of numerous streams, and had to pass through the villages of Oivi and Gorari before arriving at the Kumusi River which presented him with a raging torrent that rushed between widely separated, steep banks. There a bridge suspended by wire cables and aptly known as 'Wairopi', the 'pidgin' for 'wire ropes', allowed safe passage across the river.

Farther on, the village of Awala was the starting point of many hot steamy tracks that led through lowlands and swamps, in the vicinity of Sangara Mission and Popondetta to reach the coast and the settlements of Buna and Gona. Buna was the administrative centre for the district, while Gona was an Anglican mission. They were only small outposts, but they were later to become the scenes of some of the most bitter and yet least publicised fighting of the Pacific War.

Private Bert Ward, 2/27th Battalion:

> Once you got on that trail there was for most people that sense of personal pride or ego, call it what you like, to keep battling, to go a bit further, a bit further, and not realising a bit further was getting you more and more into trouble and to the stage where it didn't matter how severe things had been up to that point, the next day was going to be worse, and the following day was going to be worse again.[4]

The next day was nearly always worse again, because the soldier was slipping farther and farther away from his headquarters' ability to supply and therefore sustain him. Wireless sets were primitive in those days, particularly in mountainous terrain, and consequently communication with the outside world consisted for most of the campaign of a single telephone line back along the Trail to headquarters.

Native carriers, despite superhuman efforts, could not cope with the demands of brigade-strength forces fighting in such conditions. Whenever supplies were dropped by air they were often either lost due to the nature of the terrain or to defective dropping techniques, or destroyed, totally or partially, upon impact.

Many medical problems were the result of living in an environment in which a change of clothing, a hot meal, and a reasonable period of sleep were impossible dreams rather than regular occurrences. Thrust into this green nightmare, the young soldier was thus faced with a titanic struggle against an environment that would impose upon him a very great physical penalty for every ignorant, thoughtless mistake that a totally inexperienced staff in Port Moresby could make.

4

No do-or-die stunts

Having been ordered to supply a force for the protection of Kokoda and its airstrip, Major-General Morris was faced with a logistics nightmare. As he had undertaken no reconnaissance of the Kokoda Trail, he was confronted with the immediate prospect of having the commitment to action of that small force develop into a major battle for the survival of his garrison and Port Moresby itself. The fact that he knew little or nothing about the ground is best portrayed by his own words:

> . . . even if the Japanese do make this very difficult and impracticable move, let us meet them on ground of our own choosing and as close as possible to our own base. Let us merely help their own supply problem to strangle them while reducing our supply difficulties to a minimum.[1]

The Battle of the Coral Sea had put an end to the seaborne attack on Port Moresby and forced the Imperial Japanese Army to adopt a different strategy. The Japanese were about to embark upon a campaign that was quite practical, by

40

a twin thrust of operations on the Kokoda Trail and at Milne Bay. They were to fight on ground of their choosing and not on that of Morris's choice. But the crucial factor in the forthcoming campaign would be that the problem of supply that Morris referred to, would be the tragic and unhappy lot of the Australians, long before it could threaten to strangle the Japanese.

Morris had no transport aircraft based in Port Moresby. His only means of supply would be the traditional one—native carriers. He was fortunate indeed to have the services of some personnel who had both a knowledge of the natives and some degree of expertise in travel in the region. Highly credentialled among such personnel were Captains H. T. Kienzle[2] and G. H. Vernon.[3] Then an officer with the rank of Lieutenant in ANGAU,[4] Kienzle was given the tasks of taking charge of all ANGAU and native personnel for the purposes of building staging camps along the Kokoda Trail and of maintaining supplies for both newly arriving and already committed troops. Major Noel Symington, who was later to rely heavily on Kienzle's knowledge, remembers him and Vernon well.

> Kienzle was a second generation planter, a bloke of six feet two. He was big, eighteen stone of muscle. He had a good brain and successfully ran a plantation. He was very highly regarded in the civil community up there, a very good operator. I do not consider that sufficient recognition was made to this gallant officer by the army commander or his country. They gave him an MBE or something; a bloody insult.[5]

Doctor Vernon was given responsibility for maintaining the health of the native porters. His hard work and energy were destined to benefit not only the natives; his compassion and skill were to be of immeasurable value to the young militiamen of the 39th Battalion.

A very gallant medical officer. I first met him at Deniki. I ascertained that he'd been a medical officer in the First World War; he'd been awarded a Military Cross in that capacity. He'd been a planter, trader and part-time medical man in the New Guinea area since the First World War. A very widely read bloke, quite opposite to Kienzle physically, but mentally, probably equally alert.[6]

Doctor Geoffrey Vernon was to die in 1946 at the age of 63 having achieved much in his last years with scant recognition from the authorities. A native hospital at Maipani in a remote part of Papua New Guinea serves as his only memorial.

The events which led Kienzle to his newly allotted task portray both the magnitude of the job confronting him and the rapidity of developments.

About midnight on the 31st of March, 1942, I was awakened by a loud knocking to be confronted by a native constable of police, who handed me an important message from Kokoda. It was a message from H.Q. Port Moresby to the effect, I was to 'close down mines and plantations, and report to H.Q. immediately' . . . I reported to Kokoda, where Lieutenant Brewer instructed me to take a number of 'deserters'; these were natives who had deserted their employ, during the earlier air raids on Port Moresby, back to their villages, and I was to escort them back to Port Moresby. It was my first crossing of the now famous 'Kokoda Trail', and it took me 7 days to reach Koitaki with my line of about 64 'deserters' . . . On the 29th of June, 1942, I received an urgent message to report to H.Q. Port Moresby immediately. I was instructed that I was to take charge of approximately one thousand native labourers on a line of communication to Kokoda, being established between Ilolo (McDonald's Corner) and Kokoda immediately.[7]

The order issued to Kienzle must surely be amongst the most ludicrous in all history:

C.O. Angau to make arrangements to fulfil requirements up to a maximum of one thousand native labourers. Construction of road to Kokoda to commence not later than 29th June. Road to be completed by 26th August, 1942.[8]

A road along the Kokoda Trail! Lieutenant Kienzle's reaction is a masterly piece of understatement:

> It is asking too much to organise (a) a line of communication with suitable stages/depots/camps en route, all equipped and manned with sufficient carriers and (b) to build a road over this mountainous terrain within a time limit. I have heard of superman but have yet to see him in action![9]

Lieutenant Kienzle found Templeton and B Company, 39th Battalion, waiting for him at Ilolo. In order to lessen the men's burden, supplies and equipment were carried round to Buna on the north coast, by the lugger *Gili Gili*. Approximately 120 native carriers assisted the men by carrying some of their packs and rations. Ahead of the main body journeyed Sergeant-Major Maga of the Royal Papuan Constabulary and a further 130 natives, to erect a staging camp at Ioribaiwa. One of Templeton's three platoon commanders was Lieutenant Arthur Seekamp, promoted and transferred from the 2/10th to the 39th Battalion; he, and another AIF officer, Lieutenant Harry Mortimore and their platoons were to be the first soldiers of Maroubra Force to confront the Japanese on the Kokoda Trail. Lieutenant Arthur Seekamp:

> We had about 250 carriers taking us through and half of those were going through fast; as soon as we camped in the morning they'd go through, dump their load at the next station's point and then they'd build us a shack and get the fire going. First thing next morning they'd do the same thing again.[10]

Following Kienzle's plan and guidance Templeton led B Company through Nauro, Menari, and Efogi until on 12 July, the troops toiled up to Kagi, where they were met by Lieutenant F. P. Brewer,[11] the Patrol Officer at Kokoda. Brewer had some further 186 carriers for the task of assisting B Company on to Kokoda. Kienzle released his carriers to journey back to Uberi for the task of building up supplies as far forward as Kagi. He recalled:

> I found that to have carriers based at each stage and to carry only between two stages, was the best method, making the carrier line feel more settled and contented, with a reduction in 'desertions'. The trail from Uberi to Kagi is a series of steep ascents and descents, crossing six ridges en route. It is indeed a test of endurance. A steady stream of urgent rations, supplies, medical, ammunition had to be planned and put into operation immediately and maintained on the Line of Communication from Ilolo or Owers' Corner to Kokoda, to help provision a company of men. Little did I know or was advised at this stage, that this was to be my responsibility for a full battalion, then a brigade and later a division.[12]

It was thus planned that separate groups of locally based carriers would journey continually back and forth between adjacent staging posts on the route from Uberi to Kagi, and that Brewer's natives would work the stretch from Kagi to Kokoda. On 15 July, Templeton's company reached Kokoda with help from the natives and the lugger *Gili Gili*. The troops had been sorely tried, and were in need of rest although B Company had had a rather easier time than would succeeding contingents.

After supplying the company with food from his own plantation, Kienzle journeyed back towards Port Moresby to assess the supply situation more thoroughly. He quite accurately predicted that the natives were going to be incapable of maintaining adequate supplies to the troops.

A carrier carrying only foodstuffs consumes his load in thirteen days and if he carries food supplies for a soldier, it means six and a half days supply for both soldier and carrier. This does not allow for the porterage of arms, ammunition, equipment, medical stores, ordnance, mail and dozens of other items needed to wage war, on the backs of men. The track takes eight days, so the maintenance of supplies is a physical impossibility without large-scale co-operation of plane droppings.[13]

Kagi offered a site where supplies could be dropped far enough forward to enable carriers to move them to combat areas in sufficient quantities to allow troops engaged there to manoeuvre with greater freedom. Such a course of action was considered by Kienzle on or about 19 July. The Japanese landings at Gona two days later suddenly highlighted the problem which was quite obviously not the fault of Kienzle but rather a sad reflection upon the foresight and planning of Major-General Morris and his staff in Port Moresby. At the very worst, a man of Kienzle's stature could have, and indeed should have, been ordered to examine the problem of movement and supply over the Kokoda Trail soon after the fall of Singapore.

In anticipation of an enemy thrust there, Brigadier John Field[14] with his 7th Brigade had arrived at Milne Bay on 11 July. His 'Milne Force' was under the direct command of General Blamey and his headquarters. It included, in addition to the 9th, 25th and 61st Battalions of his own brigade, part of the 55th Battalion, anti-aircraft and anti-tank artillery and engineers as well as various American personnel involved in airfield development, defence and service. Field was given three objectives. The first was to prepare and defend an airforce base at Milne Bay. The second was to defend south-east New Guinea by preventing enemy penetration and by denying, by air attack, Japanese use of nearby island groups and the surrounding seas. The third objective was to maintain active air reconnaissance over the area. It was anticipated that, with the development of Milne Bay and with the addition of a forward air base near Buna, offensive operations against the Japanese at Rabaul could be undertaken.

At approximately 2.40 pm on 21 July the Japanese gained the initiative by a float-plane machine-gunning of the Buna station followed by the appearance of a convoy off the coast near Gona. Despite some spirited defence by Allied aircraft, the Japanese began landing troops late in the afternoon; and, under the cover of darkness, the disembarkation was completed unchallenged during the night.

At this time the Allies had three militia brigades defending Milne Bay and Port Moresby. While the Australians had decided to fight the initial battles in New Guinea with a largely unblooded and ill-equipped force, the Japanese, in contrast, deployed crack troops, superbly trained and equipped, and committed to a well-conceived and viable master-plan. The Battle of Midway had frustrated their attempt to subdue New Caledonia, Samoa and Fiji. At no time, however, were the Japanese prepared to abandon their plans for the capture of Port Moresby. Such a gain would have a number of advantages. Firstly, it would protect their right flank with the rich oilfields, rubber plantations and tin mines of the Dutch East Indies. Secondly, it would deny the Allies a firm base from which to attack strategic targets such as Rabaul. Thirdly, it would provide a base suitable for the bombardment of northern Australia and would therefore also be a frustrating influence upon American plans to reinforce and strengthen that undermanned land. The seriousness with which the Japanese adhered to this strategy is best demonstrated by the master-plan and the forces chosen to execute it.

On 14 June, Lieutenant-General Hyakutake, commander of the 17th Army, was ordered to prepare an overland attack upon Port Moresby. That attack was not to be instituted until a preceding force had landed near Gona and had reconnoitred the area between Buna–Gona and Kokoda. If the overland trek was deemed to be a realistic aim, a far larger force would then be landed. This initial reconnaissance was to be undertaken by Colonel Yosuke Yokoyama. His force included a large portion of the 15th Independent Engineer Regiment which would clear roads and pathways and construct depots. The combat arm of this initial force was to be the 1st Battalion 144th Regiment commanded by Lieutenant-Colonel Tsukamoto who was to have the task of engaging any Allied troops between Gona–Buna and Kokoda. In support of these two groups would be some units of the 55th Mountain Artillery, some anti-aircraft batteries and, significantly, a company of the crack 5th Sasebo Naval Landing Force. In addition, it was decided to land approximately one company of Formosans of the 15th Naval Pioneer Unit. For the later assault across the Owen Stanley Range, overall command would pass to Major-General Horii whose South Seas Force was built strongly round the 144th Regiment. The eventual Japanese build-up if the thrust was to be given the all clear, would comprise some 13 500 troops; 10 000 of these were seasoned combat troops, veterans of victory, before Rabaul, in major campaigns in Malaya and the Philippines. Against the initial Japanese force, the Allies were to commit the 39th Battalion. The brunt of the Japanese attack would fall upon Captain Sam Templeton and B Company.

In response to the Japanese landing at Gona on 21 July, Major-General Morris was ordered to concentrate one battalion at Kokoda forthwith. Consequently, he ordered Lieu-tenant-Colonel Owen of the 39th Battalion, to leave by air for Kokoda on 23rd July, to command all Papuan Infantry Battalion troops and his own 39th Battalion—to be called 'Maroubra Force'. While Owen was given orders to block further penetration by the Japanese through to Kokoda, it was anticipated that the Japanese intention was to occupy Buna–Gona for the purpose of constructing an airfield and base.

In the days preceding the Japanese landings, Captain Sam Templeton had not been idle. He had personally reconnoitred the area around Buna and had also checked upon the unloading of supplies from the *Gili Gili*. Although at least 50 years of age, Templeton possessed reserves of energy and enthusiasm that few younger men had. He burned to show his energy and leadership qualities. After he had been refused entry into the AIF because of his age and flat feet, a benign providence had given the inexperienced youngsters of B Company 39th Battalion a leader whose self-sacrifice and courage were an inspiration to those around him. Lieutenant A. G. (Judy) Garland:

> He'd fought in the Irish Rebellion, the First War and this was to be his last fling. He set an example to the whole of his company, in other words, I think he realised that we were a lot of young blokes . . . A man that you couldn't get to know very well, but he always said that if he went into action against the Japs, he wouldn't come back and that's exactly what happened, he told me that.[15]

Rather than delegate tasks to his subordinates, Templeton repeatedly undertook tasks that carried unnecessary risks for a company commander and at times were ill-advised. To an experienced officer from the AIF, Templeton's individualism and drive were harder traits to understand. One of his platoon commanders, Lieutenant Arthur Seekamp recalls that:

> The amount of time that we had Sam Templeton with us, he always was going somewhere by himself; he never took any runners or anything with him, he left Kokoda to go to Buna by himself and then started to come back. At Oivi he wanted to go back and see if there was another platoon coming down. He always seemed to be by himself—he never seemed to delegate or didn't want to. He was a funny bugger![16]

Hurrying back from the Buna area, Templeton arrived at Awala on 22 July and summoned his 11 Platoon (Lieutenant Seekamp) forward to that village with 12 Platoon (Lieutenant Mortimore) closing in from Kokoda and 10 Platoon (Lieutenant Garland) remaining behind to guard the airstrip. Having completed orders for the deployment of his platoons, Templeton left Major W. T. Watson of the PIB in command, and headed back to Kokoda to meet his Commanding Officer, Lieutenant-Colonel Owen.

On 23rd July, Seekamp's platoon withdrew from Awala to Wairopi on the Kumusi River and Watson, destroying his stores at Ongahambo, also fell back to join him with what remained of his PIB contingent, most of the Papuans having 'gone bush'. By early morning on 24 July, Seekamp's men and Watson's small group were on the western side of the Kumusi. At around 9 am Templeton contacted Seekamp:

> Reported on radio broadcast that fifteen hundred to two thousand Japs landed at Gona Mission Station. I think that this is near correct and in view of the numbers I recommend that your action be contact and rear-guard only—no do-or-die stunts. Close back on Kokoda.

The Australians awaited contact across the broad barrier of the swift Kumusi. Early in the afternoon the Japanese appeared on the east bank of the river. Fire was exchanged and then, once more, Watson's mixed command fell back, to positions in rear of Mortimore's men near Gorari.

The same afternoon Lieutenant-Colonel Owen flew to Kokoda and, in the night, he and Templeton pushed on to reach Gorari at about 2 am on the 25th. Owen decided to make a stand at Gorari with Mortimore's platoon in an ambush position about half a mile east of the village. Having completed his dispositions Owen returned to Kokoda to await reinforcements who were expected by air. He had gone before the

Japanese walked into Mortimore's ambush and sustained some fifteen casualties. With their position no longer tenable the ambushers fell back to Gorari. The enemy followed and attacked so determinedly that they forced the two Australian platoons and their Papuan auxiliaries to withdraw to Oivi.

Lieutenant-Colonel Owen had only an already tired B Company and some PIB natives under Watson's command to commit against the full force of the Japanese attack. Late on the night of 25 July he requested that two of his rifle companies from the 39th Battalion be flown into Kokoda, as there was nothing other than his small force between Oivi and Captain A. C. Dean and his C Company who were only a couple of days march out of Ilolo on their long journey to reinforce him.

In response to Owen's request for two companies one plane made two trips the next day, 26 July—it was only a twenty-minute flight. The first contingent, Lieutenant McClean[17] and fourteen others from his 16 Platoon, D Company, were sent, on landing, posthaste to Oivi. The second load consisted of Sergeant Morrison[18] and the fifteen remaining men of the platoon with its two just-issued Brens still in their packing grease in their brand new boxes. They, too, were hurried off along the track towards Oivi.

When the Japanese, aggressively following up Mortimore's and Seekamp's men, attacked again at Oivi, Templeton's meagre force numbered but two and a half platoons. The raw young soldiers of the two B Company platoons were experiencing a very testing baptism of fire; exhausted and depleted, thrice pursued and thrice engaged with little opportunity for food or rest, they were almost spent. And McClean's half-platoon, arriving without its Bren guns after a four-hour march from Kokoda, was hardly a formidable column.

The Japanese had employed what were to become standard and predictable tactics against Australian troops. They would execute a frontal attack; they seemed only too happy to incur casualties and then feel for their enemy's flanks with a view to the encirclement and annihilation of their adversary. Lieutenant Doug McClean, 39th Battalion:

> We had a most tremendous mass of misinformation about the Jap being a little fellow, and the first Jap I hit under the ear with a grenade was six feet two inches and fifteen stone, with a silver anchor on his belt, meaning that they were marines. Their movement in the bush had to be seen to be believed, because they'd just vanish! Their field craft and movement was magnificent.'[19]

At Oivi, McClean informed Templeton that he could expect to be reinforced by the remainder of his (McClean's) platoon, and the remainder of D Company. Unbeknown to Templeton at this time, was the fact that Captain Bidstrup and the last two platoons of his D Company would not be joining him; they did not leave Port Moresby that day. Templeton was only too well aware that if the Japanese defeated his small force at Oivi, there would be two daunting consequences. One would be that Lieutenant Garland and his 10 Platoon at Kokoda would face annihilation. Another would be that the Japanese would then be in a position to advance far along the Kokoda Trail unhindered until confronted by Captain Dean and his C Company. However, the most important would be the loss of the Kokoda airstrip and the only possible chance that Morris would have of a speedy and potent reinforcement of Maroubra Force. Dudley McCarthy:

> The attackers were halted at first by the fire of the forward section, then outflanked it and forced it back to the main positions on the plateau on which Oivi stood. The defenders then went into a tight perimeter defence of diameter about 50 yards. The two opposing groups maintained a desultory fire during the afternoon, the Japanese sometimes pressing to within

a few yards of the perimeter before they were killed. About
5 o'clock Templeton went to examine the rear defences and to
warn the second half of McClean's platoon …

There was a burst of fire from the gloomy forest. Templeton
did not return.[20]

Lieutenant Mortimore has been able to clarify the events of
that day to some degree:

When we went into Oivi, I was on the Kokoda side. Sam went
through me on his way out and Doug McClean had just
arrived with one plane load of troops and he said there was
another load of troops behind him. He said 'In case they pull
back along the track as it gets dark, I'm going back to meet
them and bring them on.' I never heard any shots but someone
said they heard a shot.[21]

Following well-laid plans, and deploying crack marine troops,
the Japanese were able to encircle the Australians at Oivi and
concentrate much of their force and firepower to the rear of
the defenders, who answered with grenades and rifle fire until
some degree of panic broke out just prior to their abandoning
a position they could no longer hope to hold; some pushed
forward to their less threatened original front while others
moved towards their rear and almost certain death.

Major Watson was fortunately able to rely on the leadership
and discipline of the platoon commanders—Seekamp, Mortimore and McClean—to rally their men and organise their
extrication. Together they pulled back Captain Stevenson,[22]
Templeton's second in command, and some of the men who
were heading with him into the strongest Japanese positions
on the Kokoda side of Oivi. And the regathered force was
undoubtedly saved by the skill and resource and guidance of
one remarkable soldier, Lance Corporal Sanopa, a Papuan
policeman serving with the PIB. He had found an escape route

by way of the creek below the village and was to lead the stumbling column through water and jungle, by ravine and mountain-side, all the way to Deniki. Lieutenant Harry Mortimore, 39th Battalion:

> Sanopa went off and he found a gap on one side; actually the village was a little way up from the creek; we came out of the village down into the creek and then we spent from, I think it was 10 o'clock at night until just about daylight next morning, going up that bloody creek. We pulled in early next morning into a village which was possibly Fila. All we could do was knock a few coconuts down. That was the only meal we got and then we kept on going to Deniki. Sanopa saved two platoons and Doug's (McClean) troops from getting wiped out.[23]

With dramatic events unfolding at Oivi, Lieutenant-Colonel Owen had been waiting anxiously at Kokoda with Lieutenant Garland's platoon while Sergeant Morrison, unable to pierce the Japanese lines, had established a defensive position between Kokoda and Oivi. When some B Company men, cut off from Oivi, told Morrison they had been surrounded, he returned to Kokoda at about 2 am on 27 July to inform Owen who thereupon prepared to evacuate Kokoda. Later that morning, leaving some of the buildings ablaze with stores that could not be carried, he set out on the climb to Deniki where he discovered Watson, Stevenson and the main body of his force from Oivi. Next morning he was more than a little surprised to learn that the Japanese had not yet taken Kokoda: six men from B and D Companies, the last to leave Oivi at about midnight on 26 July, had reached Kokoda on the following day and had slept the night there. Owen was faced with a predicament. He had previously radioed Port Moresby reporting his decision to evacuate Kokoda. It was thought that the Kokoda Trail could be far easier to defend than Kokoda, particularly when it is emphasised that Owen had some 80 men at his disposal, pitted against about a battalion of crack Japanese troops. But Kokoda was the key—the key to reinforcement and therefore to the best chance that Maroubra Force would have of blocking Japanese access to the Trail and progress towards Port Moresby.

Owen decided that time might afford him the chance to be reinforced by air. He therefore decided to leave Lieutenant McClean and two of his sections at Deniki and hasten to Kokoda. Doctor Vernon, who had left Ilolo on 29 July, arrived at Deniki just in time to provide the only qualified medical help available for the young militiamen as they journeyed back to secure the Kokoda airstrip.

Warrant Officer John Wilkinson,[24] who had accompanied B Company over the Kokoda Trail and through their subsequent actions had been, up until Vernon's arrival, the only available person to administer medical aid. His description of Vernon's arrival is illuminating:

> Captain Vernon arrived out of fog. Very pleased to see him. He had some instruments and dressings in two triangular bandages. He nearly got shot when first seen owing to his unregimental dress. Captain Vernon had shorts, which were really strides rolled up; a blue pullover with the arms tied around his neck and hanging down his back; a felt army hat, worn as no hat ever should have been worn, and a long newspaper cigarette in his mouth. A small dillybag and some army biscuits and tobacco in it. He saw me and spoke, 'Jack, I heard there was some action up here and thought you may need some assistance. Where do I start?' What a man![25]

By noon on 28 July, Owen had deployed his force around the administration area of Kokoda. As a consequence of his unchallenged re-entry into Kokoda, he radioed back to Port Moresby requesting more troops and some mortars, and also informing headquarters that the airstrip was open for Allied

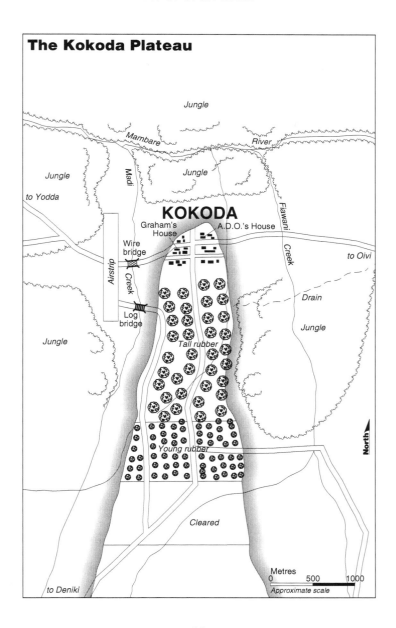

The Kokoda Plateau

Jungle

Mambare

River

Jungle

Jungle

Madi

to Yodda

KOKODA

Graham's House

A.D.O.'s House

Fiawani

Wire bridge

Creek

to Oivi

Airstrip

Creek

Drain

Log bridge

Jungle

Tall rubber

Jungle

Young rubber

North

Cleared

Metres

0   500   1000

Approximate scale

to Deniki

55

planes. He predicted that the main Japanese thrust would come from the Buna–Oivi–Kokoda track and therefore posted Garland's platoon on his right flank with most of his Papuan force on its left. Seekamp's platoon was placed on the tip of the plateau with Morrison's section from 16 Platoon on its left. Mortimore's men were in dug-in positions among the rubber trees astride the track to Deniki.

Shortly after Owen had deployed his meagre force, two droning Douglas transport aircraft circled the airstrip while the garrison cleared its obstacles aside. On board were the 39th Adjutant, Lieutenant Keith Lovett and Captain Bidstrup with another platoon of his D Company. Captain Bidstrup:

> I flew over the Owen Stanleys that morning. We were supposed to have two planes; we got two planes. I flew over there with the bulk of my company and the Yanks wouldn't put us down, because they reckoned there were Japs around. I could see our own troops on the ground at Kokoda. And I asked them to hang around; those people were clearing the barricades on the strip. No they wouldn't, they went back.[26]

Another, and indeed the last, realistic opportunity to reinforce Owen at Kokoda had been lost; the exhausted young militiamen could not be expected to hold Kokoda against the overwhelming odds they faced. It would seem that the only logical explanation for the lack of zeal and determination of both the pilots and the staff in Port Moresby and for their failure to appreciate the significance of Kokoda, lies with their total ignorance of Japanese intentions and of the ground upon which Maroubra Force was being committed. It was still believed that the Japanese were merely attempting to procure ground for an advanced air base. It was also believed that any Japanese thrust over the Owen Stanley Range could be successfully held by a numerically weaker force using the terrain of the mythical 'Kokoda Gap'. One can only speculate on the feelings of utter rejection and despair that must have swept through the minds of the young defenders, outnumbered and outgunned, as they witnessed the exit of critical reinforcements from the skies above Kokoda and, with them, the departure of hope for the forlorn force below.

At Kokoda, on 28 July 1942, the precedent had been set for the treatment of the 30th and 21st Brigades in the succeeding weeks of the campaign. Deficiencies of supply and equipment and the withholding of much-needed reinforcements were to hamper effective deployment and offensive action and to compel the piecemeal commitment of inadequate forces until, by distant Ioribaiwa, the long Japanese thrust was to be blunted and broken on the still defiant and unwavering Maroubra Force shield.

With Owen thus isolated and so greatly vulnerable, the Japanese spent some hours deploying their troops for the attack upon Kokoda. At around 2 am on 29 July, they mortared the Australians' positions and laid down concentrated machine-gun fire. The Australians possessed no mortars with which to reply to this bombardment. Captain Bidstrup had an interesting interview before being ordered to walk over the Owen Stanley Range with his D Company from Port Moresby:

> I'm told there's a general to see me. And there's Basil Morris. 'Believe you flew over?' 'Yes Sir.' 'What's the track like?' I said that I was quite surprised. There were quite a few open spaces where I believed we could use mortars. And he said 'Rot boy! Bloody rot! The mortars would burst in the tree tops!'[27]

At approximately 2.30 am the Japanese launched an all-out attack up the steep slope at the northern end of the area where Lieutenant Seekamp was deployed. Extremely close fighting ensued with the Australians responding with rifle fire and grenades. Lieutenant Garland well remembers the events of that night:

Kokoda—the first battle

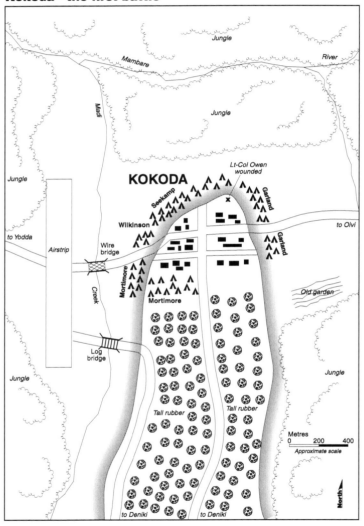

When Owen came to us we were on the perimeter of Kokoda. He was a fine man. He formed us around the perimeter of Kokoda because this was where the Japanese would attack. He was another one similar to Sam Templeton, that wanted to show his leadership, and he walked around the top of the perimeter where we were all lying down; naturally you would because you could see the Japs a couple of hundred yards away forming up. And I said 'Sir, I think you're taking an unnecessary risk walking around amongst the troops like that.' 'Well' he said, 'I've got to do it.' I suppose a half an hour later he got shot right through the forehead.[28]

As the events of this fateful night unfolded, the young Australians were quickly becoming disorientated and separated. Before long, the plateau became a confused mass of attackers and defenders as perimeters were pierced and flanks penetrated.

. . . it was difficult to tell friend from foe in the misty moonlight. At about 3.30 Brewer and Stevenson moved out from what had been the Assistant Resident Magistrate's house— about 40 yards below the centre of the melee—towards a group of men over whose heads Stevenson threw a grenade as he called upon them to assist in repelling what seemed to be a new facet of the attack. Then a cross-fire from both defending flanks swept the group while, from their right, someone began to throw bombs at the two officers. The men Stevenson had called to were Japanese.[29]

The Japanese, seemingly unconcerned at the prospect of incurring heavy casualties, paid dearly for their assault.

Soon it was clear that the attackers were through the northern positions and both flanks. The Australians were falling back, leaving Owen unconscious and with only a few minutes to live. Watson, Stevenson, Brewer and Morrison were among the last to withdraw. Just behind them were a Bren gunner named 'Snowy' Parr and his mate, reluctantly giving ground. A group of 20 or 30 of their enemies appeared in the cleared area close to Parr. He blasted them deliberately at close range. Brewer said later 'I saw Japs dropping.' Parr thought he got about 15 of them. 'You couldn't miss,' he said.[30]

Doctor Geoffrey Vernon has left an extremely vivid account of his experiences that night. It is of interest to note that even to a man of Vernon's familiarity with the region, the terrain and particularly Kokoda provided an incredibly eerie and all-consuming backdrop to men engaged in bitter fighting for their lives. Vernon's brilliant evocation of the scene is well worth quoting at some length:

On arrival, I reported to the 39th Battalion and then inspected and arranged the police house, which had been converted into the R.A.P. . . . Dusk fell early, a grey, misty, cheerless evening though the moon was at the full. Jap scouts had already been reported, and about 7.30, cat-calls and a stray mortar shot or two came ringing across the Mambare. Thereafter, there was increasing noise and salvoes of firing, mostly I think, from the Japs, who had a big mortar with them, at shorter and shorter intervals. By midnight, the firing on both sides had become almost continuous . . . About one o'clock on the 29th a hand touched my shoulder. It was Brewer, with news that Colonel Owen had been wounded. The moon was now in full strength, and shone brightly through the white mountain mist as I hurried with Brewer past the old magistrate's house, now the H.Q., where we picked up a stretcher and several bearers . . . Major Watson came in to see him, and then we had four or five casualties in rapid succession who, when dressed, were told to get back to Deniki as soon as they could. Wilkinson held the lantern for me, and every time he raised it, a salvo of machine-gun bullets was fired at the building. This particular enemy machine-gun was as yet a little below the edge of the escarpment, probably just behind Graham's back premises, so its range was bound to be too high, and while the roof was riddled, those working below could feel reasonably safe . . .

We had now evacuated our walking wounded, and there was a lull in our work. Presently, Wilkinson came bursting into the R.A.P. and said that an order for all to retreat at once had been given . . . Before leaving, I spent some five or ten minutes in the R.A.P. during which we fixed up Colonel Owen, who was now dying as comfortably as possible—moistening his mouth and cleaning him up. Then I stuffed our operating instruments and a few dressings into my pocket, seized the lantern, and went out towards the rubber. Outside, the mist had grown very dense, but the moonlight allowed me to see where I was going. Thick white streams of vapour stole between the rubber trees, and changed the whole scene into a weird combination of light and shadow. The mist was greatly to our advantage; our own lines of retreat remained perfectly plain, but it must have slowed down the enemy's advance considerably, another chance factor that helped to save the Kokoda force . . .

I thought on reflection that I should remain for a while, at least till I had met some responsible officer, and I called to several withdrawing parties to ask if there were any officers amongst them. The men seemed neither to know, or greatly care; their orders to leave had been definite enough, and they were carrying them out. By now, I had gone nearly half a mile through the rubber, and I turned back and hid behind the trunk of a tree just at the edge of the Kokoda clearing, in sight of the R.A.P. and the station garden. The firing had almost died down, and the parties making for the hills were smaller and came less frequently. Finally, after a long period, during which no-one passed and I was beginning to think I had better leave too, Major Watson, in company with Lieutenant Brewer and a couple of officers of the 39th Battalion passed along the track. I felt considerably relieved, and leaving my hiding place, called to

Watson, who said, 'Come on, we are the last out.' Actually, two men followed us a little later. I heard afterwards that the station was then full of Japs, but in the mist, I recognised none, nor was I molested in any way . .

. . . It was an experience I would not have cared to miss, and among the impressions of that exciting night, none stands out more clearly than the weirdness of the natural conditions—the thick white mist dimming the moonlight, the mysterious veiling of trees, houses and men, the drip of moisture from the foliage, and at the last, the almost complete silence, as if the rubber groves of Kokoda were sleeping as usual in the depths of the night, and the men had not brought disturbance.

When Kokoda fell to the Japanese, the youngsters of the 39th had already endured much—they had been thrust headlong into the initial stage of what was to become a bitter and desperate battle for the survival of Port Moresby. For the raw teenagers, appallingly ill-equipped, untrained and unsure venturers in a strange environment, the arduous week of combat, the lack of sleep and food and the tragic loss of the brave Templeton and Owen combined to foster feelings of isolation and despair. Warrant Officer John Wilkinson:

Reached Deniki after daylight, very buggered. Dr. Vernon, Don Barnes and self worked all morning on wounded. Took up position on road and new section under Lt. McNamara arrived. Don Barnes left with wounded. Some others also left with him by mistaking orders. My nerves on edge. Slept with Peter Brewer and Captain Stevenson. Many others on edge. Troops dejected about Captain Templeton. He may still come back as some others have. He was Uncle Sam to all.[31]

The scene was now set for the remaining companies of the 39th Battalion to join the battered vanguard at Deniki. Kokoda was lost. The battle for the Trail to Port Moresby was about to begin. But a young Major sent to assume temporary command of Maroubra Force was now hurrying to Deniki. He was not prepared to abandon hope for the acquisition of the airstrip with its strategic importance. His plans for an attack to retake Kokoda would involve the 39th Battalion in a desperate gamble that could bring triumph or tragedy.

5

A desperate baptism

During the week following the death of Lieutenant-Colonel Owen and the withdrawal of B Company from Kokoda to Deniki, the Australians and the Japanese consolidated their respective positions and prepared for the confrontation that could decide the future of Port Moresby. For the Japanese, phase one, the landings near Gona and the occupation of Kokoda had been accomplished. They had confirmed that, so far, the Kokoda Trail was a viable route to Port Moresby. Patrols were pushed out seeking possible Australian forces beyond their flanks. Supplies were hauled to Kokoda and, most importantly, Major-General Horii and his main force would now land and come forward for the launching of phase two—a concentrated thrust over the Owen Stanley Range.

While the Japanese were thus occupied, the Australians were confronted with two pressing problems which needed immediate consideration—supply and concentration of force.

The problem of supply was to be the Achilles' heel of the Australian efforts to hold the Kokoda Trail from the time of the original Japanese landings near Gona, right through until fresh brigades would later pursue the depleted and exhausted Japanese from their abandoned positions at Ioribaiwa in September. By that time the disruption of supplies would become more deadly to the Japanese than to the Australians. In the meantime, the Australian force was to have two exacting enemies—the Japanese, and the limiting and debilitating supply situation which inhibited the commander's ability to concentrate his force and left the soldier underfed, ill-equipped, poorly clothed, cold and wet.

Lieutenant Kienzle, having been allotted the chief task in addressing that supply situation, realised that a new and reliable drop zone must be found.

August 1, 1942. I started off from Isurava for Eora Creek at 1000 hours. Stopped at Alola Village, where I met Lt. Mortimore, B Company 39th Battalion and showed him tracks leading to and from this village to Seregina (on the southern slopes of Owen Stanley Range) and Abuari, a village on northeast of Eora Creek valley and opposite to Isurava in the same valley. I called in two Biagi natives to act as guides to troops. I then returned to Eora Creek, where I met Major S. Elliott-Smith, who had walked in from Port Moresby.

August 2, 1942. I left Eora Creek at 0800 hours for the main range to locate the 'Dry Lakes' for a suitable dropping ground. We made camp at the head waters of a clear, slow-moving creek which flowed south and proved to be the head waters of Efogi Creek. At 1800 hours erected shelters from pandanus leaves. There was an abundance of these palms in the area and this proved an advantage in establishing a large camp as base. Water supply was good. I had to huddle up around fires with my natives all night as it was bitterly cold. At 6000 feet it can get very cold indeed.

August 3, 1942. We broke camp at 0700 hours and arrived at first 'dry lake' at 0725 hours. Only 20 minutes walk from where we had camped the previous evening. It presented a magnificent sight—a large patch of open country right on top of the main range of the Owen Stanleys. It was just the very thing I had been looking and praying for to assist us in beating the Japanese. The 'dry lake' is a patch of open ground measuring roughly about one and a quarter miles long by one-third of a mile wide, a creek running through the middle, a tributary of Efogi and swampy, each side covered with a sharp reed and the higher ground with short tufts of grass. The finding and locating of this area of Myola, was to prove of immense value to our war effort and was indeed a turning point.

August 4, 1942. I left Myola at 0800 hours for Eora Creek, and blazed a new trail north-east over the 'Gap' by following a ridge. The junction of this new trail with the Kagi–Eora Creek track is where I established another camp and named it 'Templeton's Crossing' in memory of Captain Templeton.[1]

Lieutenant Kienzle spent the next few days requesting plane supply drops at the new camp, and also instigating the building of shelters and latrines at Myola and the laying of a phone line between Myola and the main Kokoda track. By 4 August, the most forward Australian positions at Deniki were now in contact with Port Moresby, due to this phone line. Kienzle's contribution to the logistical maintenance of Maroubra Force had been quite outstanding, particularly when it is remembered that he had been given so little time.

However, the inescapable fact concerning supply up until this time, and indeed for the immediate future, was that Maroubra Force still depended largely upon the ability of the native carriers to sustain it. Doctor Geoffrey Vernon:

The native carrier starts with a physique and constitution considerably inferior to that of the white soldier, nor is he anything like so carefully selected medically for service. The medical examination on entrance, even in the best of hands, does not aim at a very high standard, and only obvious disabilities debar service. A standard similar to that adopted for the A.I.F. or A.M.F. would almost deplete the force. In addition, the native resisting powers to disease is inferior to the white man's and both physically and mentally he is more likely to succumb to sickness. The sole advantage is that he is more used to the country and to the hardships (inferior diet, exposure to rain and cold, excessive walking, climbing etc.) it imposes on all who are working along the Main Range route . . .

During this period,[2] which roughly corresponds to the entire Japanese forward move from Kokoda to Ioribaiwa, conditions for carriers were at first but little improved on account of the pressing need for the Australian troops who were given preference in portable goods. Thus at that time many carriers were without a single blanket, rice was practically the only food issue, meat was withheld for two or three weeks and tobacco scarce; the regulation governing the reduction of loads to 40 lbs was often ignored and excessive weights and distances imposed on the carriers as if they were merely pack animals. No day of rest could be given for weeks.[3]

The second pressing problem for New Guinea Force and, therefore, Major-General Morris at this time was that of concentration of force. As a tentative step towards its solution companies of the 39th Battalion were ordered to cross the Owen Stanley Range to stem the Japanese advance.[4] Captain Noel Symington, MC, 39th Battalion:

When you're on a job like that, going from Moresby to Deniki the first time, and having no information coming to you from any quarter about how Templeton's getting on, you are aware that you don't know whether anybody's much behind you; you don't know where the bloody Japs are; it's raining all the time, every day it rains; its dreadfully difficult to describe the grotesque situation that exists. You're virtually running a long range patrol.[5]

The 39th Battalion companies either had left before the deaths of Templeton and Owen, or were to leave before any significant news of them was received in Port Moresby; furthermore, the telephone line provided little information even to those who did not reach Deniki before it. Each of the company commanders was issued with a small piece of note paper showing the names of the villages and the approximate time, in terms of hours of marching, between villages. Lieutenant Hugh Dalby, MC, 39th Battalion:

> The biggest fear I think that I had was that we got issued with Thompson Sub-Machine Guns the day before we left, and my men had never ever fired a Thompson Sub-Machine, never seen one in their lives. Whenever we had ten minutes to spare at one of these camps, we'd get the machine-gunners to let off a bit of a burst . . . [6]

The young militiamen had not only been poorly armed; they had been left lacking in suitable clothing and pack supplies. They were handicapped by a lack of ground sheets, spare clothing, boots, laces and the multitude of gear necessary for warfare. Jungle uniform is now considered a most basic requirement for a soldier in jungle conditions. The Japanese soldier wore it; the Australian soldier was handicapped by an absence of it. The Bren gun was the standard light machine-gun used by the AIF since early in the war. A small number of these highly prized weapons found their way into the hands of D Company thanks to a swift move by Captain Bidstrup:

> There's a story about how I got those Brens. The night before we were due to leave for Deniki, there's a truck landed up to my Company Headquarters and the bloke asked for the whereabouts of Brigade Headquarters. And I said 'Why do you want Brigade?' He said, 'I've got some guns for him, six Brens.' I said 'right here'. So I scribbled a signature and took the guns. [7]

The death of Lieutenant-Colonel Owen had prompted New Guinea Force to promote Major Allan Cameron[8] to temporary command of Maroubra Force. Cameron had served with the 2/22nd Battalion at Rabaul and, after its fall and his escape from New Britain in a 21-foot boat, had been promoted to Brigade Major, 30th Brigade, at Port Moresby.

When he arrived at Deniki, he found that Maroubra Force comprised 33 officers and 443 other ranks of the 39th Battalion, eight Australians and approximately 35 natives of the PIB and two officers and about a dozen natives of ANGAU. Cameron's arrival is recorded in the pages of Warrant Officer John Wilkinson's Diary.

> 4/8/42. Changed to A Company. Major Cameron arrived later and took charge of all troops. Very bitter towards men. Says they are cowards. Must have met up with the few who shot through.[9]

The men referred to were some of the youngsters of B Company who had 'gone bush' during that company's baptism of fire at Oivi and Kokoda. Cameron refused to acknowledge these men, and considered that the company had lost its good name; he considered it adequate for no more than a reserve role in the future. Two points are worth noting. First, Major Cameron had only just arrived in the area and had promptly branded members of battle-weary B Company cowards and deserters, when in view of the relative strengths of the opposing forces, he desperately needed all possible troops at his disposal. Secondly, these young men had suffered the full brunt of the Japanese advance to Kokoda, and had lost both Templeton and Owen in the process. B Company's later efforts at Isurava under a more perceptive commander were to be the equal of those of any on the Kokoda Trail.

Upon his arrival, Cameron decided to mount an attack to retake Kokoda. The motive(s) for his decision are unclear.

Raymond Paul[10] in *Retreat from Kokoda* claims that Cameron was intent upon disrupting the inevitable Japanese offensive upon Deniki:

> However, Cameron was not content merely to introduce his inexperienced troops to battle in a defensive role. To have done so would have run very much against his grain. The role he created for them was to carry the battle down to the Japanese at Kokoda. He had a two-fold purpose in this—to thrust the untried elements of the 39th Battalion aggressively forward to their baptism of fire, and by taking the Japanese unawares, to disrupt their preparations for the offensive he anticipated against the Deniki perimeter.[11]

When a commander brands as cowards a handful of troops from a battle-scarred company, withdrawing along a jungle track, and then contemplates 'blooding' their untried sister companies in an unnecessary attack against a superior force, his military wisdom must be open to question. Paull also asserts that the Japanese 'rightly concluded' after Cameron's attack that no plan existed in Port Moresby for a reinforcement of Maroubra Force at Kokoda, by air. This is untrue. The 49th Battalion had troops packed and ready to fly to Kokoda upon its capture.[12] Captain Symington, Officer Commanding A Company, 39th Battalion, was also told by Cameron that he would be reinforced by air upon his recapture of Kokoda.[13]

However events in Port Moresby had a considerable bearing on the likelihood of reinforcement. Major-General Morris had but two transport aircraft. Incredibly, they were taken back to Australia on 5 August, and returned shortly before Cameron's attack. The aircraft were American DC 3 transports. Their optimum capacity was for twenty fully equipped soldiers.[14] Therefore the airlifting of one company would have entailed eight plane trips—four each by two planes. To influence the battle effectively Morris would have needed to reinforce Symington with a battalion, as the Japanese had at least 1500 combat troops in this initial stage of the campaign. Such an airlift would have required some dozen or so planes to make four to six trips each. This was beyond the capacity of Morris's resources. Further, the weather conditions for the airlifting of troops and equipment to Kokoda would have limited flights to an average of two or three drops per day due to the excessive rain and mist which often prevailed. Allowing for the necessary equipment and planes, was Kokoda in August 1942 a suitable base for such an operation? Captain H.T. Kienzle, ANGAU:

> Yes; this was actually carried out by U.S. American DC 3 planes after our recapture of Kokoda on the 2nd of November 1942. Within days transports landed at Kokoda Airstrip. I saw up to 6 DC 3 aircraft on that small airstrip in the first week of November unloading food, stores, ammo, medical supplies etc for our forward drive through Oivi, Gorari, Wairopi and on to the beachheads at Gona, Sanananda and Buna. We should have had the Air Force support in early 1942.[15]

Thus, while the feasibility of such a reinforcement was undoubted, the capacity of New Guinea Force to stage it was denied by a lack of aircraft.

On 5 August, as a prelude to the Kokoda attack, Cameron sent three patrols out from Deniki.[16] The first was under Captain Jesser[17] and had as its task, a reconnaissance of Kokoda, to ascertain enemy dispositions and strength. He returned at 6 pm without having made any contact with the enemy. The only activity reported was of working parties building defensive positions on the western side of the rubber plantation at Kokoda.

The second patrol was led by Lieutenant Sorenson[18] of A Company and Lieutenant Brewer of ANGAU, and had as its task a reconnaissance of an 'old' track believed to have been formerly used by the natives as an entrance to Kokoda. They were to ascertain if the Japanese were using the track and whether or not there were any signs of their knowing of its existence. The patrol reported no contacts and no evidence of any use of the track.

The third patrol was under the command of the Intelligence Officer, and Sergeant Evenson (PIB).[19] It had orders to find a suitable ambush point on the Oivi–Kokoda track. This patrol returned on 6 August, having reached a position half an hour's march beyond the village of Komondo. They reported that the junction of the Komondo–Oivi, and the Oivi–Kokoda tracks was an excellent ambush position. The patrol also reported seeing 58 Japanese carrying stores in the direction of Kokoda.

On the basis of the information gained from these patrols and acting upon his desire to gain time against a Japanese thrust farther up the Kokoda Trail, Major Cameron decided to mount a three-pronged attack to retake Kokoda. His plan involved Captain Symington and his A Company in a movement along the 'old' track to Kokoda reconnoitred by Lieutenants Sorenson and Brewer. Theirs would be the task of occupying the Kokoda airstrip pending reinforcements. Captain Bidstrup and his D Company would have the task of marching to the Oivi–Kokoda Track and, by establishing an ambush, preventing any Japanese reinforcements from reaching Kokoda to oppose A Company. Captain Dean and his C Company were given the task of attacking the Japanese along the main Deniki–Kokoda track.

Captain Symington vividly remembers attempting to convince Cameron of the futility of the attack and the very grave risks involved:

> . . . when receiving the orders from Major Cameron, I
> questioned the advisability of the whole operation with him,
> pointed out the lack of patrolling in the area described; the

quite unknown numbers and equipment of the enemy in the Yodda Valley, and the complete lack of any information from the rear headquarters, of the number and equipment landed in the Gona area. Was it a battalion, brigade or division or an army? Major Cameron had no answers to these questions. I personally considered that the perception [*sic*] of the attack was ill-conceived, and highly dangerous bearing in mind the topography of the country. I was amazed that Major Cameron ordered me to fire a Verey light cartridge if and when I occupied Kokoda plantation. I did not think the Deniki outpost would be able to see it, nor did they. The first indication Major Cameron received of our occupation was when a police boy arrived at Deniki from Kokoda with a notebook containing records of the enemy campaign in Malaya and a map which depicted the Kokoda Trail as the route of the Japanese advance on Port Moresby. Its annotations suggested that the enemy had a considerable knowledge of the terrain and the geography of Papua.[20]

The inescapable fact is that the three patrols did not ascertain the whereabouts of the main Japanese force—a force vastly superior in number to that which Cameron commanded. Captain Bidstrup is of the same view:

We did not have sufficient information about the positions of the Japs or the size of their force; no reconnaissance. Remember, our forward troops were kicked out of Kokoda to Deniki. The last time I saw Cyril Dean was on my way down to this Oivi exercise. He didn't survive that day. He knew as well as I knew, that to attack down there on a straight track without sufficient intelligence as to where the enemy was; all they had to do was to enfilade that track, which they did—and that's it![21]

Major Cameron's attack to retake Kokoda was thus doomed from the outset—New Guinea Force did not have the capacity

Major Cameron's attack on Kokoda, 8–10 August 1942

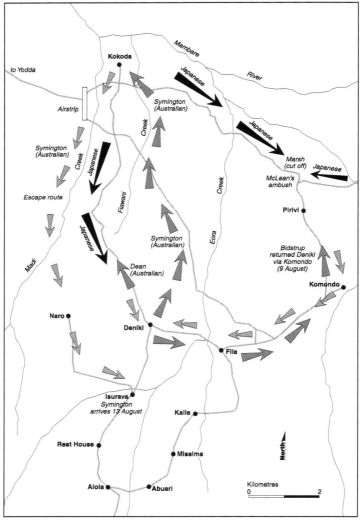

to both reinforce and supply Symington at Kokoda. Major Cameron was also neglecting a prime principle of war; concentration of force. By mounting his three-pronged attack he was diluting his potential for success. If, as Raymond Paull asserts, he was using the attack as a means of blooding the 39th Battalion, the risks involved and the manner in which they were taken, imply a scant regard for the welfare of his force.

Lieutenant-Colonel Ralph Honner[22], who was to command Maroubra Force some eight days after its Kokoda attack, and who was at this time, about to journey over the Kokoda Trail, is also a constructive critic of this attack:

> Not without more reconnaissance. I would not mount an attack
> unless I had a reasonable chance of success, based upon
> thorough reconnaissance; [not] when my orders were to stop
> the Japanese from moving across the mountains towards Port
> Moresby. And I would not separate my force into three separate
> prongs out of touch with each other. I would keep my attacking
> force under my command.[23]

At 6.30 am on 8 August, Captain Bidstrup and his D Company journeyed out from Deniki towards Pirivi with the purpose of ambushing Japanese attempts to reinforce Kokoda from the east. With him went Warrant Officer Wilkinson, Sergeant Evenson and sixteen Papuans. At 7 am Captain Symington and his A Company moved out towards the 'old' track and their mission of the occupation of Kokoda and its prized airstrip. With him journeyed Lieutenant Brewer (ANGAU) and the ever-reliable Sanopa who had previously led B Company out of Oivi. At 8 am Captain Dean and his C Company left Deniki in the company of four Australians and seventeen Papuans of the PIB advancing down the main Deniki–Kokoda track. Captain Jacob,[24] Dean's second in command, remained at Deniki with a skeleton force, while Captain Merritt and his E Company were at Isurava in reserve.

The exhausted and disparaged B Company were deployed farther back at Eora Creek.

Captain Dean and C Company had only just crossed the creek below Deniki when they were confronted with the crossing of a reasonably open gully dominated by the main Japanese force which, unlocated by the patrols on 6 August, was in a prime position to inflict heavy casualties upon venturers along the main track. Dean's troops did not have strength either to dislodge or to do much damage to the Japanese. Very soon after being pinned down, Dean moved forward to examine the situation. He was almost immediately shot, and was dead before the RMO,[25] Captain Shera,[26] could render aid. Lieutenant McNamara[27] was appointed by Cameron to assume command of the attack.

Despite the fact that Dean's death inspired an aggressive surge forward by C Company, the extreme violence of which forced forward Japanese out of their positions and killed some of them, C Company was doomed to be turned back by a vastly superior force. Captain Shera had selfless and devoted help that day. Chaplain Earl[28] assisted Shera and comforted the wounded by giving them cigarettes taken from dead Japanese. Captain Bidstrup MC, 39th Battalion:

> Father Earl, Nobby to us heretics, and whom he liked to be
> called by us who were not of his faith; never have I met a
> man who has made such an impression on me by his absolute,
> simple faith; and if I was asked to say what my definition of a
> thoroughly happy man was I would say Nobby Earl. He owned
> nothing and yet he owned the world.[29]

Another attempt was made to push on by C Company. The 39th Battalion Unit Diary:

> The advance was again held up by machine gun fire at a bend
> in the track, about 400 yards from the river. Two sections were

sent out on either flank to recce another route and if possible, to silence the guns. At 1600 hours the advance was still held up, the sections not having succeeded. As it was considered impossible to reach Kokoda before nightfall, orders were given to withdraw. The withdrawal took place along the main track, the company resuming its original position at Deniki.[30]

The Japanese followed the C Company withdrawal and were firing upon the Deniki position by 6 pm on 8 August. It would be approximately 9 o'clock that night before relative quiet returned to Deniki. The first prong of the three-pronged attack upon Kokoda had failed.

Captain Symington and his A Company had followed in the tracks of D Company, passing through lower Deniki to Eora Creek, and had then turned north along the creek. Using the 'old' track they had an undisturbed journey along the base of the escarpment, and then climbed onto the Kokoda plateau and thus into the rubber plantation. The very small group of Japanese standing in a clearing beyond the rubber trees quickly took to the bush upon sighting the Australians. Kokoda was retaken.

Raymond Paull's account of the consequences of the acquisition of Kokoda is interesting:

> Symington and his men were no less surprised than the Japanese to have recaptured Kokoda so easily. However, having succeeded, Symington began immediately to prepare for the counter-attack that would fall upon him when a nervous Japanese, braving his commander's wrath, informed him that the attack from Deniki had been nothing more than a feint to divert his attention while the Australians walked in and took possession of his headquarters.[31]

Captain Dean's attack was not a feint. He and Captain Bidstrup were given direct orders to converge upon Kokoda after their respective battles.[32] A notebook and map were

77

found by A Company and sent back late that afternoon to Major Cameron. At dusk, as ordered, Company Sergeant Major J.P. Cowey fired a Verey flare to proclaim A Company's taking of Kokoda. Raymond Paull: 'Nobody imagined that Cowey's Verey flare would go unnoticed at Deniki.'[33]

As already noted, Captain Symington had questioned the chances of its being sighted with Cameron before the attack. Thus, as Symington deployed his force around Kokoda, the situation was that C Company had been unsuccessful in its mission and had lost its commander, and that Symington had taken Kokoda and had fired a Verey Light that had gone unnoticed at Deniki. The first news Cameron was to have of A Company's success was to be given him by the native sent by Symington with the captured Japanese notebook and map. The native arrived at 10 am on 9 August, in the company of Sanopa. Both returned to Kokoda soon after.

Before A and C Companies had been thus committed, Captain Bidstrup and his D Company had left Deniki at 6.30 am on the 8th, with the purpose of cutting off any force coming along the Buna–Oivi–Kokoda track to assist the Japanese at Kokoda. D Company met their first opposition at Pirivi where they accounted for two Japanese in the village and one in an adjacent garden before being delayed by snipers for over an hour. During this engagement, Captain Bidstrup sustained light casualties. One of the wounded was Lieutenant Crawford,[34] who decided to go back to Deniki alone and was not seen again. Bidstrup gave command of Crawford's platoon to Sergeant Marsh.[35]

Arriving at the track junction, Bidstrup then placed Lieutenant McClean's platoon in position on the eastern side of the junction and Marsh's platoon on the western side. Lieutenant Hirst and his platoon were held in reserve. News of D Company's arrival in the area did not take long to reach the Japanese positioned at Oivi, to the east, and another force between Bidstrup and Kokoda. Although the Japanese knew that an Australian force was in the area they fell into D Company's waiting ambush. Some 45 of them were killed and possibly a similar number wounded.[36] A larger enemy force, following up, felt for the Australian flanks. Australians and Japanese engaged each other in the jungle. Marsh's platoon found itself confined to a small perimeter defence and sustained casualties very early in the battle. The events of the next few hours vividly demonstrated the extreme difficulty of communication in jungle such as that found on the Trail and the immense strain fighting in such an environment would place on those thrust into action there. Both Bidstrup and Marsh made attempts to get word to each other as the battle raged. Their distance apart was little more than 80 yards. Captain M.L. Bidstrup, MC, 39th Battalion:

> All of my platoons were almost within voice call. I sent two runners from one platoon to another; they never reached it and I've never heard or seen them since. What I'm illustrating, is the fact that you can get people in that short area of jungle and you don't know what bloody well happens to them.[37]

By late afternoon, Bidstrup had a number of quick decisions to make. Darkness was approaching; he had heard no firing from Kokoda; Marsh was cut off. He was confronted with a sizeable Japanese force which could add to its number at any time. He was isolated from Dean and Symington. To stay when there was no evidence that either Symington or Dean had succeeded in his mission might invite the annihilation of his own force. So by darkness, when hanging on might mean further casualties and possibly worse, the main body of D Company withdrew, harassed energetically by the Japanese. They carried their wounded with them and stayed that night at Komondo.

Marsh, having been ordered to withdraw if cut off, and unable to communicate with Bidstrup, spent the night in a small perimeter defence. When one of his men quietly slipped away into the hostile jungle in search of water for the wounded, Marsh soon found that he had lost another man—and then another looking for the first. It would be two long days before he and his men would return to Deniki, carrying their wounded on rough stretchers. D Company had lost six men killed, three missing and a smaller number wounded. Their ambush, however, had been most successful.

By the night of 9 August, the plan to retake Kokoda had clearly miscarried. C Company had not journeyed far on the 8th before being forced to stand-to back at Deniki; its commander was dead. The main body of D Company, while having successfully ambushed a strong Japanese force, was camped at Komondo, on its way back to Deniki. Symington's Verey flare signal for his acquisition of Kokoda had gone unsighted; and his later message confirming occupation could give no hope that it could be maintained without reinforcement. Warrant Officer J.D. Wilkinson:

> 9/8/42. Left for Deniki 0800 hours. Sat up all night putting hot stones round stretcher case. Sucking wound of back. Holding Rosary and Crucifix all the time. Very bad wound. No rations at all. Made Deniki 1700 hours very wet and tired. Completely buggered but felt better after a meal. Cameron chewing his whiskers. Deniki was fired on today.[38]

Major Cameron had much cause for 'chewing his whiskers'! A Company had left with approximately 100 rounds, two days' dry rations and two grenades per man. Urgent requests by Cameron via the phone line were made for supply and reinforcement of A Company at Kokoda. New Guinea Force intimated that supply drops would be forthcoming next day, the 10th. Cameron rightly informed New Guinea Force that drops next day would more than likely be too late and that careful reconnaissance beforehand would be vital.

Captain Symington knew nothing of the tribulations of C and D Companies on the 8th. He deployed Lieutenant Trotter and 7 Platoon on the plateau and overlooking the airstrip. Sergeant Guest and his 8 Platoon were deployed on the eastern side above the approach that would be taken by any Japanese force from Oivi. Lieutenant Neal[39] and his 9 Platoon were positioned 50–100 yards into the big rubber plantation to the south.

In the late morning of 9 August, the Japanese had advanced slowly and stealthily towards Neal's positions. Smeared with mud and wearing jungle uniform, they were most difficult to identify as they approached through the densely wooded cover. It was estimated by Symington that two main Japanese attacks in the late morning and early afternoon were made by some 200 enemy soldiers.

At 5.30 pm the Japanese launched their most determined and violent attack yet, committing an estimated 300 troops. They used smoke bombs, mortars, grenades and light machine-guns during an attack that was to keep the desperate defenders fighting for some two hours. But the Australians flayed the attackers with deadly rifle fire and used their limited grenade supply to telling effect. Lieutenant-Colonel Tsukamoto, fearing reinforcement of the Australian force by air, attempted to sustain the pressure upon the young militiamen by continued infiltration of their perimeter during the night. Close, desperate individual fighting broke out, where grenade and bayonet were used to repel the invaders. The extreme darkness and constant rain aided the Japanese. Two men of Neal's platoon in a forward position were found with their throats cut.

At 10.30 pm the persistent Japanese maintained the pressure with yet another attack. A captured Japanese diary reveals an insight into the stubbornness of the young Australians:

Advanced stealthily on hands and knees and gradually moved in closer to the enemy. Suddenly encountered enemy guards in the shadow of the large rubber trees. Corporal Hamada killed one

81

of them with the bayonet and engaged the others but the
enemy's fire forced us to withdraw. The platoon was scattered
and it was impossible to repeat our charge . . . The night attack
ended in failure. No. 1 Platoon also carried out an attack about
0300 but it was unsuccessful. Every day I am losing my men. I
could not repress tears of bitterness. Rested waiting for
tomorrow, and struggled against cold and hunger.

Early on 10 August, an Allied plane circled Kokoda. Despite
frantic waving from the militiamen, it left for Port Moresby
having dropped no ammunition, food or information. That
was the reconnaissance plane that reported Japanese around
Kokoda, and because of that report, the waiting 49th Battalion
company was not airlifted to Kokoda that day. Symington then
decided that if no help had arrived by approximately 7 pm he
would withdraw. His food supply was now virtually non-
existent, the last of the captured Japanese rice having been
consumed. His men had fought almost continuously for two
days and were showing the strain. He had wounded who
needed medical help. But most serious of all his problems was
that his ammunition supply was precarious. He barely had
enough with which to disengage himself from his attackers.

The Japanese had also sighted the Allied reconnaissance
plane. Its significance was not lost on Lieutenant-Colonel
Tsukamoto. As a consequence he launched yet another
determined attack just before dusk. Symington's A Company
now experienced what was to become a regular Japanese
performance prior to battle. Very loud chants were plainly
heard reverberating along the valley. A Japanese officer apparently then enquired as to whether the young Australians were
frightened. Suitable Australian replies were forthcoming that
must have indeed tested this Japanese officer's limited English
vocabulary! The Japanese then attacked, once again bringing
to bear mortar bombs and machine-gun fire in concerted
attempts to breach the A Company perimeter.

Practically out of ammunition as the renewed assaults were mounted from the south and east, Symington ordered an earlier start to his withdrawal over the western edge of the Kokoda plateau to cross Madi Creek and the airstrip and rendezvous at dawn next morning at a garden above the Yodda–Deniki track. Lieutenant Brewer was detailed to guide Lieutenant Sorenson's striking force of two sections of Trotter's 7 Platoon. They headed across the swing bridge spanning Madi Creek followed by Symington and his company headquarters with Lance Corporal Sanopa as guide. Sergeant Major Mowat's diary noted:

> 1845. Japs' attacks heavier. Heavy Mortar bombardment. 1900 Withdrawal commences. Japs swarm through. In darkness probably fight own men. Withdrawal successful. Parties lose touch. Waded through river. Crossed drome into bush.[40]

The withdrawal was only partly successful. Darkness had already fallen and the firing in the rubber to the south was at its most intense when Guest's 8 Platoon rearguard, breaking contact with the enemy on the east, gathered up two stretcher-cases and a few walking wounded—most walking wounded were back fighting with their sections—to follow Symington. But they did not follow him across the airstrip. Guest relates how his party lost touch:

> Johnny Stormont was dying and we couldn't move him, but we managed to get Les Skinner onto a blanket stretcher. I took one end of the stretcher and Ted Mitchell (our company cook) took the other. It was pouring rain as we struggled down the edge of the plateau but the firing was still intense. Then suddenly, in the darkness, we found ourselves in the waters of Madi Creek. Luckily, 'Bluey' Murray had joined in to take my end of the stretcher just as I was swept off my feet by the current to land on the creek bed held down by a haversack

full of .45 'Tommy' gun shells. I managed to get rid of the haversack and reach the far bank of the creek . . . Ted Mitchell said to me 'Les Skinner is dead' . . . So we left him there in the pouring rain and the by now almost pitch darkness and struggled on for some distance—it was a case of the blind staggering after the blind . . . I decided . . . to remain where we were until dawn . . . There were sounds of shouting coming from the plateau but I couldn't understand anything because of the pouring rain.[41]

Back on the plateau was Staff Sergeant Cowey.[42] An experienced bushman, he had volunteered to guide Guest's rearguard but, when he realised from the grenade explosions and small-arms fire from the rubber plantation that the defenders were still fighting there, he decided to stay behind to lead them out; two Tommy gunners insisted on remaining with him as a bodyguard. As was so often the case during the grim early days of the 39th Battalion's campaigns, a desperate hour produced a calm resolute leader. Jim Cowey, MC was the man for this climactic hour. He gained a commission in the Great War and was nearly 52 years old when he had joined the 39th. He was unaware that no withdrawal orders had reached Neal's isolated four-section force; he knew they were still in action and waited watchfully to gather and guide the survivors when they should extricate themselves.

When the Japanese had attacked on the morning of the 9th, Corporal 'J.D.' McKay's Section of 7 Platoon had gone forward under fire to extend the right of 9 Platoon's defensive line along a stormwater drain across the rubber plantation. The combined force had borne the brunt of enemy assaults through two days and already into a second night. Their .303 ammunition supply had been augmented from Lewis gun drums left behind by B Company in the first Battle of Kokoda but there was never enough. Corporal (Acting Platoon Sergeant) Larry Downes explains:

The closest they'd got to us until then was about 5 yards—the distance to the next row of rubber trees. That was pretty close. Then one of them would blow a whistle and they'd all go back again. They couldn't get through and that's why they were so frustrated. They never would have got through if we'd had enough ammunition. They would have had to kill every one of us—but you can't fight without ammunition.[43]

Having been under fire throughout the afternoon Neal and Downes went back in the evening gloom in the hope of replenishing ammunition for another long night. They found Sorenson, Trotter and Symington gone, the last of Guest's men moving out and Cowey waiting. They hurried back to their line to direct its defenders to the assembly point. The Japanese chose that moment to launch the full weight of their final attack so it was not easy to break contact. Lance Corporal Alex Lochhead, MC:

I sent Smythe and Dridan (both wounded) back and covered them with my Thompson. When I saw Roy Baxter fall back I emptied a drum magazine at the advancing Japs and moved back through the rubber myself . . . When I got back to the clearing Jim Cowey was waiting there. He grabbed me and said: 'Wait with me and we'll pick up a few more as they come out.' The main attack had died down but there was still some small-arms fire and grenade explosions on the right flank.[44]

'J.D.' McKay has left an account of the final onslaughts on that right flank and of what followed:

Just on dusk there was a nice little shower of rain and the first assault wave came in and we stopped 'em. My Bren gun group, Bill Drummond and Bill Spriggs, were firing and I can see the gun firing now—no kidding, you could see the bullets going up the barrel and it ran red-hot. Vern Scattergood had a Bren too and he was firing wildy. We stopped 'em again. Then there was a bit of a pause before the next wave came in and overran us. So we said; 'We'd better get out because they've gone past us.' Well old Scattergood (or should I say young Scattergood?—he was younger than me) he got excited. He was standing up firing the Bren from the hip and that was the last I saw of young Scattergood. He must have been hit. We couldn't find him in the dark and we moved back. After we came out of the rubber, we found Johnnie Stormont in the Company Headquarters dug-out. We tried to put a shell dressing on him but the wound was too big and he was dying. We had to leave him. We only moved a few more yards and we were challenged! It was old Jim Cowey, the coolest, bravest man I have ever known. There he was, in the kneeling position, with his rifle pointing at us. Jim's motto was if you were a 'digger' he had to get you out. The rest of the company had gone, but he'd stayed to get us out because he knew we'd been left behind.

Old Jim had picked up about three or four of us by now and he said 'Just stay quietly', and then he dispersed us a bit. And then he got Roy Neal and Larry Downes, and I think that was about all of us. You know most were dead then. There were no wounded in our group. Then Jim said, 'Good! We'll walk out.' I was all for running out but there were Japs everywhere. They were throwing grenades into weapon-pits, they were searching under the huts, and Jim said; 'We'll walk out. They don't know who we are.' And, if you don't mind, casually got up, put us into single file and walked us out over the bloody bridge! We walked across the airstrip into the dense scrub and then Jim said; 'Good! We'll rest here till daylight.' So he puts us down and then 'clunk', being a youth and mentally and physically exhausted, I fell straight asleep. But I suppose old Jim Cowey, being the amazing soldier that he was, stayed awake all night.[45]

Cowey was indeed awake, exploring with his Tommy gunners the airstrip and its bush perimeter in a fruitless search for stragglers. Assuming that the main body preceding him across Madi Creek had all got well away beyond the airstrip, he was quite unaware that he had bypassed 8 Platoon and its wounded charges, stopped for the night in the tangled scrub between him and the creek. It was others he sought. When his small group had filed down the track from the plateau to the bridge a burst of fire had scattered them through the bamboo thicket on the slope, separating Neal and two others from the next of the party. And more of the forgotten 'rubber' men, with their empty weapons, were likely to have been forced over the western edge by their rampaging assailants.

Perhaps he still had them in mind next morning when he led his section-sized patrol southwards, wading up flooding streams to evade the enemy before risking swifter but more perilous passage on the Kokoda–Deniki track. Along the way the missing trio led by Neal rejoined them, Alex Lochhead welcomed back Harry Barkla and 'J.D.' McKay saw his still-grinning gun crew, Bill Drummond and Bill Spriggs, walk out of the scrub with their seized-up Bren and three rounds in their last magazine. 'J.D.' McKay continues his story:

So we continue the 'advance' (as I call it) when all of a sudden a burst from a 'Juki' M.G. chops a billet of wood from a tree above Jim Cowey's head. Jim didn't even grunt—he just carefully leans against a tree, restrains the breathing slightly, and shoots the No. 1 on the 'Juki'. Then the No. 2 rolls in and takes his place. Jim restrains the breathing again after reloading at the shoulder and shoots the No. 2. Talk about coolness! Of course by this time there's Japs running everywhere and everytime one of 'em jumps down behind the 'Juki' Jim shoots him. I remember I fired a burst of 'Tommy' gun and the damn thing jams, and old Jim still firing from the shoulder, says; 'Throw that bloody thing away!' You know, they couldn't even ruffle him! And then he says 'I think we'll withdraw', and he just casually moves off the track into the scrub. So we withdraw—went around the back of 'em. And then we bump into another outpost—a listening post I think. We see them first (otherwise we would have been sitting ducks) and Roy Neal lobs a grenade into their hole and that finishes them.

We go on all day and just on dusk we're climbing a mountain when we come to this village called Naro (we were sort of hooking to the right of Deniki coming from Kokoda). So we lie there quietly for a while and have a look at it. Then old Jim (who was obviously in charge) says; 'Well, I think we'll go in and have a look'. And Roy Neal and Larry Downes go into the village with him while we sort of gave 'em covering whatever we could (we were going to throw bricks at 'em I think!). So Jim and the other two go into the village and then wave to us to follow them, and the natives wave us in too, and in we go. It was just getting dark and we could see their fire glows. And then bloody A Company walks in from the other side of the village with Symington—they had arrived there a few hours earlier and had been having a scout around.

Now when those other A Company blokes walk in there was great rejoicing all round because they'd written us off. There was Company Headquarters with some of the wounded and the rest of 7th Platoon and part of 9th Platoon—they must have pulled 'em in when they moved down the edge of the plateau. I remember that night Symington said; 'These fellas (our party) will sleep the night. Everybody else except the wounded will stand to.' So they put us in a hut and of course we were starving and the 'marys' were cooking this pumpkin. They gave us this pumpkin and I can still taste it—it was delicious you know! But it was cold and dark in the hut and I remember rolling over and a bloke saying 'Watch my arm!' and I said: 'What's the matter?' and he said 'It's got a bullet in it.' And it was Vic Smythe who'd come out with Company Headquarters with some other walking wounded.[46]

Late on the following day, the 12th, a native from Naro arrived at Deniki with a message from Symington reporting that A Company was moving back but needed help with the wounded. Warrant Officer Wilkinson volunteered to patrol to ascertain their position and assist their wounded.

12/8/42. I volunteered to go for them and left 1715 hours with guide and P.I.B. native troops as carriers. Deniki expecting attack when I left. Japs on track to A Company but we sneaked through long grass. Held my breath for nearly half an hour, or it seemed like it. Worst trip I have ever made. Jap coughed about ten feet away. I shrivelled up into almost nothing. P.I.B. lads stuck and we had to hold each other to keep on path. In the forest luminous fungus took on all sorts of shapes and made for weird effects. All fell off the track at times. Eventually lighted fire and used fire sticks for guides. On into old garden in light rain. Too black to see six feet. Could see Naro Village outline on top of hill. Was told troops were there. Five of us fell into a deep ravine from a log we were crawling across. Heard voice from top of hill and got scared that troops would fire on us and I would lose carriers. Swore loudly and long to let them know it was an Australian there. Also because I had fallen on top of one native but three more had fallen on me. Heard someone say faintly, 'That's Wilkinson down there. I recognise the way he swears.' Reached NARO Village by 2320 hours. A bit buggered. No food. Several wounded. Peter Brewer very weak with dysentery, but still able to smile. All food dropped to troops in Kokoda fell in Jap lines. Symington very annoyed.

13/8/42. Left 0600 hours. Arrived W.T. station 1200 hours. Still no food. Peter Brewer still able to move feet but unable to stand. Most troops tired but still a fighting force. Very little ammo. Fr Earl had long stick in one hand and Rosary in other. He shivered every time a mortar went off in the hills. Then he said to carriers 'Come on, they won't hit us', and the carriers followed him. We raided line and shared a tin of salmon with every two men. Cut my tongue licking tin. Hell, I was hungry. Reached Isurava 1730 hours absolutely done in. Only one big building. Rain all night. Mud everywhere . . . [47]

89

The battle to retake and hold Kokoda had been a desperate baptism of fire for the young, raw and poorly equipped 39th Battalion. Its survivors, who had withstood all that the Japanese had thrown against them, had begun to develop into hardened veterans; they had lost a battle but had gained experience. However, experience of equal value could have been acquired at less cost and to greater advantage.

History will assess the abortive attack on Kokoda as ill-conceived, based upon a threadbare reconnaissance, upon an unfounded expectation of support and supply from Port Moresby and, crucially, upon a desperate gamble where the stakes so recklessly risked were at least two companies of an already grossly outnumbered force. Captain Noel Symington MC, 39th Battalion:

> . . . I think we would have all done better at Deniki, because we had the high ground. I think we would have all done better not to have expended the energy we did in this operation. We would have had more mutual support to defend from Deniki. Deniki was not indefensible. It was quite a good spot. It overlooks Kokoda. It's a very high area and I think you'll find if you had the choice and if we'd been able to dissuade Cameron from attacking we would have imposed as great a delay possible with less casualties from Deniki.[48]

6

On our last bloody legs

The valiant but unsuccessful attempt by the 39th Battalion to retake and secure the prize of Kokoda during the period 8–10 August, had a number of important consequences for both the Japanese and the Australians.

For Lieutenant-Colonel Tsukamoto, the initial shock of having an enemy force secure a foothold close to the vital airstrip so unexpectedly and swiftly, must have been more than a little disturbing. Although able to force A Company's withdrawal from Kokoda, Tsukamoto had sustained significant casualties and had lost some two to four days which could have been utilised exploiting his gains rather than protecting his rear. However he must have taken great heart from some very obvious factors concerning his position after Kokoda. The fact that Kokoda was the key to the domination of the Kokoda Trail was obvious to both sides. Having denied the Australians the objective of Kokoda, Tsukamoto knew that they were now committed to a long and debilitating supply line, with a six to eight day march for reinforcements to the front and also for the wounded to be evacuated. Thus the initiative lay quite decisively with the Japanese.

Over 40 years after the event, many 39th Battalion veterans believe that their determined attempt to capture and hold Kokoda confused the Japanese as to the strength of Maroubra Force.[1] This is a valid point. Had Tsukamoto known that he was fighting against barely company-strength opposition, he would have undoubtedly pressed home his enormous numerical superiority with more vigour. A jungle environment, particularly that found on the Kokoda Trail, can conceal the size of a force most effectively. However while the environment may have caused a degree of confusion for the Japanese, Major Cameron's attack to retake Kokoda must have given Tsukamoto two key insights concerning Maroubra Force. Firstly, the failure of the Australians to land troops during their command of the airstrip must have made it apparent to Tsukamoto that his enemy did not possess a capacity to reinforce its forward troops by air—they were thus isolated far from their base. Secondly, the Australians' attempt to hold Kokoda was extremely limited in view of the significance of their objective. Tsukamoto would have therefore quite quickly realised that Major Cameron could not sustain an attack, ie he did not possess a large force in comparison with the Japanese force.

As a further boost to his confidence, Tsukamoto could look forward to the arrival of Major-General Horii and the main body of his crack South Seas Force—and to the vigorous exploitation of his gains.

The soldiers of Maroubra Force had, for nearly three weeks, been engaged in a deadly struggle against both the Japanese and the totally uncompromising environment of the Kokoda Trail. The demands made upon their physical fitness were enormous. Their sleep was drastically curtailed by the obligations of battle and battle-readiness, by the discomforts of wet clothes in muddy posts and by the lack of dry blankets to allay the chill of night. And, despite the incredible efforts of the native carriers and the first intermittent fruits of the droppings of supplies at Myola, food shortages became a constant concern. Lieutenant Hugh Dalby, MC, 39th Battalion:

Bully beef and biscuits! Man, I could have eaten you and sat up and begged for mint sauce after the first five days! Once you get up into the high altitudes, it's cold, it's enervating; you have a tin of bully a day. Sometimes if you were lucky you might get a tin of peaches between about ten. We later got some rice at Isurava. I had a batman called Kennedy. He was a wizard. They brought up a kerosene tin. Now I couldn't light a fire, there was no way known you could light a fire, except this bloke Kennedy. And he cooked the rice. We all got a dixie full of it. By the Lord living Moses! . . . I was the last one to get fed. I could have eaten twice the quantity. A solid something in your stomach![2]

However, in spite of the setbacks and the conditions, the young veterans of Wairopi, Gorari, Oivi and Kokoda still demonstrated the retention, even the enhancement of three unmistakable qualities. Although isolated, fatigued and outnumbered, their morale, determination and humour seemed to have never deserted them. Sergeant John Manol has a vivid recollection of a sample of Lieutenant Doug McClean's sense of humour:

They found a pumpkin and cooked it up. McLean did the right thing and made sure that all the men got theirs first . . . and then he said to me, 'Moey?' 'What is it Doug?' 'Close your eyes and think that you're at Maxims. This isn't pumpkin, imagine this is souffle!' I said to him, 'Close your eyes and cross your bloody legs, and it's still bloody pumpkin!'[3]

Despite the sterling efforts of Lieutenant Kienzle and his carriers, the situation of the 39th Battalion at Deniki was soon at an extremely critical stage. On 12 August, the young militiamen awaited the inevitable Japanese attacks upon their thinly manned positions. The 39th Battalion Unit Diary:

As it was obvious that A Company badly needed rest it was decided that when they reached our lines they would be sent back to Eora Creek, and that the Machine-Gun Company should come forward to occupy A Company's former positions, while B Company would replace Machine-Gun Company at Isurava. Orders were signalled to B and Machine-Gun Companies at 1245 hours to move immediately. During the afternoon enemy troops were seen from Deniki to be marching out of Kokoda towards the main track to Deniki indicating that our positions were to be attacked, and all troops were ordered to stand to. Machine-Gun Company did not arrive at Deniki until after 1700 hours and consequently many of their positions were taken up in the dark and no recces could be made of their area. Careful watch was kept throughout the night, but the enemy remained quiet, and no attack materialised. It was notified that a further Company of the 53rd Battalion was being sent forward and that Brigadier S.H.W.C. Porter D.S.O. Commander of 30th Australian Infantry Brigade was also coming forward to command Maroubra Force.[4]

By the early morning of 13 August, E Company, commanded by Captain Merritt, were occupying the left Deniki flank, Captain Jacob and his C Company held the village of Deniki, and Captain Bidstrup and his D Company occupied the right flank. B Company were held in reserve at Isurava. E Company did not have to wait long for its baptism of fire in the form of an extremely violent and determined attack against Lieutenant Simonson's[5] platoon occupying the extreme left position, a patch of dense scrub, fifteen yards wide and 30 yards deep on the crest of a blunt-nosed spur. During a lull at midday, Simonson heard muffled sounds of the lunch time employment of Japanese mess tins; he crept forward, saw the enemy, and with grenades eliminated two machine-guns and a number of men. But as the battle raged during the afternoon, Simonson suffered numerous casualties and, while forced to yield some ground, his men later struck back with the aid of a liberal supply of grenades which dislodged the Japanese from their hard-won gains.

The Japanese persisted with their favourite tactics of attacking the high ground, probing Simonson's positions for a vulnerable spot and relentless with their pressure. Heavy rain followed by the familiar mist heralded nightfall and the vigilance and fatigue of a dark, wet night were to be interrupted only by spasmodic rifle and machine-gun fire until approximately 1 am on 14 August. Lieutenant Dalby was ordered to take command of Lieutenant Simonson's men. He ventured along to his new position without his own troops. Lieutenant Dalby:

> Simonson was having a firefight. He had a section of ten men. And Captain Merritt said to me 'Hugh, I want you to go down and look after that section for me.' I said, 'I'll pick up my men' and he said, 'No, leave your platoon here, Simonson will look after them' . . . Well that's a funny thing, but you don't tell a Company Commander to go fry his eyebrows so I went down there. There were a couple of dead men there . . . First thing they started dropping mortars in the area. They hit one bloke, he didn't come back. I sent him off with two stretcher bearers and I don't know what happened; it's an unfortunate story that one. I think the Japs got them.[6]

The early morning of 14 August saw the Japanese commit fresh troops to the fight as they redoubled their efforts to pierce the E Company positions. Amid the heavy fighting, the Japanese, despite stout-hearted resistance, used their overwhelming superiority in numbers to get behind some of Merritt's men. That move resulted in the cutting off of both Lieutenant Dalby and his front section from Simonson's platoon and Lieutenant Pentland[7] and some men from C Company. Both groups 'went bush' and stayed well clear of the track as they attempted to navigate their way back to the Australian lines, using a small compass as their only guide.

By approximately 8.30 am the relentless pressure being applied to Captain Merritt's E Company had spread to Captain Jacob's C Company positions in Deniki village in the form of concentrated mortar fire. McCarthy states:

> . . . The Japanese pressure eased and the attacking fire died away. With the lull, however, Cameron decided to withdraw and, in the confusion of the urgent and unexpected move, the men left most of their equipment, and some of their own numbers . . . [8]

Captain Bidstrup, D Company, 39th Battalion:

> It must be emphasised that the 39th Battalion got its weapons and ammunition out; what had to be left was some rations which couldn't be carried. They did not panic as McCarthy seems to infer.[9]

When the events at Deniki are examined against those of the preceding days during the Kokoda battle the word 'unexpected' cannot be realistically applied to Major Cameron's withdrawal. The fact is that whatever time he gained by the occupation of Kokoda from 8–10 August, he quickly lost at Deniki, which was a reasonably good defensive locality. Had Cameron not attacked Kokoda, he would have been in a position to have sent fighting patrols out from Deniki to harass and frustrate the Japanese preparations. At the same time he could have held Deniki with four companies all in reasonable condition and with B Company in reserve. The Kokoda battle saw his A Company hold an untenable position only briefly, awaiting reinforcement that never came; exhausted, it was sent out of battle to rest at Eora Creek. B Company, disparaged by Cameron as he reached the front, had been sent back to Eora Creek and then brought forward again, but only to Isurava. Cameron could ill-afford two of his companies left out of battle at Deniki. In addition, D Company had expended much energy and had sustained significant casualties on the Oivi track. This left Cameron with a 'fresh' E Company and a reasonably intact C Company to use in his prime defensive positions at Deniki. Concentration of force and economy of force were the key principles of war that Cameron had flouted with his attack on Kokoda. Maroubra Force should have been concentrated in one area, for control—at Deniki—with security patrolling of the Alola–Naro tracks on the west of the valley and of the track from Alola to Missima and Kaile on the east of it. At Deniki the 39th paid dearly, and prematurely, for his rashness.

The exhausted young men of the 39th Battalion dug in at Isurava using bully beef tins, bayonets and steel helmets. Cameron formed his perimeter using Captain Jacob and his C Company in the right forward position; Captain Merritt and his E Company in the left forward position; B Company and 17 Platoon, D Company, on the left flank; and Captain Symington and his A Company on the right flank. Captain Bidstrup with the main body of his D Company lay in an ambush position one hour's march north of Isurava. On the morning of 15 August, his ambush accounted for some eight Japanese deaths. Corporal Boland[10] was responsible for the elimination of the two machine-gunners amongst the Japanese patrol. Bidstrup then repositioned his ambush some 30 minutes farther back along the track north of Isurava.

The 16th saw the advent at Alola and Isurava of a new commander of Maroubra Force. On the same day a mutual respect and admiration had its genesis between the men of the 39th Battalion and their newly arrived Commanding Officer which was to grow through the Kokoda Trail and the Gona–Sanananda campaigns. Lieutenant-Colonel Ralph Honner came to Isurava with not only an impeccable military record, but also both personal courage and leadership qualities of the highest order. A schoolmaster turned lawyer he had seen a major war looming and had rejoined the militia as a lieutenant in 1936. When the 6th Division was formed and later sent to the

Middle East, Honner had journeyed with its 2/11th Battalion as one of its original company commanders. As a veteran of Libya, Greece and Crete, he had acquired abundant experience. Lieutenant Hugh Dalby, MC, 39th Battalion:

> I remember from the time I met Ralph Honner I felt a new course of blood. I thought he was the best battalion commander I ever had the privilege to serve under. He was just a man who knew where he was going and what he was doing, and never had to put on any airs and graces.[11]

Honner's orders were quite clear. He was to assume immediate command of Maroubra Force and hold the enemy on the northern side of the mountains until relieved by 21st Brigade. Prior to his arrival at Isurava he had deployed the incoming companies of the 53rd Battalion at Alola to be fresh for use by Brigadier Porter, then crossing the mountains to become the next commander of Maroubra Force. Honner soon set about examining his own positions and his new command. He perceived that Isurava provided a reasonably good delaying position. Its northern and southern extremities allowed for some view over the eastward flowing creeks, which provided obstacles, if narrow ones, for the enemy. Although thick scrub ran virtually up to both the front and rear creeks, there were cleared patches of ground on each side of the track in the central area. Isurava village lay on a flat clearing to the east of the track and south of the front creek. Through the village a steep descending track ran eastwards to Asigari, situated on the other side of the Eora Valley. The western flank was dominated by timber and extremely thick jungle beyond. A track from Naro ridge ran eastwards through an overgrown native garden to join the main Isurava–Deniki track just north of the front creek.

Its track command and its tactical advantages made Isurava an acceptable defensive proposition but it was far from impregnable and it was woefully undermanned. However, the

39th's scattered elements were consolidating and could see themselves as a concentrated force for the first time. On the 16th Honner had brought with him the last resting details from Alola. On the 15th Dalby, and on the 16th Pentland, had led in their troops cut off at Deniki on the 14th. Most welcome of all, Guest's 8 Platoon, extricated from Kokoda on the 10th with walking wounded and stretcher-cases, and adding other A Company men to its ranks, had struggled in, in three groups on the 14th, 17th and 19th.

The Japanese had three alternatives for their attack upon Isurava. The first was an advance along the eastern side of Eora Valley to bypass Isurava. The second alternative was an attack along the higher ground to the west from Naro to Alola. A direct attack upon the 39th Battalion at Isurava was the last—it had the advantages of securing the main track for movement, communication and supply without having to move far afield and over severe gradients. The element of time made the last option the most attractive. If the Japanese were to choose either of the first two, they must cut the track near Alola and then move north to deal with the 39th Battalion from the rear.

Honner deployed his companies to meet the expected attacks. The area bounded by his E, B and D Companies and the main track contained open, overgrown gardens, with some high grass and a sugarcane plantation. The only real killing ground—low grass with good fields of fire—lay west of his B Company's main positions towards the edge of the timber. The enemy should avoid it. But, because they could swing from the Deniki track to the Naro track and cross the creek to come in from the high ground through sparse jungle and rather open woodland opposite his B Company, to assemble in large numbers near the timber edge for the short rush across the killing ground, they might be tempted to try it.

B Company therefore dug in, in deep narrow weapon-pits, with forward posts in the timber edge in front of them and reserve positions behind them for their support—or their retirement in the event of a limited withdrawal.

Very dense jungle between D Company's gentle ridge and the hidden rear creek made an attack from the south unlikely. Therefore, D Company was held available to support B Company's left and prevent the enemy from slipping past.

To the east, difficulty of access, lack of an assembly area and the prospect of a very steep climb up a jungled slope made a major organised attack extremely unlikely.

On the north, the shallow creek was crossable. It did not provide a great killing ground to the defenders, whose requirement of cover for survival minimised the effectiveness of what fields of fire were available. This should be the enemy's prime target. Ample assembly areas were available north of the creek opposite E Company and south of the creek opposite B Company, with easy access to E Company by slipping past B Company's right flank. But above all, there were covered approaches, day or night, into the heart of E Company's stronghold.

The 39th Battalion could hold its open left flank while its B Company commanded its killing ground. But once the enemy penetrated E Company's locality they could pour in sufficient numbers to achieve the conquest of Isurava; and the enemy had the numbers, the capability to concentrate a large force. For the entire struggle for Isurava, this position was the prime piece of Australian military real estate. Lieutenant-Colonel Ralph Honner, DSO, MC:

> It was to cover that weak point—fatally weak once the enemy realised it and exploited it—that we had firm plans in place for quick reaction from counter-penetration and counter-attack platoons from companies not in the anticipated danger areas. It was the best we could do when we could not afford any larger gap in our perimeter than we already had, just to provide a normal reserve.[12]

If the new commander perceived a fair degree of hope from the nature of his defensive positions at Isurava, the sight of the condition of his troops must have been a sobering experience:

Physically the pathetically young warriors of the 39th were in poor shape. Worn out by strenuous fighting and exhausting movement, and weakened by lack of food and sleep and shelter, many of them had literally come to a standstill. Practically every day torrential rains fell all through the afternoon and night, cascading into their cheerless weapon-pits and soaking the clothes they wore—the only ones they had. In these they shivered through the long chill vigil of the lonely nights when they were required to stand awake and alert but still and silent. Only the morning brought a gleam of comfort—a turn at sleeping and forgetting, a chance perhaps, to lie and dry in the warmth of the glowing day.[13]

What was perhaps his most debilitated group called for Honner's special concern and a particular decision. Having served the longest at the front, braved the early battles and suffered the loss beside them of their mates—and their leaders, Templeton and Owen—and having then been disparaged by Cameron for their fraying spirit, B Company stood exposed on the left flank where the main enemy attack might be expected to come down from the high ground. During a brief conference with Honner before his return to Port Moresby, Cameron recommended that B Company be disbanded and that its men be spread through the other companies. Lieutenant-Colonel Honner:

They were the only troops I had. I had to make them as good as possible. They wouldn't have been too well received in the companies they went to, coming with that reputation. I thought that I couldn't afford to lose a company. I went there with the job of holding the Japs, and this was what I had to hold them

101

with; they were my troops and we were going to do the best
we could.[14]

After consultation with his company commanders, Honner
appointed Lieutenant French[15] to command B Company and
emphasised that his men had the responsibility of holding the
ground where the Japanese would more than likely attack—
the post of honour. Ably led by French, B Company's efforts
were to be of the highest order from Isurava until the bloody
battle at Gona in December 1942.

On Porter's arrival—and his approval of the Isurava dispositions—on 19 August, the 39th Battalion became Honner's
sole responsibility. His task remained the same—to buy time
for the build-up, behind him, of the promised offensive—and
he was not going to fritter away his limited resources; there
would be no more rash adventures, no more haphazard stands,
no more precipitate withdrawals:

> There wasn't much I could do in the way of an attack except
> hold the enemy at arm's length as long as possible to prevent
> them from finding out how weak we were and how small
> indeed was our garrison. Had they known how small we were
> they should have gone around us and cut us off from our
> supplies and annihilated us. We had to buy time and buy
> distance as long as possible and as far as possible.[16]

On 17 August, Honner inspected Bidstrup's relocated two-
platoon ambush position on the Deniki track and decided that
its task could be performed by a 24-hour platoon-strength
patrol of the fittest men from each company in turn with the
'next-for-duty' platoon on stand-by for immediate support.
On the 20th a C Company patrol was about to be relieved
when Private Hourigan came in from a forward listening-post
to warn of an impending attack. He went back to his post to
be killed when the attack was launched; it was repulsed, with

two enemy corpses left in view. Chaplain Earl went forward with a spade to bury the brave Hourigan.

The following days were spent by the 39th Battalion patrolling and preparing for the inevitable Japanese offensive. This period was used by the Japanese to assemble at the front Major-General Horii and five battalions of his South Seas Force—all three battalions of the 144th Regiment and the first two (the third to arrive at Basabua on 2 September) of the 41st Regiment. With these were deployed a formidable array of ancillary and support units including the 55th Mountain Artillery and the 15th Independent Engineer Regiment equipped to double as infantry troops.

On the morning of 26 August, the Japanese unleashed the full fury of their awesome superiority of numbers and fire-power upon the 39th Battalion. Around midday Lieutenant Simonson's forward patrol was heavily engaged by the Japanese, while Isurava was bombarded by a Japanese mountain-gun which had been manhandled up the track to press home the Japanese advantage. Japanese troops moved through the dense jungle adjoining the Naro track and thence into the thick-grassed garden beyond the front creek.

Simonson was hurriedly reinforced by Lieutenant Sword's[17] D Company platoon which had been on stand-by as the next forward patrol. The combined force pushed the probing Japanese back towards Deniki, a distance of some 200 yards, in an attempt to reach and destroy their enemy's formidable mountain-gun. Unable to locate it, they returned to their former patrol positions. At around 3.30 pm the Japanese resumed a bombardment of Isurava that did not subside until five o'clock. Then enemy troops moved through the dense jungle adjoining the Naro track. Lieutenant-Colonel Honner:

A hundred yards forward of our front line the sentry of a listening post, beside the Deniki track, ambushed the leading bunched patrol. He emptied his tommy-gun magazine into them at a range of two or three yards, then seeing a larger force swarming down through the garden, jumped across the track and crashed recklessly over the steep hillside, hurtling and slithering to the rocky creek-bed far below, there to begin the long laborious climb back to regain C Company's lines next morning. The other two members of the listening post, stationed some distance farther south—to keep him in sight and to keep themselves in view from our forward posts—seeing that he no longer needed their protection, raced back along the track and over the creek already coming under enemy fire.[18]

While Lieutenants Simonson and Sword had been engaged in halting the Japanese upon the main track, Lieutenant Clarke[19] had gathered together a stand-by C Company platoon for the purpose of relieving Simonson and Sword the following day. During the afternoon, he had journeyed out along the track with his section leaders and seconds in command to reconnoitre the forward positions. While returning at approximately 5 pm he clashed with the infiltrating Japanese in the garden forward of the front creek. Aggression was a quality quite obviously not lacking in the characters of Clarke and his men, as they ruthlessly charged the Japanese positions and drove them uphill, through the garden. They then proceeded to clear the area, stalking their enemy through the high grass with a cold-blooded persistence which resulted in the killing of eight of the infiltrators by Clarke and one of his men before descending darkness and the deepening gloom of the jungle, into which their surviving quarry had disappeared, put an end to their spirited sortie.

While 26 August saw the first eruption of Major-General Horii's offensive against Isurava, that day also brought with it the first element of relief for the 39th Battalion. Having held on gamely with little more than sheer determination and discipline to fortify them, they were to be reinforced by an influx of fresh troops who were to turn the Isurava battle into a confrontation of epic proportions. Captain Bidstrup MC, 39th Battalion:

> The 2/14th and 2/16th came up the track just as we were on our last bloody legs. We couldn't have lasted another day. We were gone for all money. Despite the fact that the blokes were down to the last human resource, they were still prepared to fight, to carry on. I have never ceased to marvel at the way those boys did carry on.[20]

7

Confident even cocksure

It's a confidence business; all war is a confidence business. If there isn't confidence in your mates and your leadership, and your weapons and your training, you're not good soldiers.[1]

When the battle-tested and victorious 7th Division AIF berthed at Port Adelaide in late March 1942, it had acquired a magnificent standard in this 'confidence business'. Its three brigades had experienced between them two testing campaigns. Seconded to the 9th Division, the 18th Brigade had fought alongside it in the now famous siege of Tobruk. The 21st and 25th Brigades had fought in the Syrian Campaign. Battlegrounds at the Litani River, Sidon and Damour were the scenes of heavy fighting against the Vichy French.

The 21st Brigade was composed of the 2/14th Battalion from Victoria, the 2/16th Battalion from Western Australia, and the 2/27th Battalion from South Australia. If the fighting in Syria had nurtured in the men of this brigade a great confidence in their mates, it had certainly also engendered a great respect for, and trust in, their leaders. The months of training prior to that campaign, and indeed the campaign itself, had tried and tested their officers.

After the conclusion of the Syrian campaign 21st Brigade's commander, Brigadier J.E.S. Stevens[2] was promoted to the rank of Major-General, and given command of the 4th Division. The vacant 21st Brigade command was given to the newly promoted Brigadier A.W. Potts.[3] A grazier from Kojonup in Western Australia, Potts had served with the original 16th Battalion in France during the Great War, rising to the rank of Captain. By the end of the war he had won a Military Cross and been mentioned in despatches. With the outbreak of the Second World War, Potts joined the 2/16th Battalion in mid-1940. By the conclusion of the Syrian Campaign, he had added a DSO to his awards and had become the commanding officer of the 2/16th Battalion. Lieutenant-Colonel Frank Sublet, DSO, MC, well remembers Arnold Potts, the soldier and the man:

> Potts was an inspiring leader. He was quite fearless and endeared himself to his officers and men by sharing danger and discomfort with them. While solicitous for his men, he was aggressive and skilful in handling his command. On the Owen Stanley track he showed himself constantly to his troops, and this did a great deal to sustain morale. Knowing that he was the senior allied commander in the battle, the outcome of which would be vital to the security of Moresby and by extension, Australia, he never allowed the responsibility to weigh him down.[4]

Captain Stan Bisset, MC, 2/14th Battalion:

> A leader, a man to be admired and respected, always mindful of the welfare of the troops under his command; courageous and could not be faulted in any way for his leadership in the Owen Stanleys.[5]

Captain R.N. Thompson, 2/14th Battalion:

> Excellent—loved by all the men. Even when men were on
> the point of exhaustion, the call 'Pottsy ahead!' made men
> straighten up.[6]

Lieutenant-Colonel Ralph Honner DSO, MC:

> Admiration for Potts went beyond his own brigade. I served
> under some distinguished brigade commanders; Morshead,
> Robertson, Savige, Vasey, Porter, Eather, Dougherty—under
> six of those in action. But to follow and to fight beside in a
> hazardous campaign, I could not have preferred any of them
> to Arnold Potts. He had a magical, yet natural, charisma of
> leadership that inspired confidence and loyalty and devotion.
> To me, he was the Bayard of them all— 'sans peur et sans
> reproche'.[7] [without fear and without reproach]

The high degree of competence of this veteran brigade's new
commander was consistent with that of the officers from
Lieutenant-Colonel to Lieutenant within its ranks. Such a
standard had not been attained by chance. The AIF had an
enormous advantage over the militia with regard to officers.
First, it had been able to deploy its officers and men away from
the homeland, living and training in the very conditions in
which it had been required to do battle. Secondly, action in the
Middle East had allowed the AIF to test and therefore assess its
officers efficiently. It also facilitated rapid promotion, due
partly to the attrition of its ranks, but partly also to the need
or demand for officers in an expanding wartime army. The
Middle East campaigns thus saw young, energetic and, above
all, capable young officers gain promotion. As a consequence
of its being the only force committed to action prior to the
Pacific War, the AIF was equipped with the best of the nation's
weapons and equipment. Thus, when 21st Brigade arrived in

Adelaide in late March 1942, it was quite definitely an elite brigade in an elite division of the Australian Army.

After the collapse of Singapore, the Australian Army had examined the complex task of defending the extensive Australian coastline with the meagre forces at its disposal. It was realised that the eastern seaboard was the vital ground to defend, and as a consequence the infamous 'Brisbane Line' strategy was formulated. The Brisbane Line marked the northernmost extremity of territory that the Army considered itself capable of defending. As a response to this assessment, 7th Division were deployed on the Brisbane Line prior to the Coral Sea battle to defend this ground. 21st Brigade were deployed at Nambour, Yandina, Maroochydore and Caloundra. Much of the brigade's time and energy shortly after its arrival was spent constructing defensive positions and roads in the area. Lieutenant Jack Gerke, 2/16th Battalion:

> The advance of the Japanese towards Australia and the meeting of American Chiefs of Staff with our Prime Minister and Service Chiefs received a lot of publicity, and it is my opinion that up to that time there had been no set plan on what 7th Division was to carry out, so that we were given the task of setting up the defences along the coast of Queensland and the Brisbane Line.[8]

As a result of the Coral Sea and Midway battles the 7th Division was given hard training in anticipation of offensive operations against the enemy in New Guinea. However, it was not generally contemplated initially that the Kokoda Trail would be the ground upon which 7th Division would be committed. Lieutenant-Colonel Sublet:

> Even then there did not seem to be much alarm about the Japanese push. Such news as I recall emphasised the insurmountable difficulties they would encounter at the

'northern ramparts of the mighty Owen Stanleys'. Reports left the firm impression that the terrain and the troops on the spot would convince the Japanese of the futility of attempting to capture Port Moresby by the land route. The ability of small forces to hold and defeat the enemy at the 'Gap' was portrayed as a forgone conclusion.[9]

Sergeant John Gwillim was at that time serving with the Victorian 2/14th Battalion:

> We were involved with battalion exercises and brigade exercises, with a composite enemy of approximately company strength, providing guerilla activity and resistance. These exercises were of approximately three weeks' duration, and included a considerable amount of work at night, and navigation across open country . . . Establishment of jungle training and obstacle courses such as Canungra were at this stage of training a thing of the future.[10]

21st Brigade therefore, received training prior to New Guinea that bore little relevance to the type of warfare to which it was to be committed—an enormous disadvantage to any force preparing for action. The training in Queensland did, however, provide the brigade with the opportunity to toughen its troops physically prior to battle, and, as a consequence, endure what lay before them. The morale of the 21st Brigade was also at a very high level, because of its victories in the Middle East.

The Japanese landed at Gona on 21 July 1942. With the imminent threat of invasion to Australia having passed some six weeks earlier, as a result of the Battle of Midway, General Headquarters, South-West Pacific Area, issued embarkation orders for the 7th Division on 3 August. On that day some companies of the 39th Battalion were congregating at Deniki prior to the attack upon Kokoda on 8 August. The intentions of the Japanese at that time must have been unclear to

MacArthur. It is most likely that he had decided to move his veteran 7th Division to Port Moresby and Milne Bay to secure his existing bases there. Extremely disciplined and efficient movement saw the 7th Division sail from Brisbane on 6 August. While en route the convoy split, taking the 2/10th, 2/9th and 2/12th Battalions of the 18th Brigade to Milne Bay to reinforce its militia garrison, and the 2/14th and 2/16th Battalions to Port Moresby.

Brigadier Potts arrived at Port Moresby by air on 8 August, and chose the Itiki–Koitaki area as a staging camp for his brigade. He had two reasons for this choice. Firstly, its high altitude minimised the risk of malaria. Secondly, it was close to the end of the motorised transport section of the road to Ilolo and therefore the beginning of the Kokoda Trail. On 11 August, Lieutenant-General S.F. Rowell[11] who had commanded I Corps since April, arrived in Port Moresby. Accompanying him was Major-General Allen[12] commander of the 7th Division. Rowell now had the responsibility of command of all forces in New Guinea. A regular soldier, Rowell had graduated from Duntroon in 1914 and had seen service at Gallipoli during the Great War. Between the wars he had graduated from the Imperial Defence College in England and, after war broke out in 1939, he journeyed with the 6th Division to the Middle East in early 1940. His highly competent staff work during the Middle East campaigns earned him the position of Deputy Chief of the General Staff prior to his appointment as Commander I Australian Corps.

Allen also came to New Guinea with very high credentials. He had served originally as a Lieutenant during the Great War and had earned a battalion command by war's end. When the 6th Division travelled to the Middle East in 1940, Brigadier Allen commanded the 16th Brigade. He participated in the capture of Bardia and Tobruk in Libya and in the fighting in Greece, before assuming command of the 7th Division during the Syrian Campaign. Potts, Allen and Rowell were all destined to play key and successful, yet ultimately controversial, roles during the battles along the Kokoda Trail.

As a result of the arrival of Lieutenant-General Rowell, Major-General Morris assumed command of ANGAU. On 13 August, Allen and Potts held a conference with Morris. Their newly issued orders were quite brief, if ambitious: 21st Brigade was required to recapture Kokoda as a supply base for further operations against Buna and Gona. The outcomes of this conference were twofold. Morris pledged that at least two plane loads of rations, wrapped in blankets, would be dropped at Myola each day, pending the arrival there of the 21st Brigade, to provide a 40 000 ration dump for its offensive. However Morris was astounded to hear Allen and Potts inform him that the troops would carry their own supplies to Myola. Morris believed this to be an impossibility. He warned that the terrain would limit the weight of the troops' packs to fifteen pounds. For their part, Potts and Allen knew that existing porterage capabilities were grossly inadequate to provision 21st Brigade's movement over the Owen Stanley Range. They therefore determined that the troops would indeed carry sufficient rations to enable them to reach Myola.

On 14 and 15 August 1942, the 2/14th and 2/16th Battalions set about the task of preparing to cross the Owen Stanley Range. A distinct sense of purpose and urgency settled over the men as they contemplated the massive green, cloud-ridden mountain obstacle that rose before them. But they were not encouraged by the inadequacy of the preparations undertaken and of the intelligence provided by New Guinea Force, reflecting the incompetence that had prevailed in Port Moresby since the fall of Singapore in February.

The troops spent much of their time preparing their weapons and equipment. While bayonets were sharpened to a razor's edge, deciding the essential contents of, and their arrangement in, a standard pack became a major task prior to departure. Unsuccessful attempts were also made

Top: Brigadier Arnold Potts—Commander 21st Brigade
Centre left: Lieutenant-General S. Rowell (AWM)
Centre right: Major General Allen (AWM)
Bottom left: Captain F.H. Sublet 2/16th Battalion
Bottom right: Captain K. Goldsmith 2/16th Battalion

Left: Lieutenant-Colonel Ralph Honner, C.O. 39th Battalion *Centre:* Lieutenant-Colonel Arthur Key, C.O. 2/14th Battalion *Right:* Lieutenant-Colonel Albert Caro, C.O. 2/16th Battalion

The great boot-sucking porridge—the Kokoda Trail, August 1942 (AWM)

After Isurava, casualties and congestion on the Trail (AWM)

Left: Major and later Lieutenant-Colonel Phil Rhoden C.O. 2/14th Battalion
Centre: Lieutenant Harold 'Butch' Bisset 2/14th Battalion K.I.A. Isurava
Right: Captain Jacob K.I.A. shortly after Isurava—C Company 39th Battalion

Left: Major Rupert Maga[...] 2/6th Field Ambulance
Right: Captain Duffy, R.M.O. 2/14th Battali[...]

Left: Captain Shera, R.M.O. 39th Battalion
Right: Captain Viner-Smith R.M.O. 2/27th Battalion

Left: Lieutenan[...] Colonel Geoff[...] Cooper, C.O. 2/27th Battali[...]
Right: Major Harry Kateka[...] Adjutant, 2/27[...] Battalion

e care of a mother, the devotion of a nurse

Goldsmith became 'Goldie', Major Hearman was 'Ben', Captain Langridge was 'Lefty', Captain McGee was 'Skeeter' . . . The manual also emphasised the ability of the Japanese soldier to live and fight on a spartan diet and his skill and ability in moving through jungle, off roads and tracks. The Japanese tactics in the advance, of moving along tracks, drawing fire, then holding the front while quickly deploying on the flanks were described in the manual and in my experience this was how they operated.[16]

Chester Wilmot's[17] reaction is noteworthy:

> The truth is, that we have been slow to learn the lessons of
> the Malayan Campaign and slower still to act on what we
> did learn.[18]

While accurate, Wilmot's statement only partially identifies the mistakes made. More importantly, the fall of Singapore immediately transformed the significance of Port Moresby. It was, from February 1942, no longer a garrison outpost, but vital ground. Then, perhaps adjectives such as 'impassable' and 'impenetrable' would not have been used as late as July 1942, nor would there have been the mythical legend of the 'Kokoda Gap', where a handful of determined soldiers could halt the invading hordes. A seaward invasion of Port Moresby was the obvious line of advance of the Japanese. However, unlike the Allies, the Japanese after Midway determined that they would land at Gona and push on to Kokoda with a view to an overland assault upon Port Moresby. They were much more flexible in their thinking, and regarded geographical features as surmountable obstacles rather than unconquerable barriers.

On the very night preceding the departure of the 2/14th Battalion, intelligence reported that a further 4000 Japanese had landed at Gona, of which some 1800 were identified as combat troops. Potts was undeterred. He believed that, provided the 2/27th was sent to him immediately and the promised supplies were awaiting him at Myola, all would be well. He had fair cause for his confidence. He could look to his command of Maroubra Force consisting of five battalions; the 39th, 53rd, 2/14th, 2/16th and 2/27th. He had an advanced drop zone at Myola for his supplies and, in addition, native carriers. On information available to him, his enemy would be of comparable numerical size.

The 2/14th Battalion commenced its journey to Myola on 16 August. It was under the command of Lieutenant-Colonel Arthur Key.[19] Key had been an original officer of the 2/8th Battalion, 6th Division, and as a consequence had seen action in Libya, Greece and Crete. He had assumed command of the 2/14th Battalion shortly before its return from the Middle East. Sergeant John Gwillim remembers his first impression of Key:

> I was rather disappointed when Lieutenant-Colonel Key was introduced to us as our new C.O. when Lt-Col Cannon was transferred in January 1942, as he had a rather fragile appearance and did not at all fit my picture of an infantry commander. He did not project an 'I would follow you through hell and high water' air, but rather an 'I need your assistance' air. It was therefore more of a shock to find that he was indeed of very tough moral fibre and had obviously learned to handle hard types during his service with the 6th Australian Division. He was nevertheless a very quiet man who did not have to raise his voice to get things done, and he made no attempt to court popularity with the troops . . . He was a very sound soldier who spared himself in no way, and was in evidence to the forward fighting troops to inspire their performance.[20]

Although by far the easiest part of the Kokoda Trail, Ilolo to Uberi, on day one, tried and tested the 2/14th Battalion. The men's aching knees and shortened breath were but niggling signs of what lay ahead. The assault upon the Golden Stairs awaited them on their second day. With the extreme weight of their packs and the slippery, irregularly spaced logs, falls and utter exhaustion were the rewards for dogged determination to achieve an end to the ordeal. Sergeant R. O. Clemens, 2/14th Battalion:

> How can one describe fully the monotony of following a trail over mountains, and climbing endless steps which had been cut up the slopes and then finishing the day's march physically exhausted, and then after a respite, move out at first light for a repetition.[21]

Corporal R. Watson, 2/14th Battalion:

> With an increase in load because of the moisture in our clothing, webbing and packs etc., the steps up were laborious and the steps down were spine shattering![22]

Captain R. N. Thompson, 2/14th Battalion:

> I was one of the fittest members, but on the second day, climbing the 'Golden Stairs' I was extremely fatigued. A small dixie of tea caused me to vomit and I could not eat. Next morning I and most others had a great craving for salt which surprisingly was issued to us . . . [23]

Such experiences were not isolated ones, but more the constant day-to-day lot of the troops from Uberi to Ioribaiwa, Nauro, Menari, Efogi and finally Myola. In addition, the effect of two heavily laden battalions of men marching mostly in single file over a narrow track transformed the track 'into a great boot-sucking porridge.'[24]

Unbeknown to his battalions, struggling so laboriously over the Kokoda Trail, two disasters struck which would drastically inhibit the implementation of the ambitious plans of Brigadier

Potts. At approximately ten o'clock on the morning of 17 August, the Japanese bombed the seven-mile airfield and destroyed two Dakota transports and three Flying Fortresses. In addition, five Dakota transports and a further five Flying Fortresses were damaged. The Dakota transports were the 'biscuit-bombers' upon which Maroubra Force was so heavily reliant. Sadly, the planes were positioned wingtip to wingtip fully laden and fuelled. Lieutenant-General Rowell had warned the Americans of the potential danger only the day before. The Japanese had struck before the orders to disperse the aircraft had been executed.

Brigadier Potts, with characteristic energy and enthusiasm, had forged ahead of his troops at Menari. The lack of promised supplies and the abominable unpreparedness for his approaching battalions at the villages on the way to Myola shocked him profoundly. In some cases no prior warning had been given the staff of the impending arrival of the 2/14th and 2/16th Battalions.[25] In other cases prior warning had not evoked a professional, businesslike organisation of facilities and supply. In short the logistic planning and fulfilling of 21st Brigade's supply needs was a shambles. But worse was to come. The sight that greeted Potts at Myola must have been truly devastating. There Potts found rations for only five days instead of for 25. A degree of controversy has since reigned as to the fate of the missing supplies. Dudley McCarthy writes:

> It is likely, however, that the rations were never dropped at all and the explanation lay in faulty work by an inexperienced staff.[26]

Closer examination produces a variety of reasons for the supply debacle. General Rowell maintained that a thorough examination of the events in Port Moresby revealed that the rations did leave Port Moresby by air and cites the inaccurate dropping of them as the reason for their loss:

All through the New Guinea campaign cargo dropping remained notoriously unreliable . . .

Besides, the pilots were mainly civilians under hire, without the sense of duty and urgency that could be expected from enlisted and trained personnel.[27]

It is a curious departure from reality to expect untrained, hired civilian pilots to navigate along one of the most dense and, at that time, one of the most unexplored jungle air routes on earth, and then to drop supplies at any given point. The *Report Into Operations 21st Brigade—Owen Stanley Campaign*[28] has identified many of the reasons for the failure of supplies and the lack of facilities at the villages. One of the main conclusions reached was that there were no army-trained supply personnel at the villages.

Sadly, the controversy does not end there. During an interview with the author in February 1989, Captain Ken Murdoch discussed the issue of the missing supplies:

I was Staff Captain Learner, or assistant to Peter Smith at the start of the show. Brigadier Potts asked me to go down to New Guinea Force Headquarters to find out what supplies were on the track. And when I went down I found all the difficulties in the world! When I finally got the A.Q., Lieutenant-Colonel . . . refused to give me the details because it was top secret, and he could not disclose what supplies or ammunition had been located on the trail. I argued with him and told him we were moving off the next day and we wanted to know what extra supplies we had to carry. And he said, 'Any extra supplies you need will be dropped to you'. He refused to give the figures to me. I went back outside to the D.A.Q.M.G. I got the same answer—he had been sworn to secrecy! He could not tell me the location nor the amount of stores or ammunition that had been located on the trail. I was leaving the H.Q. frankly in disgust, to tear back to Brigadier Potts to say 'well, what the hell, I can't get the story', when I struck a man I knew from the 2/14th in the Middle-East, Captain . . . And he said, 'Ken I know your problem, I'm sworn to secrecy. However, come around the corner.' And he said, 'I can't tell you, but you know what you want; you know the types of ammunition, you know the rations. You start nominating figures and types and if you're near it I'll nod my head.' Now that is a true story! I went back to Brigadier Potts with the story of the various locations and on the nod of a head, the amount of ammunition and supplies. The time was short. A phone call back to H.Q. couldn't get the information. They just refused to issue it. So we didn't know whether the supplies were there or not. The men carried every piece of food and ammunition that they could. Every man was asked to carry an extra bandolier of 50 rounds. Potts was certainly suspicious and I can confirm that; that they weren't going to be there.[29]

The case of the 'missing supplies' will forever remain a mystery—a shameful mystery.

That crucial principle of war, supply, had thus been flouted before Potts and his 2/14th and 2/16th Battalions had arrived at Myola. It denied him any chance to gain the initiative at Isurava. He determined, and was supported by Rowell, that he would not commit his battalions to offensive action until the lost essential supplies were made good.

This logistic nightmare did not unduly haunt the men of the 21st Brigade. Those battle-seasoned veterans were eager to face their enemy. The recollections of Lieutenant Bisset and Captain Sublet, from the 2/14th and 2/16th Battalions respectively, most vividly indicate the troops' determination and morale. Captain Stan Bisset, MC, 2/14 Battalion:

The Battalion had reached Efogi, 5,000 feet above sea level by the end of the fourth day's march towards Kokoda in August 1942. This was the last staging spot where fires could be lit and troops relax. It was a memorable occasion for me and no doubt all members of our battalion. The feeling of achievement of overcoming fantastic obstacles, of feeling fit and eager to meet and defeat our enemy over the towering Owen Stanleys, lay just ahead of us. I was the Intelligence Officer then and Butch asked me to join his Platoon No. 10's camp fire, and I remember well the sing-a-long and being asked to sing two or three of Butch's and his men's favourite songs. I remember at that time I experienced a feeling that my beloved brother might not survive. It is difficult to express this feeling which I had whilst singing.[30]

Lieutenant–Colonel Frank Sublet, DSO, MIC, 2/16th Battalion:

I fumed at the delay at Myola and, as information from the most forward area reached us via 39th Battalion wounded, I joined my superiors in roundly condemning those in Port Moresby and beyond, responsible for the debacle. When air-dropping of supplies commenced I sometimes joined my men in scouring the area around the dropping zone for supplies dropped in the jungle. While I heard 'tongue-in-cheek' grumbling and acid comment one expects from troops who are not afraid to speak their minds, there was also considerable good humoured levity and outspoken resolution; they looked forward to making the Japanese pay for these discomforts . . .

Despite all the handicaps imposed by others, the troops were at all times confident, even cocksure of their ability to throw back the Japanese.[31]

8

Unawed in the gates of death

Surely no war was ever fought under worse conditions than these. Surely no war has ever demanded more of a man in fortitude. Even Gallipoli or Crete or the desert.[1]

To a generation of postwar Australians the names Gallipoli, Passchendaele, the Somme, El Alamein, Tobruk, Bardia and Crete are identified, if at times vaguely, with significant events in a proud military heritage. For the same Australians, Isurava is a term unknown. And yet around this rain-soaked, muddy and primitive little village was fought one of the most critical battles in Australian history. The nature of the terrain and the consequent problems of supply and communications limited the number of combatants in comparison with those of Gallipoli, France and Alamein. However titanic struggles do not necessarily require massive employment of infantry, armour and equipment, but are assessed more accurately in terms of the importance of the objectives gained or denied and their immediate and long-term historical consequences. Only with the application of these prerequisites does the battle for Isurava in late August 1942 assume its full significance.

For the Japanese, Isurava would be the point at which the full and awesome might of Major-General Horii's South Seas Force would be initially unleashed. By employing a concentrated and explosive frontal assault upon the Australians at Isurava and an outflanking movement along the Kaile–Missima–Alola axis, the Japanese sought to outflank the Australians, cut them off from their line of supply and communication, and then annihilate them. Horii was at the head of a formidable and confident force. Thirteen thousand five hundred of his troops had already been landed, of whom some 10 000 formed a well-balanced fighting group, spearheaded by his first five experienced battalions, for the assault on Isurava. Horii was relying on that key principle of war—concentration of force. He had the initiative and looked to a speedy and decisive conclusion to the campaign. Only the mountains and a thin Australian force were between the invaders and Port Moresby.

Brigadier Potts enjoyed none of his opposite number's advantages. Relying upon very scant and inaccurate intelligence, he believed his enemy to number 4000 at most. New Guinea Force had failed to supply him with the rations and equipment that he required to execute his orders. And to compound his problems, one of his prized battalions was still denied him; three days after he assumed command of Maroubra Force, the Japanese landed at Milne Bay, and General Allen remained very reluctant to commit the 2/27th Battalion to the Kokoda Trail before Milne Bay could be deemed secure.

On 23 August when Potts took over command of Maroubra Force from Porter at Alola, the 39th Battalion was still the forward shield, holding the Isurava perimeter, patrolling north towards Deniki and watching the westward and eastward tracks towards Naro and Asigari. The 53rd Battalion had been held at Alola by Honner and, later, Porter. Its principal task was protecting the right flank through the track via Abuari, Missima and Kaile. In addition, that still fresh battalion had the role of patrolling out through the 39th Battalion positions at Isurava towards Deniki, and along the left flank towards Naro. The further employment of his two militia battalions became of immediate concern to Potts; denied the necessary supplies and his 2/27th Battalion, he considered three alternatives for his future course of action.

His first option involved leaving the 39th and 53rd Battalions forward and holding the 2/14th and 2/16th Battalions at Myola pending the acquisition of sufficient supplies for an offensive. This course offered two distinct advantages. Firstly, it would permit the build-up of a supply dump capable of sustaining his offensive and at the same time reduce the strain upon the supply line to his front. Secondly, and most importantly, it would allow him to keep his fresh force at Myola concealed from Japanese detection and thus preserve an element of surprise. However desirable, this first option was quickly rejected because of the poor physical condition of the 39th Battalion. On 26 August, Potts signalled Allen:

> Condition of 39th Battalion men weak due to continuous work lack warm clothing blankets shelters curtailed rations and wet every night monotonous diet combined with comparative static role last fortnight.[2]

The inability to exercise his first option must have frustrated Potts. His orders and intent were directed at the recapture of Kokoda. Had the Japanese strength in the area proved consistent with intelligence estimates supplied to Potts and had the physical condition of the 39th Battalion been satisfactory, he might well have embarked upon an offensive.

The second course of action contemplated by Potts involved the maintenance of the 39th and 53rd Battalion positions along with the deployment of his fresh 2/14th and 2/16th Battalions to the east and west of Isurava on the high ground. It would enable him to prevent a short-term outflanking movement by the Japanese and gain time to increase his Myola supply stocks and improve his line of communication—time too, perhaps, to bring forward his urgently needed 2/27th Battalion. The still critical supply problem and deteriorating physical condition of the 39th Battalion tragically inhibited the choice of this second option.

The least attractive course available to Potts was the one that circumstances forced him to adopt. He reluctantly decided to relieve the exhausted and depleted 39th Battalion with his 2/14th Battalion, maintain the 53rd Battalion at Alola and bring the 2/16th Battalion forward to Alola for whatever role developments might dictate.

During the days preceding the Japanese offensive on 27 August, the 53rd Battalion had experienced three relatively minor contacts with the Japanese. During the morning of 24 August, Lieutenant MacDonald[3] with twenty of his men passed through the 39th Battalion positions at Isurava and journeyed northward towards Deniki. Approximately one hour's march along the track, he was caught in an ambush by a Japanese patrol and his forward scout, Private MacGraw,[4] was killed. Encountering the Japanese in dug-in positions, the Australians inflicted four Japanese casualties before breaking contact and withdrawing. On the following day Sergeant Meani[5] took twenty of his fellow 53rd Battalion men out along the same route and was also ambushed. The Japanese had left MacGraw's body against a tree as a decoy. Meani's men scattered and later returned to Isurava and thence to Alola.

Events along the Alola–Kaile track on the eastern flank during 25 August, gave clear warning that the Japanese were reconnoitring that flank with a view to mounting a concerted attempt to outflank the Australians at Isurava. The 53rd Battalion had been maintaining a standing patrol at Kaile and radio communication between Missima and Alola. On that day, Lieutenant Isaachsen[6] and twenty men of his platoon left Alola to occupy Kaile as the standing patrol.

Approaching Kaile, Isaachsen's patrol was ambushed by a two-platoon strength Japanese force which attacked from the high ground, with the support of a mortar and a machine-gun. In the ensuing action Lieutenant Isaachsen was killed. Some three hours later, Captain Ahern[7] who had accompanied the patrol, abandoned Kaile after having inflicted heavy casualties upon his enemy. Upon his return towards Missima, Ahern found that village to be occupied by the Japanese. Forced into a withdrawal via Eora Creek, the patrol finally reached its own lines on the evening of 28 August, having been three days without rations.

When Lieutenant Clarke and his C Company small group of the 39th Battalion reached Isurava after their bloodthirsty sweep through the garden across the front creek, they were greeted by new faces. Captain Dickenson[8] and his C Company, 2/14th Battalion, had arrived late in the afternoon of 26 August, and immediately proceeded to relieve C Company of the 39th. The desperate plight of the 39th and the impressive bearing and physical condition of the relief force are vividly portrayed by some of those who were there. Captain H. D. Steward, 2/16th Battalion:

> . . . gaunt spectres with gaping boots and rotting tatters of uniform hanging around them like scarecrows. Their faces had no expression, their eyes sunk back into their sockets. They were drained by malaria, dysentery and near starvation, but they were still in the firing line, facing a much more powerful enemy equipped with much heavier weaponry.[9]

For the men of the 39th, morale was improved instantly by the sight of their rescuers. Sergeant John Manol has a dramatic recollection of his first encounter with the men of the 2/14th Battalion:

> That's the first time I'd ever seen a man dressed in green. That was at Isurava and this bloke jumped into our pit and I thought 'Jesus! He's a bloody nip!' 'Green uniform.' I said 'Where are you from? Who are you?' 'We're the 2/14th.' I thought Christ had come down again! We all did. We thought of them as Gods, these blokes. They were tall and they were trained . . . Clean uniforms, they were trained whereas you'd look around at your mates and their eyes were sunk back in their heads and they were pale and dirty and grubby.[10]

Dickenson's C Company assumed responsibility for holding the right front at Isurava and the forward part of the right flank covering the eastward track to Asigari. His arrival was more than a little opportune. Captain Jacob and his C Company, 39th Battalion, had been under mountain-gun shelling both morning and afternoon and, having been required to place on stand-by their platoon of fit men for the standing patrol towards Deniki, were thinly spread.

During the night of 26 August, the Japanese attacked Lieutenant Simonson's standing patrol on the Deniki track. Simonson and three other men were wounded. A chance bullet fired at Simonson by a Japanese soldier who had burst out of the jungle into the platoon headquarters and signal area struck a grenade in Simonson's pocket. The resulting detonator explosion caused burns and cuts to the legs of the startled officer. Lieutenant-Colonel Honner ordered Simonson and the other wounded men to return to Isurava along the main track. With this order also came the chilling warning that the Japanese might have cut the track between him and headquarters. The remainder of Simonson's platoon were ordered to join Lieutenant Sword's[11] D Company platoon to constitute the standing patrol between Isurava and Deniki. Simonson and his wounded comrades plodded their way back to Isurava during the pitch-black and rain-soaked night of the 26th, hearing occasional movement and other noise along their blind and desperate flight.

As the night passed, the position at Isurava was that Honner had had his C Company reinforced by Dickenson and had a standing patrol towards Deniki composed of Lieutenant Sword's D Company platoon and Simonson's E Company platoon without Simonson and his wounded. The next morning C Company's fittest men, unable to attempt relief of Sword's outpost along a track swarming with the enemy, were detailed for a new patrol assignment. Potts required a platoon from the 39th Battalion to occupy Naro to block enemy movement through it towards Alola. After his brisk action the previous evening Clarke had earned a rest; the command went to Lieutenant Pentland. The Naro track through the garden facing E Company was already in enemy hands again, so Pentland took his men west from B Company, cutting through the timber and crossing the creek to the Naro track higher up, beyond the enemy infiltration, to reach the Naro ridge unopposed.

That day, 27 August, saw the Battle of Isurava erupt in an awesome fury such as had not previously been witnessed during the campaign, as the Japanese propelled their superior numbers and firepower against the desperate defenders; while in a co-ordinated attempt to outflank Isurava they also unleashed a battalion strength advance towards Alola via the Kaile–Missima track. The hot, steamy, rain-soaked days and the chilling, dark nights at Isurava were henceforth to be the gruesome setting for a battle that would produce appalling slaughter in the wake of wave upon wave of attacking Japanese breaking against spirited and determined Australian resistance.

Having moved through the garden on the far side of the front creek and having also penetrated the thick jungle on the Naro flank, the Japanese were soon probing Lieutenant French's B Company and Captain Merritt's E Company positions.

Isurava before the attack, 27 August

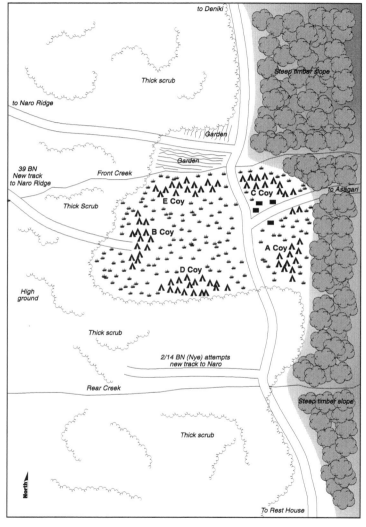

Earlier in the morning, when the closing Japanese ring had made it impossible for Clarke's stand-by patrol to relieve or reinforce Sword's two platoons, Honner had ordered Sword to delay the enemy as long as possible and then to fall back on Isurava when his position should become untenable. As the intensity of the battle increased Honner concluded that those two invaluable platoons must return to Isurava. By that time, however, the Japanese had cut the signal line.

Brigadier Potts envisaged a complete relief of the 39th Battalion on 28 August; he therefore required the recovery of Pentland's Naro patrol to allow Honner's battalion to withdraw intact; and he ordered Honner to replace Pentland's patrol with a platoon from C Company, 2/14th Battalion. Dickenson detailed Lieutenant Davis[12] and his platoon for the task.

When Davis and his patrol, guided by the 39th Battalion Intelligence Sergeant, Buchecker[13], set out to follow Pentland's route they found, upon crossing the front creek, the jungle alive with Japanese. In the ensuing action Davis lost a man killed and was then seriously wounded himself. Despite his wound, he fought a single-handed rearguard action, sacrificing his life to enable the successful withdrawal of his platoon. Buchecker was wounded in the leg, suffering a shattered thigh. Displaying their usual standard of compassion and selflessness, Chaplain Earl and the RMO, Captain Shera, moved out to the sound of the guns through the enemy-infested jungle, and carried Buchecker back to safety. The patrol followed them back to Isurava pressed closely by the enemy. With Pentland cut off, as well as Sword, Honner was without the fittest men of three of his five companies. To replace E Company's missing men Sergeant Kerslake, with the remainder of C Company after Pentland's Naro patrol had gone, was posted in the reserve platoon position with a counter-penetration role. At the same time Sergeant Murray's platoon of A Company became the battalion reserve, ready to rush to wherever it might be needed. Lieutenant-Colonel Ralph Honner DSO, MC, in *The 39th at Isurava*:

With the situation apparently well under control I went to the rear creek—outside the perimeter but our only water supply—for a wash and a shave. There were about a dozen of us there, including Merritt. A breathless runner brought me a message that the enemy had broken into 'E' Company's position. I looked over at the unsuspecting Merritt. It seemed a pity to disturb him. 'Captain Merritt', I said, 'When you've finished your shave will you go to your company. The Japs have broken through your perimeter.' Merritt didn't appreciate the Drake touch. An astonished look hung for an instant on his half-shaved face; then it lifted like a starter's barrier and he was off like a racehorse.

Odd parties of the enemy were already bursting through the thinly-held timber to be shot down in the open; . . . Then, in the middle of the afternoon, the intermittent bombardment was suddenly intensified. As the precise Japanese diarist of No. 3 Battalion records it: 'At 1538 our guns all join in together and the attack and advance begins along the whole front.'

And while bombs and bullets crashed and rattled in an unceasing clamour that re-echoed from the affrighted hills, the enveloping forest erupted into violent action as Nippon's screaming warriors streamed out of its shadows to the assault.

Across the creek they swept in a swift thrust that sliced through E Company's thin front line . . . The attacks on E Company were repulsed mainly by Merritt's own men, but with a quick counter-attack by Kerslake's counter-penetration platoon driving out the enemy breaking through one gap and with Murray's mobile reserve also racing up to the rescue. For the rest of the day B Company bore the brunt of the enemy's attacks.

Its forward platoons had occupied advanced positions near the timber edge to obtain some cover from it and to force the infiltrating Japanese deeper into the denser forest; but the violence of the enemy onset pressed them back to a better line prepared slightly to the rear to give them more open killing space on an occasion such as this. There they held, fighting magnificently, while the enemy came on in reckless waves, regardless of the casualties that soon cluttered that short stretch of open ground.

These incessant assaults were slowly sapping 'B' Company's strength—and at the end of the day, when the heaviest attack of all rolled in over French's men their endurance was stretched almost to breaking-point. Lieutenant Garland, their second-in-command, reported that they were unlikely to hold much longer unless reinforced. I gave him a message for French that he would have to hold—there was only battalion headquarters behind him. But in the light of the enemy's obviously superior strength I recognised that it would be only a matter of time before our small garrison was overrun—in the evening, the night, or next morning. There was only one source of quick reinforcement to forestall disaster.

In the middle of the afternoon Captain Nye[14] had arrived with 'B' Company of the 2/14th not to strengthen the defenders but with orders to push through to relieve Pentland on the Naro Track. Davis had already found Pentland's route through French's lines impassable, so Nye's company started to cut its way west through the jungle bordering the creek to the rear of our perimeter. It was with considerable misgiving that I watched this formidable force march out of our lines just as the big offensive was commencing. When 'B' Company was so sorely pressed at sunset I resolved to recall Nye if he could still be reached. Fortunately the jungle was so thick that two hours of laborious slashing had not taken the head of the column more than a couple of hundred yards—his rear troops were hardly off the track. They quickly returned to take part in the fight and I do not remember anything more heartening than the sight of their confident deployment. Their splendid physique and bearing, and their cool automatic efficiency—even the assembly-line touch as two platoon mortar-men stepped one on either side of the track to pluck bombs from the haversacks of

the riflemen filing past them without checking their pace—
made a lasting impression on me. And they were to prove even
better than they looked.

I sent their first platoon to strengthen 'E' Company's left, and
the second to 'D' Company's right to close the pincers from
either flank on the enemy still endangering 'B' Company; and
the pressure had already eased when the third platoon was
placed under French's command. It was dark by the time the
three strengthened companies had consolidated their positions,
and the firing died away to a silence that seemed strangely eerie
after the twelve-hour tumult. And the peace of the night was
broken only by an occasional stealthy foray—as when one of
Dickenson's men was bayoneted without seeing his assailant.

In the morning, Captain Cameron[15] and his D Company
2/14th Battalion took over E Company's positions, which in
turn allowed Nye's three platoons to congregate under his
command and assume control of his opposite number's 39th
Battalion positions. Captain Merritt's two E Company platoons
and Lieutenant French's men now occupied gaps in the lines
to the rear which had been created by Sword's and Pentland's
missing patrols.

The dogged resistance offered by the 39th Battalion at Isurava
pending their reinforcement by the 2/14th Battalion, was
of paramount importance to not only the four-day battle of
Isurava, but also to the resounding success of the Maroubra
Force fighting withdrawal to Ioribaiwa. Had the 39th Battalion
broken, Isurava would have fallen with awesome consequences.
It had held the enemy beyond arm's length to conceal weakness and to exploit surprise; it had made a tenable disposition
of an inadequate force to hold ground that was, for it, really
unholdable; it had prepared definite and trusted plans for
counter-attack—necessarily at the risky expense of defensive
gaps elsewhere; and it had built faith and trust amongst its ranks
to accept, with cool resolution, the odds against them and not

to flinch or panic. This was a superb performance in any military company—its magnitude is all the more astounding when the Isurava achievement is weighed against the garrison experience in Port Moresby only three short months before.

While the Japanese were attacking Isurava on 26–27 August they were also pressing along the Kaile–Missima–Abuari track on the eastern side of the Eora valley. On the 26th, Lieutenant McDonald's 53rd Battalion patrol found the wreck of the wireless set at Missima but no trace of its crew or of the men despatched to Kaile under Isaachsen and Ahern the previous day. They killed three Japanese before withdrawing ahead of the enemy who followed them closely to secure Abuari. Within 24 hours the consequences of that action were to be catastrophic. The first futile reaction came as darkness fell. Captain Cairn's B Company went forward to meet the enemy threat.

On the morning of 27 August, Potts ordered the 53rd Battalion to retake Missima. Lieutenant-Colonel Ward now sent his D Company to reinforce B Company and recapture Missima. Force Headquarters received information that the two companies of the 53rd were advancing towards Missima at approximately 5.30 pm. Ward was apparently acting on the same information, as he pushed on through Abuari in company with Lieutenant Logan[16] at approximately 6 pm. Tragically both unsuspecting officers—and an unlucky private with them—were ambushed and killed.

As far as could be ascertained later, B Company did no more than make contact with the enemy but broke and scattered, while it is doubtful if D Company did more than make contact with the enemy. At 1620 hours a runner from 53rd Battalion informed Brigade that the Japs had come around the waterfall and were making towards the river crossing and Alola. 53rd Battalion were ordered to hold Abuari Village, waterfall and river crossing with the remaining companies pending the arrival of 2/16th Battalion. At nightfall the position on the right flank was as follows:—B and D Companies, 53rd Battalion, out of contact with Brigade and reported to have pressed on to Missima. Jap patrols thought to be in occupation of Abuari Village. In addition seventy of 53rd Battalion on patrols NOT reported in and subsequently found to have taken to the bush.[17]

It would be 8 am on the following morning before approximately 70 men of the missing D and B Companies of the 53rd Battalion were able to regain contact with their headquarters. Another small group returned via the waterfall at around 2 pm. The remainder had scattered—some had perished.

By nightfall on the 27th, the position on his shattered right flank around Abuari was one of deep concern for Potts. A major part of the 53rd Battalion was out of contact with his headquarters and the leaderless and aimless remainder were close to the Eora Creek crossing below Alola. Forward on the left flank Honner was being reinforced by a third company of the 2/14th and was holding Isurava but against a great enemy strength that would still require the committal there of the rest of the 2/14th.

The 2/16th Battalion had been in the process of moving Captain McGee's[18] A Company and Captain Sublet's B Company forward to spearhead the Australians' right flank advance from a firm base at Alola to Missima. The failure of the 53rd Battalion to carry out its orders and to provide any semblance of co-ordination or order on that crucial flank forced Potts to commit his 2/16th Battalion company by company, upon arrival at Alola, to the rescue of the defence and dashed any hopes he held for a co-ordinated offensive operation.

The 27th was also an important day for the Japanese. If ever Horii was to have a chance to wreak utter havoc and defeat upon the Australians, then this would have been his golden opportunity. He had the Australians pinned down at Isurava and had, at minimal cost, extended his left flank enormously towards Alola. His only opposition between Missima and

Alola was a militia battalion which had scattered upon contact and had failed dismally to contest his advance. There can be only conjecture as to why he failed to exploit his gains. Horii's master-plan involved an encirclement and consequent annihilation of the Australians at Isurava. Yet, presented with the realisation of his objective, he instead dug in near Abuari and extended patrols forward. Perhaps this was an instance where the jungle and terrain worked in favour of the Australians. Firstly, the Japanese may have been unsure of the magnitude of the enemy force confronting them; their intelligence may have been poor. Secondly, communication on foot or by radio in the jungle in this environment was a nightmare. Thirdly, Horii may have felt loath to overextend his left flank advance until Isurava had fallen. Whatever his reason, he forfeited his chance of a speedy and decisive conclusion to the campaign on 27 August.

The next day was unaccountably quiet on the right flank. This was a rare piece of good fortune for Potts as he moved his A and B Companies, 2/16th Battalion across Eora Creek to close on Abuari by nightfall after the Japanese had been seen from Alola moving towards that village. But the 28th had been a busier day on the left flank. At first light Captain Cameron's D Company, 2/14th Battalion, which had reached Isurava the previous evening, took over the creek covering positions of Merritt's E Company, with Dickenson's C Company established beyond the main track to its right and Nye's reunited B Company taking over French's 'killing-ground' front to its left rear, the defensive responsibility of the 39th companies contracting to the less threatened south and east sectors of the perimeter.

Dawn was shattered by the menacing roar of a Japanese mountain-gun and mortar and heavy machine-gun fire which were to continue uninterrupted until approximately eight o'clock that morning. Through the still echoing shock waves of the subsiding bombardment stormed tall, confident Japanese veterans of recent jungle victories in Malaya and the Philippines.

They initially attacked in company strength, twice upon Captain Dickenson's positions. The seemingly insane, fanatical frontal assaults had begun. Bodies began to litter the approaches as the attackers were met with concentrated, lethal fire and, when necessary, grenade and bayonet. Dickenson's men remained unmoved, disciplined and in absolute control of the situation.

Employing what was becoming standard procedure, the Japanese turned their attention towards Cameron's Company in the centre positions, and upon Nye's Company on the left flank. Having spent adequate time prior to their attacks observing the Australians' positions, they devoted much of their aggression to Lieutenant Moore's 11 Platoon. Before the fighting eased Lieutenant Moore had made the supreme sacrifice and a number of his men had been wounded. Lieutenant–Colonel Ralph Honner DSO, MC in *This is the 39th*:

> There were already four times as many men holding our front
> and flanks as there had been the previous day; and when 'A'
> Company and part of Headquarters Company of the 2/14th
> arrived it was possible for the first time to provide a powerful
> reserve. So Isurava seemed secure when Lieutenant-Colonel Key
> of the 2/14th marched in at midday and took command,
> relieving the 39th which was due to leave for Port Moresby. But
> I told Key I considered the holding of Isurava against the
> strength the enemy had shown the previous day would need
> more than one battalion, and I would not leave him in the
> lurch. The two of us then convinced Potts that the 39th must be
> allowed to stay and fight.

The Japanese sustained their attacks upon Dickenson and Nye until mid-afternoon. Having attempted to pierce the Australian positions at a number of points, they again turned their attention towards Captain Cameron's D Company later in the day. They had good reason to do so. First, it had become obvious to them that the beleaguered young men of the 39th Battalion had been reinforced. Secondly, their attacks through cleared passages of ground had cost them dearly. Cameron's positions were now seen as the best possibility of a break-through. His 17 and 18 Platoons occupied ground with some vision of the enemy's daylight approaches. However, his 16 Platoon commanded by Lieutenant Pearce[19] was sited, to prevent inroads through the tangled hiatus between D and B Companies, in very thick jungle that allowed little observation of its front and limited the capacity of its sections to support or even communicate with each other. It was at this point that the determined Japanese launched a spirited attack. Using superior numbers and firepower, they were able to overrun a part of Pearce's positions. Disciplined resistance and a counter-attack led by Lieutenant Hutchinson's platoon from Captain Buckler's reserve A Company enabled the 2/14th Battalion to clear its D Company position by nightfall, inflicting heavy Japanese losses in the process.

As the darkened, cold and wet final hours of 28 August petered out, neither Major-General Horii nor Brigadier Potts saw much cause for contentment with his battle situation. Major-General Horii was already some days behind his schedule for the acquisition of Port Moresby. He must have known that time in this environment posed countless problems. Time was a deadly and unforgiving enemy for both sides. It placed enormous pressure upon supply lines and carriers and upon exhausted shelterless soldiers.

For the Japanese and the Australians alike, every soaking, shivering, sleepless night on the Kokoda Trail conspired to further the general debilitation of the troops. The Japanese standard of hygiene was less than demanded by such an environment. As the Australians doggedly contested their advance, time became their ally—dysentery and diarrhoea were to occur in almost plague proportions amongst the Japanese. The Australians, while observing far superior standards of hygiene, were also to fall victim to dysentery and a multitude of other disorders. Time. Time was the key.

With critical hours slipping away from him by 29 August, the fourth day of his great offensive, and despite appalling losses in earlier wholesale attacks, Horii decided to commit his considerable reserves to a final massive assault upon the Australians at Isurava. Brigadier Potts, meanwhile, was engaged in reinforcing his right flank with his 2/16th Battalion and repeatedly requesting the despatch of his much needed 2/27th Battalion from Koitaki, as without that strengthening of his force he was reduced to conducting his unequal battle with grossly inadequate resources.

On 29 August, the 2/16th Battalion was committed to the right flank along the Alola–Abuari–Missima axis. Its role was to stabilise the right flank, and if possible, push on to Missima. The Commanding Officer of the battalion was Lieutenant-Colonel Albert Caro.[20] Captain F. H. Sublet MC, 2/16th Battalion:

> Lieutenant-Colonel Albert Caro was a courageous officer who displayed plenty of military knowledge. To me he seemed a little too forgiving and his compassion was pronounced. I held him in the highest esteem as a commanding officer, and as a man of great goodness.[21]

In order to execute Potts's directive, Caro despatched his A Company under the command of Captain McGee and his B Company under the command of Captain Sublet, who recalls:

> All was quiet around Abuari when I reached there and almost immediately I made a reconnaissance with a couple of men along the track to Missima. About one hundred metres down this track we came across the bodies of Lieutenant-Colonel Ward, C.O. of the 53rd Battalion and his Adjutant or Intelligence Officer. I concluded they had been ambushed, and firing on my right rear told me that A Company had

contacted the enemy. Soon afterwards I received orders to take command of both A and B Companies, and I did so. When A Coy scouts discovered the enemy in position above Abuari Village, the Company Commander ordered 7th and 9th platoons to attack, and they went in with gusto and continued to press the Japanese all afternoon. 9th platoon killed about fifty of the enemy and captured several light machine guns while 7th platoon continued their assault. In accordance with Colonel Caro's wishes, I had handed over B Coy to Captain George Wright when I assumed command of the two-company force and I decided that B Coy should move and attack the enemy's right flank while A Coy continued their frontal attack. I judged that at least one hundred Japanese were holding well prepared positions covering the partially cleared area of the village and the Missima track where it emerged from the cover provided by a thirty foot cliff at the top of a sidling track up which we had travelled from the deep gorge below Alola. In view of the threat of Japanese reinforcements from Missima, B Coy was to post a strong standing patrol to secure their left flank.[22]

By mid-afternoon it was clear to Sublet that if he was to push on to Missima he must mount an attack using his A Company in a frontal assault, his B Company on his left flank, and a fresh third force along his right flank to fall upon the Japanese rear. He requested that a 53rd Battalion company come forward to accomplish this last task.

The initial 2/16th Battalion action had been executed with standard 21st Brigade confidence and skill. Captain F. H. Sublet, 2/16th Battalion:

All day I had heard the shattering noise of the other battle taking place about two miles away on the other side of the Eora Creek gorge but received no definite news as to the likely outcome . . .

139

During the day's fighting we had suffered many casualties and I was particularly sad that so many of the 9th Platoon (my first command) had been killed. But I was proud that in their first battle against the vaunted Japanese men of the 2/16th had, to quote Kipling, 'glared unawed in the gates of death'.[23]

While the situation on the right flank was poised inconclusively, the battle for Isurava was becoming a titanic struggle. Against overwhelming odds the 2/14th Battalion, supported by the exhausted remnants of the 39th Battalion, was locked into a desperate battle against a vastly superior force.

From daybreak until dusk, the Japanese mounted furious frontal attacks upon the 2/14th Battalion positions. B Company's 10 Platoon, commanded by Lieutenant Harold (Butch) Bisset,[24] had relieved 11 Platoon towards the previous evening. The Japanese mounted eleven determined attacks upon Bisset's men, each of company strength. During these attacks the enemy penetrated 10 Platoon's perimeter with the result that any movement during such close-quarter fighting brought down a withering hail of fire. This caused the treatment and withdrawal of the wounded to be undertaken at great peril. By dusk, the 10 Platoon perimeter had become a splintered graveyard for no fewer than 200 Japanese soldiers.

During the late afternoon, Bisset, whilst distributing grenades to his men, was mortally wounded by a burst of machine-gun fire. The withdrawal became a nightmare for the survivors of 10 Platoon as, burdened with their wounded, they struggled over uneven ground in the encroaching darkness, turning repeatedly to inflict delaying casualties on the closing enemy hotly pressing the pursuit. Amidst all of this, they would not leave the dying Bisset. His brother recalls that fateful night:

Butch was shot in the stomach by a machine-gun and as the platoon later withdrew his men carried him out . . . Don [RMO Captain Don Duffy][25] and I were with him,

Don administering morphine, whilst I held his hand, and at times we talked. He died at 4 am. No man had a finer brother.[26]

The 2/14th Battalion had lost one of its favourite sons:

Perhaps no other single death could have more deeply shocked the Battalion. 'Butch' was one of the most strongly individual men in the Unit, and every man's friend. He had all the manly virtues together with a rollicking sense of humour. Above all he loved his men unto death and his men returned his devotion.[27]

11 Platoon also fought under intense pressure and strain on that fateful afternoon. Lieutenant Treacy[28] having assumed command of the platoon after Lieutenant Moore's death, provided sound leadership and inspiration to his men as he calmly held back the enemy and personally attended to the recovery of the wounded and the making of stretchers whilst the withdrawal was in progress.

Whilst 10 and 11 Platoons of B Company had been thus occupied, 12 Platoon had experienced a quiet morning. It bore no resemblance to the period of confrontation that was to follow—particularly in the case of Corporal Charlie McCallum.[29] Having been subjected to four spirited counter-attacks during the afternoon, the Japanese launched a determined attack upon the 12 Platoon perimeter, pushing in telling reinforcements as they gained ground. As the order came for 12 Platoon to withdraw, McCallum provided covering fire with his Bren blazing and a wounded comrade's Tommy gun used from the left shoulder. When his Bren magazine ran out, the Japanese stormed his position, only to be met by a torrent of fire from his Tommy gun while he changed magazines with his right hand. His brave action was fought at such close quarters that one of his enemy actually managed to pull his utility pouches off as McCallum pulled away from him. Apart from saving many of his comrades' lives, McCallum inflicted no fewer than 40 casualties upon the enemy. And this most gallant action had been performed after McCallum had been wounded three times.

Dogged resistance had also been offered by Dickenson's C Company. The Japanese having been repulsed on a number of occasions, mounted a determined attack upon Dickenson which resulted in numerous C Company casualties. In order to stem the Japanese attacks, Lieutenant-Colonel Key sent Lieutenant Cox[30] from A Company, with his 9 Platoon to bolster the dwindling C Company defences. Cox had barely reached the company lines before he was fatally shot. Corporal Bear,[31] displaying cool and determined resolution, assumed command of the platoon and, despite sustaining two wounds, accounted for some ten to fifteen of the enemy with his Bren gun at very close range. The Japanese persisted with their frenzied attacks, showing scant regard for their mounting casualties. But the 2/14th Battalion continued to produce soldiers of all ranks whose initiative and bravery dominated the events around them. The Japanese had now gained ground through the 13, 15, and 9 Platoon positions.

Sergeant Thompson[32] from Headquarter Company journeyed forward with a number of men to once again stem the Japanese advance which was threatening the very survival of the battalion. Lieutenant Clements[33] of C Company mounted a desperate counter-attack, employing some of his own men, and Thompson's men. The wounded Corporal Bear and Privates Avery[34] and Kingsbury[35] from Lieutenant Cox's platoon insisted on accompanying their comrades.

Perhaps the thoughts and actions of brave selfless men are beyond accurate interpretation. The instinct of self-preservation might be expected to dominate in a situation of terror. However, the esprit de corps amongst soldiers of a seasoned, successful and disciplined battalion produces in the hour of impending defeat or triumph, extraordinary courage. Private Kingsbury displayed such courage as Clements's counter-attack gained momentum.

[Kingsbury] rushed forward firing the Bren-gun from his hip through terrific machine-gun fire and succeeded in clearing a path through the enemy. Continuing to sweep enemy positions with his fire and inflicting an extremely high number of casualties on them, Kingsbury was then seen to fall to the ground shot dead by a bullet from a sniper hiding in the wood.[36]

Following in Kingsbury's path the determined foray restored the position and thus denied the Japanese their much-sought-after breakthrough. Kingsbury was the first Australian to win the Victoria Cross in the South-West Pacific Area and, more importantly, the first Australian to win the British Commonwealth's highest award for bravery upon Australian soil.

D Company, virtually cut in two the previous day, had also been busily engaged. Their left flank had been under constant attack by the Japanese who had managed to drive a wedge between them and 8 Platoon of A Company, by late afternoon. The part of D Company that could be reached was ordered to move to the assistance of B Company who were being savagely assailed from two sides. To facilitate this movement, Corporal Craig[37] and Privates Wallshaw and Gibson, dashed forward with grenade and Tommy gun in order to blaze a path for their comrades. In this desperate close-quarter action, Corporal Craig was killed. But his death was not in vain—B Company were reinforced.

By nightfall, the situation was grim. Although the 2/14th Battalion had inflicted over 500 casualties upon their enemy and had held their locality against monumental odds, the Japanese had nonetheless penetrated the Battalion area and still held the high ground to the west. Key needed reinforcement. Responding to this request from Key, Brigadier Potts ordered a company of the 53rd Battalion to move from Alola to Isurava. That company was to be of little use then or later. It simply camped by the track at Isurava Rest House while others performed its allotted role.

But Key was indeed destined to gain a reserve that day. It was by no means of the size needed and it came from a most unexpected quarter. The 2/14th Battalion, in its magnificent performance in the leading role during the last days at Isurava, was supported by the depleted and exhausted 39th Battalion, still committed to battle after declining orders to leave the front line. There can surely be no finer examples of that brave battalion's discipline, esprit de corps and dogged devotion to duty than that of its invalid contingent sent out of battle but coming back to it and that of its returned patrols led by Lieutenants Pentland and Sword. Lieutenant-Colonel Ralph Honner, DSO, MC:

> When, on the 27th, the complete relief of the 39th was ordered for the following day, I had sent back, under Lt Johnston, the weakest of the battalion's sick to have them one stage ahead on the long march to Moresby—they were too feeble for the fast-moving fighting expected at the front.[38]

Two days later with his band of wounded and wasted comrades, Johnston learnt of the plight of the 2/14th and 39th Battalions back at Isurava. Lieutenant Johnston led the volunteers, the fittest of the unfit, back to Isurava to report for duty.[39]

'J.W.B.' in the book *We Were There*, provides a moving account of the incident:

> The battalion was in trouble, so twenty-seven out of thirty went back. The three who didn't were minus a foot; had a bullet in the throat, and a forearm blown off. We never did it for God, King and Country—forget that. We did it because the 39th expected it of us.[40]

Cut off for four days behind enemy lines, the missing 39th Battalion standing patrol commanded by Lieutenant Sword, returned in company with Lieutenant Pentland's missing platoon from Naro Ridge. These exhausted, starving men had been forced to journey through extremely thick jungle surviving only as a result of their having kept well away from the Japanese and the tracks under their use. They were in an appalling physical condition, the jungle having cut at their ragged clothes and bodies. Lieutenant-Colonel Ralph Honner, DSO, MC:

> A corporal of the 2/16th told me afterwards, 'It was enough to make a man weep to see those poor skinny bastards hobble in on their bleeding feet.' They were greeted with the news that the 39th and 2/14th were fighting for their lives. Without a word, or a thought for the food their stomachs craved, they turned and hurried off to Isurava as fast as their crippled feet could carry them.[41]

Lieutenant-Colonel Key had a reserve again.

As night descended over the battle-scarred perimeter, the 2/14th Battalion had still denied the enemy the prize of Isurava despite having been outnumbered in the order of six to one, and having been bombarded continually while having no suitable weapons of reply. But after a magnificent see-sawing defence of its positions on the high ground, B Company had been driven off its ground for the fourth time and this time was unable to regain it. The *Report Into Operations 21 Brigade* gives a perceptive insight into the determined and, above all, cool and measured manner in which Brigadier Potts exercised his command of Maroubra Force. He was an aggressive and extremely professional officer whose intent was always focussed upon offensive action where possible:

> The situation at Isurava had deteriorated so rapidly and to such an extent that at 1800 hours the Bde Comd. had to review the psn. Courses considered were:
>> A Deal with right flank first. Considered this might be only a diversion on that flank, the main threat being on the front.

B To hold right flank and put in a solid attack around the
ridge on the left of 2/14th Battalion position, thus taking
the enemy in the flank and rear.

C Withdraw 2/14th Battalion and 39th Battalion.

Obviously the risk attached to course (B) was that *all* reserves
would be committed. Opinion was, however, that the situation
warranted this risk. Consequently Lieutenant-Colonel Caro was
ordered to call in OC's C and D Coys 2/16th Battalion who
were given the tasks of getting along the Naro Ridge and
encircling the Jap positions forward of 2/14th Battalion. At this
stage, however, Comd. 2/14th Battalion telephoned the Brigade
Command to say that the position had deteriorated to such an
extent that he asked for permission to withdraw to the line of
the Isurava Rest House Ridge . . . The Brigade Command
considered Lieutenant-Colonel Key's request and granted
permission to withdraw to the position indicated. This meant a
complete change of plans and a force to cover the 2/14th
Battalion occupation of Isurava Rest House Ridge had to move
immediately. The role of C and D Coys 2/16th Battalion was
changed to this task.[42]

C and D Company's 2/16th Battalion were unable to perform
this task owing to the terrain and darkness. As the battle situation deteriorated they were kept at Alola pending the
outcome of the action of their A and B Companies engaged
along the Missima track.

The withdrawal of the 2/14th and 39th Battalions was
completed during the late hours of 29 August. It was a grim,
deathly quiet and backbreaking experience, as the sleepless and
worn troops of the two battalions, assisting their wounded,
made their way back along the track through the mud and
darkness to the Rest House. By 2 am on the 30th both battalions had occupied their new positions and awaited their
enemy. The 39th Battalion numbered 150 men. Lieutenant-
Colonel Key had sustained casualties of two officers and ten

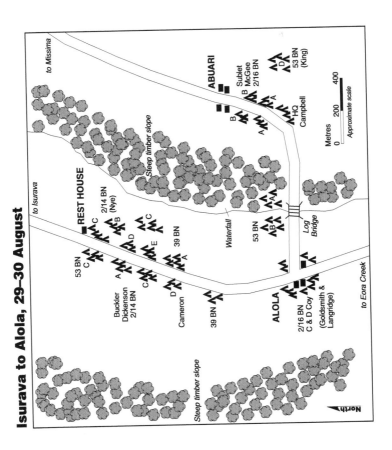

Isurava to Alola, 29–30 August

men killed and three officers and 45 men wounded. In addition, he knew that many of his troops were missing, the bulk of them from D Company.

On the left at Isurava and out of touch with the rest of the 2/14th Battalion, Lieutenant Pearce[43] and a large portion of 16 and 17 Platoons gamely carried on their fight. For two long and desperate days they repulsed repeated Japanese attacks upon them and were forced to withdraw only when their ammunition stocks ran perilously low. Pearce, although wounded, covered the withdrawal of his embattled little force aided by a small number of volunteers. His rearguard rejoined the 2/14th lines five days later, whilst the main group under Sergeant Irwin[44] struggled through to Uberi after an amazing journey over trackless terrain lasting 21 days—nineteen of them without food.

While the 2/14th and 39th Battalions were disposed at Isurava Rest House on 30 August, Captain Sublet, commanding A and B Companies 2/16th Battalion, prepared to attack the Japanese on the right flank. He had, on 29 August, requested a company for that purpose and Captain King's D Company, 53rd Battalion, given that role, had been ordered to attack early next morning. As the 2/16th companies would then be quite out of touch with King it was agreed that Sublet's attack would begin upon hearing the first shots fired by King's men. Captain F. H. Sublet MC, 2/16th Battalion:

On the next morning—30th August—A and B Coys prepared for their roles in the attack and we waited for the sound of firing on the enemy's left flank, which was to be the signal for our assault. However no sound came from where I hoped the 53rd Company would be, so I decided that A and B Companies would attack as planned. Earlier at my request, the C.O. had directed H.Q. Coy to take up positions on the track between A and B Companies and Alola to secure my Line of Communication, and this they did, during the afternoon of the

29th of August. I had eliminated the 53rd Company from calculation and timed the attack by A and B Companies to commence at 1100 hours.[45]

The resulting 2/16th Battalion attack, unbeknown to its A and B Company participants, was made against a Japanese force of battalion strength. B Company's role (Captain Wright) was to move around the Japanese positions, while A Company was to be engaged in a frontal assault. Captain McGee's A Company attacked with great spirit although suffering heavy casualties, and his 9 Platoon (Lieutenant Christian) and his 7 Platoon (Lieutenant Blythe) inflicted telling casualties upon the Japanese.

B Company 2/16th Battalion was confronted by a large, well-positioned Japanese force and in the resulting action its 10 Platoon, under the command of Lieutenant Gerke, was ambushed and cut off. This company also inflicted heavy losses upon their enemy. For Lieutenant Gerke's platoon it would be some days before they were able to rejoin their lines. The role of this 2/16th attack transpired to be a vital one, as it frustrated the Japanese attempt to cut the Kokoda Trail at Alola. For the 2/14th and 39th Battalions, the consequences of the success of that attempt would have been catastrophic. The recollections of Lieutenant Gerke bear grim testimony to the nature of the fighting on the Kokoda Trail and also to the tragedy that befell the inexperienced 53rd Battalion soldiers:

My platoon found a number of the 53rd Bn in and around Abuari, in the jungle, they were not aware of what was going on, had little or no food or ammunition and some were without weapons. As I had a mission to fulfill at the time, they were instructed to keep behind us and out of sight. They appeared most grateful and relieved to see us. At no time did I use them during the four days that they were with me, and they were not a problem, other than we had to ration out our food as we had been cut off from our main forces. At the Waterfall near Abuari we located a large 53rd Battalion patrol that had walked into an ambush, and all had been killed. Their bodies had been dragged off the track and into the jungle, out of sight . . .

A similar fate could have happened to us, but one of the forward scouts in the platoon noticed fallen branches and damaged trees from bullets passing through them, which resulted in our locating a Jap machine-gun post further down the track which we disposed of before we could advance to carry out the task allotted to us. I took the particulars from the dead bodies, removed any food or ammunition and some personal items that they had, marked the spot and proceeded with the task ahead. This delayed us about 3 or 4 hours which eventually resulted in our being cut off, although when I received my orders and instructions from my O.C. (Frank Sublet) I, with 11th platoon, was to take the high ground covering the track to Abuari at the same time that a company of the 53rd Bn was to attack the Japanese positions below. I believe this never eventuated, and it was some of these troops that we picked up and took with us.[46]

While Sublet's force was thus engaged on the right flank, Potts was forced to react to a very rapid deterioration of the position at Isurava Rest House. Lieutenant-Colonel Key had insufficient men to attempt to cover the high ground to the west, where a platoon of the 2/16th Battalion had been posted. When they were driven into Key's defensive perimeter in the late morning of 30 August, the Japanese began to bypass the front positions and prepared to fall upon his rear. Potts ordered Captain Sublet to fall back upon the Alola side of the waterfall which was approximately halfway between Abuari and Alola. Captain Sublet MC, 2/16th Battalion:

We were still attacking when news was received that the battle on the other side of the gorge was going badly for our forces, and that a withdrawal was likely. I was told to withdraw my companies to a position covering the track as it passed behind a waterfall—thus forming a narrow defile—and which would prevent or severely impede any attempt by the Japanese to outflank Alola from Abuari ridge.[47]

While Sublet was engaged in repositioning his force to the rear of the waterfall, a further deterioration took place at the Isurava Rest House. Already aware that the Japanese were bypassing Key's troops by their movement along the high ground, Potts concluded that the Isurava Rest House area was no longer defensible. At 3 pm he ordered a complete withdrawal to Eora Creek as he was only too well aware that Alola provided only a very poor defensive position.

To facilitate an unimpeded withdrawal Key ordered Dickenson and Cameron to clear the enemy from the timbered slopes above the Australian positions. Just before five o'clock C and D Companies swept into a wide attack along the covered hillside and a brisk fire-fight developed there at the same time as a strong attack came along the lower track-side ground against the rearguard A and B Companies. Key and his Battalion Headquarters group, assembled on the track ready to move, suddenly came under the most intense fire from the opposite slopes that forced them over the edge of the precipitous descent to Eora Creek. Corporal H. W. Fielding was amongst that party:

> I was cut off with Lieutenant-Colonel Key, the Adjutant Captain Hall, and fifteen others at the Rest House when the Japs attacked our rear. We tried to make it around the enemy lines and link up with the 2/14th and 2/16th Battalions. On the following morning Lt-Colonel Key advised us to break up into two parties each of nine men.[48]

Lieutenant-Colonel Key was captured some ten days later by the Japanese and subsequently executed. Lieutenant Bisset and a handful of companions regained the battalion lines five days later. Some of the remaining Headquarters men were missing for a number of weeks. The unobtrusive, quietly spoken Key had led his 2/14th Battalion with great distinction during a battle that had demanded the dual qualities of sound, decisive, professional judgment, and cool determination.

An hour of desperate fighting ensued before the men of A and B Companies 2/14th Battalion repulsed the Japanese attacks upon their rear. Captain Nye and most of his company reached the new positions. Lieutenant Treacy and a number of his men remained behind to construct stretchers and withdraw the wounded. This was done under continual fire. Captain Buckler and a part of his A Company also rendered selfless help and protection for these men by fighting the rearguard action. An additional hour passed before this collection of A and B Company men could follow in the path of their comrades. The Japanese had not been idle during this time. Apart from dispersing Key and his Headquarters they had cut the track between Buckler and his battalion south of Alola. Buckler assigned the task of clearing the track to Sergeant Gwillim and a small patrol under his command. The Japanese ambushed Gwillim and killed three of his men. Gwillim and Corporals Smith[49] and Metson[50] were wounded. Sergeant Gwillim:

Personally I was knocked about a bit, as a result of a gunshot wound in my left shoulder which smashed the collarbone and shoulder blade before exiting from a couple of holes in the back. We were subsequently cut off from the main body and did not rejoin the main body for almost seven weeks.[51]

The subsequent adventures of Buckler and his men were marked by extreme hardship, deprivation, tragedy and above all the triumph of the human spirit. No finer example of this spirit could ever be cited than the story of Corporal Metson. Having been shot through the ankle, Metson refused a stretcher, knowing that it would hamper the progress of his comrades and particularly the eight men that would be needed to carry him. He defiantly wrapped his knees and hands in bandages and proceeded to crawl unaided over the mud trails of the Owen Stanley Range. His tragic murder by a Japanese patrol occurred some three weeks later.

The fiercely fought withdrawal of the 2/14th and 39th Battalions from the Isurava Rest House late on the afternoon of 30 August placed Captain Sublet in a desperate situation. Positioned to the rear of the waterfall between Abuari and Alola, Sublet, with most of his A and B Companies, 2/16th Battalion, waited anxiously for the return of Lieutenant Gerke and his 11 Platoon. Captain Sublet MC, 2/16th Battalion:

It was late in the day when we took up our positions round the edges of a cleared area and I waited anxiously to be rejoined by B Coy HQ, 11th Platoon, and other elements of B Coy to whom I had apparently not been able to convey my order to withdraw. I felt frustrated at the lack of telephone contact with 2/16th Bn HQ, but eventually a signaller found a break in the line, repaired it, and was able to bring me a message confirming the Brigade withdrawal and warning me NOT to attempt to bring my troops through Alola after 1900 hours. I was left to guess where the Brigade was withdrawing to, but I knew it would be somewhere down the single track. It was pitch dark when we reached the fallen tree crossing the fast-running creek swollen by the regular afternoon rain, and there was no prospect of getting the straggling line of men through Alola in time. As it seemed the Japanese were not on our heels, I directed the troops some hundreds of yards upstream and rejoined them to remain quiet in the thick undergrowth on the left bank of the stream. I then clawed my way up the steep track to Alola to try and judge whether our people were still holding the village. When I reached the top of the track I found all was dark and silent. Forced to make a judgement, I decided that, rather than risk taking my party consisting of A Coy, HQ Coy and about half of B Coy, up the track and through Alola, I would wait about four hours to moonrise, when the rain should have ceased, then move upstream until we located the remainder of the 2/16th Battalion. Soon after the morning mists rose, Australian troops were spotted on a kunai spur to our right front and I reported my force back to Colonel Caro before midday. The afternoon was unusually clear and sunny and I watched with chagrin a parade and apparently some sort of celebration by Japanese troops in the hilltop village of Alola which had seemed so secure when I first arrived there.[52]

The Battle of Isurava Rest House concluded late on 30 August. For the Japanese—another victory. Isurava Rest House and Alola had fallen and many of the defenders had been cut off from their line of supply and communication. Significant Australian casualties had been inflicted and Major-General Horii could still enjoy the advantages of a grossly superior and more heavily armed force. The application of continued frontal assaults combined with outflanking movements still afforded him the potential to encircle and annihilate his enemy. However, he must have had two extremely sobering thoughts during that fateful night. First, he had sustained very heavy casualties in relation to ground gained and, more importantly, his timetable had been frustrated by some four decisive days—days that meant an additional strain upon his supply column and additional exposure of his force to the harsh environment of the Kokoda Trail.

Brigadier Potts viewed the Isurava battle with great frustration. New Guinea Force had failed dismally to sustain his force with rations and equipment. He had been forced to wage his battle upon costly, faulty intelligence. The consequences of such inadequacies of intelligence and supply were devastating. By a piecemeal commitment of his force Potts was continually reacting to the Japanese possession of the initiative. In command of a force of inferior size, Potts had to cope with one militia battalion's abject failure to achieve any of the very modest goals that he set it. In addition, his experienced 2/27th Battalion had been denied him because of the Japanese landing at Milne Bay, when its intervention at Isurava could have been vital.

By 30 August Potts knew that he faced two critical challenges. A strategic withdrawal is but a part of the ebb and flow of the art of warfare. He must preserve his force intact, while buying time for ground. Behind him lay his 2/27th Battalion and a potential for the introduction of the fresh 25th Brigade. Behind him also lay a shorter supply line and ahead of him a lengthening Japanese supply line. Captain Bisset's view is an accurate one:

> As for tactics, I believe he was initially defeated at Isurava and ultimately at Ioribaiwa. He suffered extremely heavy casualties as was discovered later when Cha-force came through . . . When they [Japanese] became threatening, our units would withdraw to a new ambush position and establish a killing ground. This procedure went on throughout the entire withdrawal to Ioribaiwa Ridge, the enemy gradually being whittled away even though he still employed the same tactics, and all the time his supply problem was becoming more and more difficult.[53]

The achievement of Isurava will forever stand as a memorial to the unshakeably professional and resolute 2/14th Battalion and that haggard, but defiant 39th Battalion. Captain F. H. Sublet MC, 2/16th Battalion:

> In my judgement as a participant, the morale and fighting spirit of the troops upheld in unsullied purity the deathless tradition of Australian Arms—they were superb![54]

9

Rupert's clinic

Warfare is a curious human phenomenon. It evokes an incredible range of complicated human character traits and emotions. The most obvious of these characteristics are hatred, extreme violence, fortitude, courage, pain and very often, a scant regard for the value of human life. Paradoxically, it also calls forth compassion and self-sacrifice and, indeed, the soldier's love for his fellowman.

Perhaps the most famous and legendary Australian story of such compassion and self-sacrifice is embodied in the Gallipoli episode of Simpson and his donkey. The battlefields of Europe and Africa were the scenes during two world wars of countless deeds of courageous devotion by those who sought to provide care and comfort for their wounded comrades.

On the Kokoda Trail during July–September 1942, a small but dedicated group of young medical officers ably assisted by their stretcher-bearers and often the fighting troops themselves, emulated the deeds of those who had undertaken equivalent roles in both long past and quite recent battles. There were numerous 'Simpsons' on the Kokoda Trail. There were no donkeys, for the terrain forbade any form of animal or motorised assistance. However there was help—the story of the medical personnel is vitally interwoven with the super-human efforts of the ANGAU staff, and the native carriers who are forever immortalised and remembered simply as 'The Fuzzy-Wuzzy Angels'. The treatment and evacuation of the wounded on the Kokoda Trail is a story to uplift the heart.

As a direct response to the more fluid and mobile nature of warfare during the Second World War, the medical procedure for the care and evacuation of the wounded had become quite sophisticated. A wounded soldier's recovery from the battlefield was usually undertaken by his battalion's stretcher-bearers, who often had a secondary role as members of a battalion band. Such stretcher-bearers displayed great personal bravery in that they often recovered their comrades under enemy fire. The casualty was then carried to the Regimental Aid Post (RAP) where basic but vital first aid was administered by the Regimental Medical Officer (RMO). Each battalion had one such officer (attached from the Australian Army Medical Corps) who invariably became a personal counsellor and adviser in addition to discharging his medical responsibilities. The RMO was thus a well-known and respected figure in the battalion. From the Regimental Aid Post the casualty passed to the Field Ambulance for emergency surgery or further dressing of his wound(s). If his condition warranted additional treat-ment, or, if he had been subjected to an operation, he was then conveyed by motor transport back to the Casualty Clearing Station and thence to a hospital. This process from stretcher-bearer to hospital was efficient and speedy and gave the patient an optimum chance of survival.

The Kokoda Trail negated this proven and efficient system of medical evacuation. The medical staff in the Owen Stanleys created their own system under enormous pressure and with minimum time. The senior medical officer of the 7th Division AIF was Colonel Norris.

Norris had the 2/6th Field Ambulance available for use in the Kokoda Campaign. This team were not strangers to the 7th Division, as they had served it with distinction during the Syrian Campaign. Norris knew that, because of the nature of the terrain, the supply situation and the type of fighting, he could not efficiently deploy and use all of the 2/6th Field Ambulance. He therefore decided to appoint a senior medical officer for the campaign and limit the number of medical staff, using the criteria of age and fitness as well as competency. The post of senior medical officer was given by Norris to Captain Magarey[1] who was to be promoted to Major. Magarey was ordered to select his team and to design and implement a plan for the treatment and evacuation of the wounded.

Unable to discover much information concerning the terrain and conditions, Magarey journeyed out from Uberi on 17 August.

Left road head with Captain Oldham[2] and thirty-one other ranks in composite party consisting of engineers, Brigade signals, Brigade A.S.C. and other details, and A.A.M.C. medical equipment carried by personnel. The thirty-one other ranks included ten orderlies to be left in pairs at the 5 staging posts to Myola.[3]

Magarey assigned the five pairs of orderlies to the villages of Uberi, Ioribaiwa, Nauro, Menari and Efogi. He then left the balance of his medical team at Myola, where he could expect the bulk of his supplies to be dropped and then proceeded on from Myola.

Upon further investigation forward, Magarey found Captain Shera and his 39th Battalion RAP were at Isurava, while Captain Wallman[4] was administering an Advanced Dressing Station (ADS) at Isurava Rest House, twenty minutes to the rear of Isurava. Captain McLaren[5] was in charge of a smaller ADS at Eora Creek, while Captain Hogan[6] and his 53rd Battalion RAP were at Alola between those two stations.

Prior to the battle for Isurava from 26–29 August, Magarey attempted to accommodate within his plan for the evacuation of the wounded Brigadier Potts's desire to move forward and capture Kokoda. Magarey therefore saw Kokoda as the key point from which his casualties could be flown out to Port Moresby, avoiding being laboriously carried back to Uberi by stretcher. Major Magarey:

> As this plan never came into operation, it will not be given in detail; but it should be mentioned that it embodied the unusual feature of a medical evacuation forward, ie to Kokoda for evacuation by air. Hence the general policy was to push medical posts forward and hold all patients as far forward as possible, to avoid the waste of labour—and labour was always the biggest problem—of a carry two ways over the same track.
>
> R.M.O's 2/14th and 2/16th Australian Infantry Battalions as they came through were appraised of the plan and the methods of evacuation—by native carriers from the R.A.P.'s.[7]

The withdrawal of Maroubra Force from 30 August until relieved by the 25th Brigade in mid-September, forced Magarey to change his plans radically. He had two main concerns with regard to this withdrawal; firstly, the evacuation of the wounded over arguably the worst terrain yet faced by Australian soldiers and, secondly, the physical debilitation of the troops as a result of the conditions.

Every single Australian soldier who could walk, however slowly, and subject to whatever pain, discomfort and inconvenience that had to be endured, walked, staggered or stumbled out of the Owen Stanley Range. Major Magarey:

> It was necessary to be quite ruthless in this respect. Every man who could possibly walk had to, and over and over again men

arriving at medical posts could be given only short rests and then had to be pushed on again. The fortitude and cheerfulness shown by the majority of these men was beyond praise, and the feats of endurance performed by some of the wounded, particularly those with wounds of the lower limbs, were almost incredible.[8]

Chester Wilmot, that doyen of Australian reporters, journeyed over the Kokoda Trail:

> They must be going through hell on this track—specially those with leg wounds. Some have been hit in the foot and they can't even get a boot on, but they're walking back over root and rock and through mud in bare feet, protected only by their bandages. Here's a steep pinch and a wounded digger's trying to climb it. You need both hands and both feet, but he's been hit in the arm and thigh.
>
> Two of his cobbers are helping him along. One goes ahead, hauling himself up by root and branch. The wounded digger clings to the belt of the man in front with his sound hand, while his other cobber gets underneath and pushes him up. I say to this fellow he ought to be a stretcher case, but he replies 'I can get along. There's blokes here lots worse than me and if we don't walk they'll never get out.'[9]

At each staging post the walking wounded were the first to be sent on their way to avoid congestion both in the small and primitive villages and on the track. These men were rarely the recipients of a warm, comfortable rest but were instead always kept moving as the pressures of the general withdrawal mounted.

The evacuation of the wounded by stretcher on the Kokoda Trail must surely rank amongst the most exhausting and remarkable feats of human endurance ever undertaken in Australian military history. The terrain to be traversed made the standard, reasonably comfortable and long-used army stretcher obsolete. Major Magarey:

> The ordinary ambulance stretcher was of little use. A few were used and it was found that the spreaders almost invariably broke and the canvas rotted and tore. The handles were not long enough and the natives would always lash these stretchers on to the frames they made themselves. In addition the carrying surface is too flat and the patient is very liable to be tipped off. The stretchers used were made by the natives, using blankets, local wood and native string. The blanket was doubled round two long poles and the edges tied together. The poles were kept apart by spreaders lashed across them at each end.[10]

The performance of the native bearers affectionately memorialised as 'The Fuzzy-Wuzzy Angels' is best assessed by the veterans of the campaign. An RMO, Major Steward:

> Many tributes have been paid to these carriers and their work, but none can adequately match the reality. They carried up supplies, and then were loaded down on the return with our wounded. The men on stretchers they tended with the devotion of a mother and the care of a nurse. A quick word from an A.N.G.A.U. man that the doctor needed shelter for his wounded, and instantly black arms were at work with machetes, poles were cut, leaves collected, and a rough but almost rainproof lean-to rose before your eyes. When a stretcher went 'bugger-up finish' they lashed a new one together in a matter of moments.[11]

Major Magarey:

> As stretcher bearers the natives were excellent. They can get stretchers over seemingly impossible barriers and not only get them over but give the patient a comparatively comfortable

ride as well. The care which they show to the patient is magnificent. Every need which they can fulfil is fulfilled. If night finds the stretcher still on the track they will find a level spot beside the track and build a shelter over the patient; they will make him as comfortable as possible, get him water and feed him if any food is available. They sleep four each side of the stretcher and if the patient moves or requires any attention during the night it is instantly given. The labour of carrying was extremely arduous but was never shirked and the natives practically never left the patient until they had brought him to his destination.[12]

The day-to-day grind, the compassion shown also by the troops towards their fellow men, and the fortitude of the stretcher cases are simply but dramatically recorded for posterity by Chester Wilmot:

—now and then we pass a stretcher case. The stretchers are only two saplings with a blanket strung between them and sewn up with lawyer vine. But they do. It's hard enough to keep your feet with only a pack and rifle on your back. It's a miracle how they carry those stretchers. But they get through, even though it takes eight men all day to move one stretcher case back three or four miles. But the troops up forward are holding on, giving them time to get all the wounded out. They put one stretcher down by the track for a moment to give the fellow a rest from the jolting. He's got a bedraggled half-damp fag in his mouth and he asks for a match. Mine are damp—they've been damp all the week—but Ossie has some waxies he's carefully preserved in an oil-silk tobacco pouch. We give him a light, roll another cigarette for him and he says— 'Thanks mate . . . a smoke helps a lot . . . I'll be O.K. now.' They lift him gently but he winces as the slow agonising jolting begins again. Then a fellow I went to school with calls down the track. He used to be a good left-hand bowler, but he won't bowl for a while. 'How did you get that, Bill?' 'Oh, we were out on patrol . . . trying to clear that ridge on the left . . . we got 'em off it . . . but three of the boys got knocked. We started to carry 'em in . . . but the nips saw us and got behind us just at dark. First we knew was a shower of grenades. We blazed around and after a bit they pulled out, but it wasn't easy fighting and looking after the wounded too. They got Butch Bisset and most of us got hit somewhere, but we carried 'em all back.' I watch him go off down the track . . . It'll be nearly a week before he reaches hospital and *he* has sound legs—for fellows with leg wounds and for stretcher cases, it may be twice as long.[13]

The withdrawal of Maroubra Force severely limited and frustrated the medical staff with regard to the actual treatment of wounds. Prior to the withdrawal from Alola, all possible surgery allowing for the conditions and lack of equipment, was performed. But after that withdrawal all surgery performed for several days—crucial days when casualties were high—was limited to the arrest of haemorrhaging and other lifesaving measures. The restrictions on surgical procedures had some devastating consequences. Sir Rupert Magarey:

If you got an abdominal wound on the Kokoda Trail you might as well have given up. You never told the troops that, but you knew bloody well that that was what would happen. To deal with an abdominal wound you have to have an operating theatre, an anaesthetist, a surgeon, possibly an assistant surgeon and a good deal of gear! So you gave them a shot of morphine . . .[14]

Major Steward, RMO, 2/16th Battalion:

My saddest sight at Butcher's Hill was that of a 23 year old former golf professional. He had a ghastly, gaping wound of the throat, and although my eyes could see only darkness and death, his saw light and hope. They were asking me something with all the mute urgency that eyes can convey. Eyes, the windows of the soul, show every facet of the inner feelings— love, joy, hope, fear, guilt, pity, hatred, and even bodily sickness or health. Looking as dispassionately as possible at that man's throat, I hoped he couldn't sense the lump in mine. Emotion clouds calm clinical judgement, but the hardest thing is not to flinch from the gaze of the man you know is going to die. Evacuation by helicopter (as later in Vietnam) or the good fortune of having a surgical team nearby might have given him a fighting chance.[15]

One can only ponder what must have gone through the troops' minds concerning the possibility of a severe wound in the conditions that prevailed on the Kokoda Trail.

It is to the everlasting credit of Magarey, his staff, the RMOs, the native carriers and the troops themselves, that not one wounded digger known to them was left at the scene of the battle during this whole campaign. This professionalism and devotion to duty must have been very greatly appreciated by troops who were only too well aware, after the Japanese atrocities in China and the shameful Japanese Tol Plantation massacre near Rabaul, of their fate if left behind. An excellent illustration of this devotion to duty is embodied in the story of three patients who were cared for at Eora Creek during the withdrawal. Two of the men had abdominal wounds and the third a sucking chest wound. Due to the extreme shortage of morphine it was decided not to administer further injections as they were all moribund[16] and comfortable. As no further casualties were expected into Eora Creek Magarey and his men left the village at dusk:

I went through the clearing and up into the jungle like everybody else, just lay down and got what rest I could for the night. The next morning there wasn't anyone at Eora Creek and one of the doctors told me that they'd all been alive when he left! I went back down to this hut. One was dead, one died while I was there and the third one looked up at me and said 'Aye! Doc, I thought you were going to take me out last night when you put me on the stretcher.'[17]

The man was hurriedly removed after the necessary carriers were found and was withdrawn to die amongst his wounded comrades rather than left.

The treatment of casualties and their subsequent evacuation presented Magarey and the medical personnel with their biggest challenge. However the appalling campaign conditions seriously affected the general physical well-being of the fighting troops. The medical staff could do little to alleviate their plight. What they did do was observe it and interpret its magnitude, with two resulting advantages. Firstly, from this campaign came lessons which were learnt for the benefit of future campaigns and men's lives. Secondly, their observations have left the historian with a wealth of documentation on the Owen Stanley Campaign. Major Magarey:

> It should be borne in mind that many of these men for a week or more, had been wet through and cold continuously, had had little, if any sleep; had been almost continuously either fighting or marching, and had lived solely on an often inadequate supply of bully beef, biscuits and water.[18]

It was indeed more than a week! The 39th Battalion had existed in these conditions from mid-July until early September, while the 21st Brigade's 2/14th and 2/16th Battalions were subjected to nearly three weeks of much more intense fighting. The consequences of those conditions were extreme. Major Magarey:

> A large majority of sick were bowel disorders varying from mild diarrhoea to true bacillary dysentery with the passage of blood

and mucus. These began to occur in serious numbers about the
1st and 2nd September and from then on steadily increased. It
was felt that the majority of cases which fell into the mild
diarrhoea category were due to the living conditions which
were dreadful and the constant ration of bully beef and biscuits,
often inadequate, and that if these cases could be held for one or
two days in conditions where rest and sleep, dry clothes and
adequate food could be provided, they could clear up. This was
repeatedly attempted but with only a very partial success. Firstly,
it was rare to be in a position where the patients could be held
long enough. Secondly, the majority of cases were so exhausted,
that a condition which would normally clear up in one or two
days, required under the circumstances, at least a week.[19]

It was therefore relatively common to see exhausted men with
the backside cut out of their shorts or trousers traversing the
Kokoda Trail while suffering continual and debilitating dysentery or diarrhoea. But infection was not the only ravager of the
human frame. Shortages of food and lack of rest and sleep,
combined with excessive demands on body, mind and will (particularly the almost superhuman exertion involved in unending
fighting and frantic movement under extraordinary burdens of
weapons and ammunition and wounded) drained the physical
and psychological reserves of the emaciated and hungry.

However, it is well worth recording that the medical
personnel on the Kokoda Trail reported little or no incidence
of self-inflicted wounds, malingering or neurosis in the 39th
Battalion or the 21st Brigade—a measure of the soldierly
conduct, professionalism and sheer courage and fortitude of
those remarkable troops.

Major Rupert Magarey's 'clinic' on the Kokoda Trail
operated under deplorable conditions. It lacked equipment,
decent accommodation and speedy transport to and from its
posts. Lieutenant-Colonel Sublet, in a pen picture of his RMO
Major Steward, portrays the qualities common to all of the

very fine young men who worked so tirelessly in conjunction with Rupert Magarey's clinic:

> In accordance with faithful compliance with medical ethics, Captain Steward showed absolute devotion to the sick, wounded and dying, totally regardless of his own safety. He did a great deal to restore the spirits of men who had been despondent, downcast, or afraid.[20]

10

Full of fight but utterly weary

There's heavy machine gun fire from just over the ridge and every few seconds the valley rumbles with the crump of mortars. And the Brigade Major says, '. . . It's no use your going forward, Chester . . . we're coming back . . . They broke through on the left of Crofty's crowd this morning and now they're swarming over the ridge above brigade. They shot us up just before we left and we've sent the old and the bold to clean 'em up.' 'No doubt' he says 'they'll deal with this party but by tomorrow the Nips will be there in hundreds. Albert's bringing his battalion back now and the others are going to make a clean break at dark and withdraw through 'em. I'm going back to reconnoitre the new positions. I think you'd better come back too.'[1]

That was the first day of one of the most gruelling and yet utterly resolute withdrawals in the history of Australian arms. Wilmot's meeting was with Major Challen[2] the Brigade Major of the 21st Brigade, on the afternoon of 30 August.

The ensuing night will forever remain burnt into the minds of the young soldiers who endured it. Exhausted, ragged men struggled, groped, slipped and fell through the pitch-black darkness holding on to the belts or bayonet scabbards of the men in front of them. The 39th Battalion were amongst the last Australian troops to leave the Isurava Rest House area—on the twenty-fifth day of their full battalion involvement in the battle-zone.

Lieutenant-Colonel Honner had moved to Eora Creek to reconnoitre the next Maroubra Force defensive position. Behind him stumbled the gaunt, exhausted remnants of the battalion that had endured so much. Sergeant Russ Rosengren well remembers:

> The only clothes I had after we dropped our pack before Deniki were a pair of shorts; a pair of boots and an army jumper; that's all my clothes consisted of. No blanket, no groundsheet. In fact anyone lucky enough to have a blanket, maybe a half dozen of us would share it. If someone had a cup or a dixie, maybe a dozen of us would use the same implement and share out what food we had.[3]

Lieutenant Hugh Dalby, MC:

> My condition feet wise had deteriorated because my boots had worn out. I had pulpy feet; like crevices; ridges a quarter of an inch thick. You were soaking wet all the time. White puffy skin just started to peel off. Your clothes stank. My sergeant cut my hair with a safety razor blade and then I cut his hair with the same blade. It was all matted with dirt; you couldn't wash it properly because you had no soap, so with long hair you would grab handfuls of it, slash it with a razor blade and thereby get some of the muck out of your hair.[4]

Laurie Howson, 39th Battalion:

The days go on. You are trying to survive, shirt torn, arse out of your pants, whiskers a mile long, hungry and a continuous line of stretchers with wounded carried by 'Fuzzy-Wuzzies' doing a marvellous job. Some days you carry your boots because there's no skin on your feet. But when I look around at some of the others— hell! They look crook! Then I have seen the time when you dig a number of holes in the ground and bury your dead. Nothing would be said, but you think 'maybe it will be my turn next.'[5]

'Your turn' could indeed be next. Heavily outnumbered, outranged by the enemy's weapons and caught in an environment where death could come from literally any direction, the psychological pressures upon the men were immense.

Nor were the Japanese the only source of tragedy during the withdrawal. After having survived the attack to retake Kokoda, and having also survived the carnage of Isurava, the 39th Battalion suffered the tragic loss of one of its finest young officers during that fateful withdrawal. Captain Jacob, affectionately known as 'Tubby' to his troops, had assumed command of C Company after the death of Captain Dean at Deniki. He relieved an exhausted young man of the burden of his rifle during the night of 30–31 August. Unbeknown to Jacob, the safety catch on the rifle was not 'on' and as Jacob slipped over a tree root the rifle discharged a bullet which hit him in the groin. Padre Earl, a Catholic priest, read the Anglican Last Rites as Jacob's life passed. He was at the ripe old age of 22.

Of the four battalions engaged forward of Alola the Victorian 2/14th was the one that bore the brunt of the heaviest fighting. The battalion gave far in excess of what could reasonably have been expected of it, and paid so very dearly in terms of casualties and hardship. The main body of the 2/14th withdrew from Isurava Rest House between 5 pm and 6 pm on 30 August. It was to be around 11.30 pm before all its men who had not been cut off were back and in position.

The Withdrawal—Alola to Efogi

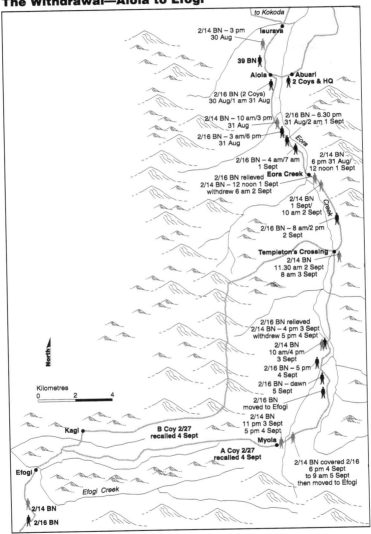

to Kokoda

2/14 BN – 3 pm
30 Aug — **Isurava**

39 BN

Alola • **Abuari**
2 Coys & HQ

2/16 BN (2 Coys)
30 Aug/1 am 31 Aug

2/14 BN – 10 am/3 pm
31 Aug

2/16 BN – 6.30 pm
31 Aug/2 am 1 Sept

2/16 BN – 3 am/6 pm
31 Aug

2/14 BN
6 pm 31 Aug/
12 noon 1 Sept

2/16 BN – 4 am/7 am
1 Sept

2/16 BN relieved
2/14 BN – 12 noon 1 Sept
withdrew 6 am 2 Sept

Eora Creek

2/14 BN
1 Sept/
10 am 2 Sept

2/16 BN – 8 am/2 pm
2 Sept

Templeton's Crossing

2/14 BN
11.30 am 2 Sept
8 am 3 Sept

2/16 BN relieved
2/14 BN – 4 pm 3 Sept
withdrew 5 pm 4 Sept

2/14 BN
10 am/4 pm
3 Sept

2/16 BN – 5 pm
4 Sept

2/16 BN – dawn
5 Sept

2/16 BN
moved to Efogi

North

Kilometres
0   2   4

2/14 BN
11 pm 3 Sept
5 pm 4 Sept

Kagi •

B Coy 2/27
recalled 4 Sept

A Coy 2/27
recalled 4 Sept

Myola

2/14 BN covered 2/16
6 pm 4 Sept
to 9 am 5 Sept
then moved to Efogi

Efogi •

Efogi Creek

2/14 BN

2/16 BN

171

Its diminished strength bore stark testimony to its role in the actions at Isurava and Isurava Rest House. It had completed its concentration at Isurava on the 28th with 542 troops. After 'stand to' on the morning of the 31st it mustered 160, 30 in HQ and A Company, 54 in B Company, 42 in C Company and 34 in D Company—little more than a company at full strength. On the 30th alone—the first day of the withdrawal—or as a direct result of it—48 men lost their lives, and, in addition to those, 44 had been cut off, including the CO, Adjutant, Intelligence Officer and nearly half of A Company with its commander. The command of the battalion passed to the very competent Captain Rhoden[6] who, the following year, was to be promoted Lieutenant-Colonel to command the 2/14th again until the end of the war.

By early morning of 31 August, the 2/14th Battalion was deployed about a mile south of Alola, Brigade Headquarters was set up halfway between Alola and Eora Creek, the 39th Battalion was occupying defensive positions at Eora Creek and the 53rd Battalion was being sent out of battle. Goldsmith's and Langridge's companies and the headquarters of the 2/16th Battalion had withdrawn through the 2/14th positions and were astride the track near Brigade Headquarters, to be joined later in the morning by Sublet with HQ Company, A Company and about half of B Company who had moved back through the moonlight and the morning mist beside the creek, well east of the track.

Meanwhile, the Japanese were busily engaged in widening tracks using Formosan, Korean and native labourers. And with fresh reinforcements coming forward after the capture of Alola, Horii was able to use the Abuari track to shorten his line of communication. But, although in total command of the initiative and enjoying the enormous advantages of superior numbers and weaponry, he was still faced with worrying problems.

When the Australians are forced to retire, they show a tendency to first destroy their establishments. They must be attacked, captured, and any fires extinguished . . .

Because the quantity of arms and ammunition within the detachment is limited, the method of using captured arms and ammunition should be studied . . .

The progress of the operation must be swift, brave and resolute, and much practical use can be made of captured supplies.[7]

Such was the air of confidence displayed by the Japanese command in Rabaul before Horii's force landed at Gona, Basabua and Buna between 21 July and 22 August. The Japanese supplied their combat troops with about eleven days' rations. At the outset of the Owen Stanley Campaign it was hoped that these light rations and captured enemy supplies would see them through to the capture of Port Moresby. The sparse nature of the Japanese private soldier's rations was noticed repeatedly by the Australians. Sergeant John Manol, a member of the 39th Battalion Intelligence Section observed this Japanese trait when examining their dead:

I often had to go through their equipment. And you'd see a bloke; his rations, . . . he'd have a little dixie there with a ball of rice and a couple of bits of seaweed, and that'd do him for twenty-four hours.[8]

In hindsight, the Japanese might be seen as taking an enormous military risk by employing their Spartan logistic policy. However, they had not, so far, known defeat. In fact the rapidity and magnitude of their victories had surprised them no less than their enemies.

Major-General Horii's advance to Efogi would now increase his supply difficulties to a critical level. And the disciplined, defiant and resolute Australians of Maroubra Force were not obliging in their surrender of the very few supply dumps that they were forced, during September, to abandon. Supplies that could not be carried out from Myola for example, were destroyed. Bully beef tins were punctured, the contents contaminated and rice scattered in the mud. Desperate, weary and starving men are not discerning gourmets. The fouled food jettisoned by the Australians was to be the cause of widespread dysentery amongst the Japanese. And the Japanese were not hygiene-conscious troops. Excrement and rotting corpses breed horrific consequences for men already hungry and debilitated.

From 31 August until 15 September, a decisive military game of 'cat and mouse' was staged along the Kokoda Trail. Potts did not possess a force of sufficient size to make a stand of the magnitude of that at Isurava. It would be only at Efogi that such a stand could be even contemplated. The tactic employed by Maroubra Force was obvious in conception but intricate in execution. Exhausted, sleepless and hungry men were required company by company, platoon by platoon, to hurriedly withdraw, stop, prepare positions, defend dourly until their comrades could pass through their positions and then, often within a mere 20–30 yards of the enemy, break contact at dawn, or dusk, or perhaps late at night and trudge wearily up hill and down to repeat the process—again and again. To withdraw too early was to allow the enemy a too speedy acquisition of ground. To withdraw too late meant outflanking, encirclement and annihilation. Captain F. H. Sublet MC, 2/16th Battalion:

> During the step-by-step withdrawal the operation was executed with text book precision and control; no man left his post before his turn came; we left no wounded and no prisoners . . .
>
> The highly professional performance of the 21st Brigade and the 39th Battalion was all the more praiseworthy because, until after the Efogi battle there seemed no likelihood of relief.[9]

By the early afternoon of 31 August the 2/14th Battalion had moved back through the 2/16th to occupy their next defensive position just south of Eora Creek (where the 39th held both sides of the crossing) with Potts's relocated headquarters near by. Although in occupation of a very poor defensive position, C and D Companies, 2/16th Battalion held their ground long enough for the recovery of later elements of Sublet's force still coming in from the Abuari Track and for the securing of time and space for the safe passage of the Maroubra Force stretcher-cases to Eora Creek and beyond. At nightfall, the 2/16th Battalion moved back about 45 minutes' march along the track. However its new position was dominated by high ground to the west and, at a company commanders' conference early that night, Lieutenant-Colonel Caro issued orders for a further withdrawal at 2 am on 1 September. Captain Keith Goldsmith, 2/16th Battalion:

> So I sent a runner off to the three platoons to withdraw through D Company and come back to the track and with my headquarters, you know, a couple of runners and sigs, etc. and went back through D Company along the track. And I'm waiting for the three platoons to come out of the bush . . . and they never came.[10]

By the morning of the 1st the 2/16th were in a new position farther back towards Eora Creek with Goldsmith's ungathered rearguard platoons under increasing pressure that forced them eastwards to cross the creek lower down. Soon after first light the battalion commenced another withdrawal—over the three long logs, perched end to end on great boulders in the fast-flowing rapids, that constituted the crossing of Eora Creek. The 39th (regrouped into two companies with an average strength of about 70) were holding the ridge above the eastern bank. Merritt's composite company was sent down to the creek-side to cover the 2/16th move and to destroy the crossing when all their men were over. Major Hearman (second in command of the 2/16th) informed Merritt that Paterson's 17 Platoon was still fighting the rearguard action along the track, and Merritt delayed his demolition. But the next troops to arrive were Japanese—in large numbers and with a Juki adding its firepower to the weight of their attack. Merritt's exposed company scattered to scale the steep slope— under covering fire from the ridge above them—ignoring the too visible steps up the face of the knoll. Paterson had been killed and his sergeant wounded when the noise of the firing behind them warned them that they had been outflanked and cut off. Like the C Company rearguard before them they escaped to the east over another crossing.

After the main body of the 2/16th had completed their crossing at about 8.30 am they strengthened the Eora Creek defences guarding the approaches, mainly from the north. At 10 am Potts ordered the 39th to Kagi to hold the tracks through there. The sick and the slightly wounded from the rear echelon at Myola, who could still travel, reached Kagi at 5.30 pm. The fitter companies from Eora Creek made a forced march along the Kokoda Trail through Templeton's Crossing and over the top of the Owen Stanley Range to hold that night a position, chillingly cold in the wet mud, two miles east of Kagi. At first light on the 2nd, Bidstrup's company moved on to Kagi leaving Merritt's company in ambush.

At noon on the 1st the 2/14th had handed over the defence of Eora Creek to the 2/16th and had fallen back to a position between Eora Creek and Templeton's Crossing. From that point Rhoden sent a C Company patrol of twenty men under Lieutenant McIlroy up the steep westward track from Templeton's Crossing—the route taken by Honner on his way to Kagi—to guard against Japanese infiltration from that direction. McIlroy's orders were to maintain a standing patrol on the track for three days or until relieved. He was not relieved, and it was to be a long 'three days'.

On the evening of the 6th, after a four-day struggle over the mountains, McIlroy picked up two soldiers cut off that day from Lieutenant Bell's patrol of the 2/27th. On the 9th, two clashes with the Japanese near Menari cost two killed and one wounded but two eluded the enemy and rejoined the 2/14th on the 14th. The next day the patrol was split in two. Of the main body seven linked with another homing party under Sergeant Irwin (out of Isurava two days after Key's withdrawal) to arrive, spent and worn, at Uberi on 21 September—but of four of them there was no word. McIlroy's party continued south to the west of the main track. They were very weak with one wounded and one injured who had to be carried; so on the 16th four men were sent ahead. Treacherous natives killed two of them and the two survivors, one with a spear wound in the back, reached safety on 3 October. McIlroy and one helper stayed with the casualties until one of them died. His three friends, joined by two more of their battalion who had been in the jungle since the fighting at Isurava, struck the Brown River on 6 October and a patrol of the 6th Independent Company on the 7th.

Early on 1 September, the situation was that the 2/14th Battalion had moved to the rear of the 2/16th Battalion and was about halfway between Eora Creek and Templeton's Crossing.

Back at Eora Creek the 2/16th had the task of holding positions overlooking the crossing and covering tracks from the north and east from midday on the 1st until 6 am on the 2nd. It was heartened by the return of Paterson's leaderless D Company platoon and of Gerke's longer lost platoon, in at last from the Abuari Track with 53rd Battalion auxiliaries it had gathered on the way, including those surprised at Missima on the eve of Horii's main offensive. They were followed in by the Japanese, soon mounting ever increasing pressure upon the Western Australians who, on the high ridges, were cut off from the water below and suffered severely from thirst. Most of the attacks were against Langridge's defences on the right. There, 16 Platoon became the rearguard while 17 and 18 Platoons dug in farther up the hill. By dusk 16 Platoon had withdrawn to the dug-in positions.

During a pitch-black night of heavy rain the persistent Japanese stormed at them again and again. Every attack, every infiltration, was countered.

During the night of 1–2 September, amidst very heavy rain, a number of attempts were made by the enemy to infiltrate the D Company positions. To be ever vigilant whilst occupying ground in pitch-black darkness and in heavy rain requires extraordinary fire discipline and coolness when it is known that the enemy is within yards, or indeed feet—or on occasions, touches you before either party is aware of the other's presence:

> One got so close that he grasped Private Bill Waldron's fixed bayonet to help him up the hill, evidently in the belief that he had hold of a sapling or branch of a tree. Private Jack Currie, who was behind Waldron, coolly rested his Bren-gun on Waldron's head and gave the visitor a burst . . .
>
> Another raiding Japanese crept up close to our lines and whispered in English: 'Where are you, Digger?' Lance-Corporal Alex Salvaris answered with studied politeness: 'Here I am', and fired point-blank to prove it.[11]

As groups of the infiltrating enemy pressed forward, the Australians tossed grenades amongst them and, in the flashing glare of the explosions, cut them down with quick concentrated volleys. The midnight deluge doused the fire of the last fierce assaults; and, in the cold, wet light of the withdrawal, some 170 enemy dead littered the outer limits of the defiant defences.

Potts was seeking a suitable defensive position at which he could make some reasonable attempt to hold the enemy. A position between Myola and Efogi was initially chosen. To have to pull so far back was a bitter tactical pill for Potts to swallow. Myola was his main supply dump; its dry lake-bed had been the focal point of his 'biscuit bomber' supply drops. The tragedy was that just as supplies had been forthcoming in a regular pattern for some days, he was forced to abandon Myola. The whole supply debacle was quite simply a tragic case of far too little when it mattered most, and almost too much when all seemed lost between Myola and Kokoda. The key factor in Potts's decision to give up Myola was the terrain. While Myola was an ideal venue for the dropping of supplies it was an extremely poor defensive position against a large enemy force. In addition, Myola lay quite near to one of two tactical 'loops' in the track. Away to the west of Myola stood the village of Kagi, on the other loop was the Kokoda track which the Japanese could readily use to outflank the Australians and thus cut them off from their line of communication near Efogi. Potts therefore determined that a stand would be made between Myola and Efogi with the Kagi track junction held to protect his left flank.

Accordingly, at dawn on the 2nd, the move from Eora Creek began. By 8 am the 2/16th, strengthened by the return of Goldsmith's platoon cut off on the last night of August, had passed through the 2/14th and halted an hour's march north of Templeton's Crossing. Rhoden led the 2/14th through the 2/16th about 10 am and about an hour later a standing patrol from Sublet's left forward company shot ten of the advancing enemy. The Japanese pushed into closer contact with the main positions and moved around the left flank to threaten the route to the south. Caro decided to leave the track, moving out to follow the ridges to the east. His men, leaving their secure positions as the day waned, were rushed by the alert enemy and some close fighting followed with the attackers sustaining the heavier losses.

The next day, hungry and thirsty, the 2/16th struggled across rough country, tearing their way through thick bush and drinking the moisture oozing from the moss-covered trees. In the late afternoon they emerged where the 2/14th were waiting, between Templeton's Crossing and Myola, and they settled there while the 2/14th continued their journey to Myola. With them went a welcome reinforcement; Lieutenant Bisset, Warrant-Officer Tipton and eleven others cut off at Isurava Rest House, had returned in the wake of the 2/16th.

Even by day the track to Myola was an abomination of a thousand pitfalls—a steeply ascending and descending, slippery, muddy bog; in the dark the invisible obstacle course became a disorientating, disjointing, shattering nightmare. The 2/14th reached Myola late in the night of 3 September and early in the morning of the 4th, most so tired that they dropped to sleep in their sodden cold clothes. But they were to wake in a 'promised land' providing luxuries so long denied that they seemed unready for them with their utterly weary faces, their sunken sleep-starved eyes, their drained grey skins and their mud-matted hair. Clothes were almost immediately removed and cast away and fresh, clean uniforms acquired. Boots were cut away, socks often cut away and in many cases away too came the rotten skin with them. The men's feet were exposed to fresh air as Corporal Clark, the unit chiropodist, set about the task of paring away rotten tissue and smoothing out the wrinkles. Men bathed and washed, and slept the sleep of the reprieved. Most welcome of all came the tantalising odour of food—hot food. The cooks at Myola worked with the most humble of ingredients and recipes; but a hot bully beef stew with dehydrated tinned vegetables, rice and hot tea seemed like 'Maxim's of Paris' to these men.

While the 2/14th Battalion enjoyed their all too brief respite, the 2/16th Battalion were busily withdrawing towards Myola under increasing pressure. They were slowed by the burden of their stretcher-cases and by their own physical deterioration and lack of sleep. At approximately

2 pm on 4 September, Lieutenant Hicks[12] who had led a
patrol out to the west, reported to Captain Sublet (who was
commanding the battalion while Lieutenant-Colonel Caro
was at a conference with Potts) that the Japanese were rounding
the left flank in considerable force. Not long afterwards
McGee's company was attacked in the forward battalion
positions. Sublet wisely chose to withdraw to the high
ground to his rear. What then happened has a comical twist
many years after the event, but would have been less than
amusing at the time:

> When Hicks reported to me (I was I/C of the battalion at
> this stage) that a large party of Japs had passed our left flank,
> I luckily guessed they were making for exactly the higher
> position behind us to which we then withdrew. The Japs put
> in a strong frontal attack as we were thinning out. When I
> arrived back at the previously selected holding position Sgt.
> Morris[13] very irately told me that I had mistakenly allocated
> his Company to a position that was already occupied.
> However a quick inspection disclosed that the position
> (a key one) WAS occupied, but by Japanese! The dynamic
> Morris reacted like a flash and waded in with his men,
> evicting the Japs in short order. Morris' determined and
> full blooded action no doubt saved the battalion from a
> difficult situation.[14]

While a signal received by Brigadier Potts from Major-General
Allen on the afternoon of 3 September gave him great heart,
its contents also portrayed the almost unbelievable ignorance
that even then prevailed in Port Moresby concerning the
plight of Maroubra Force.

> Expect to have Ken here for dinner approximately 6 September . . .
> Supply situation demands vital necessity for holding Myola as
> dropping area . . . We cannot allow enemy to use Myola.

Kokoda Trail—Kokoda to Eora Creek

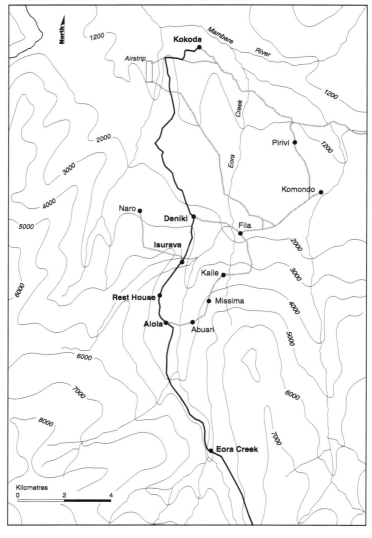

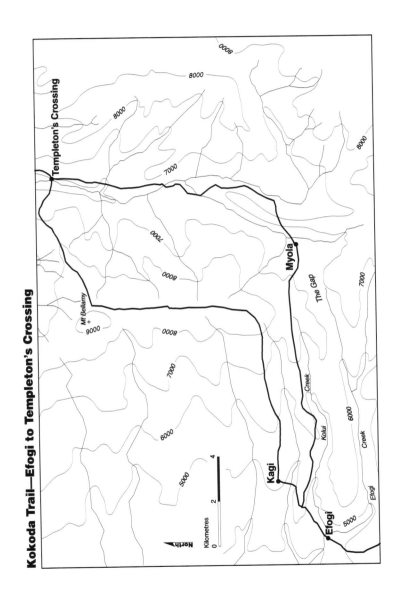

Kokoda Trail—Efogi to Templeton's Crossing

Therefore we must establish firm base forward of Myola as soon
as possible. Is it possible to revert to offensive action now?

The significance of Allen's dinner guest was immediately
obvious to Potts. It told him that Brigadier Ken Eather,[15] and his
25th Brigade, 7th Division, was expected in Port Moresby
within days. Potts could look towards brigade reinforcement and
an ever lengthening Japanese supply line. In hindsight, the
second part of Allen's message does little to enhance this fine
officer's military reputation. There can be no excuse for a divisional commander to have been so hopelessly out of touch with
so many key and yet basic components of a battle that he was
directly responsible for. Such basic notions as terrain, supply and
the magnitude of the enemy force opposing his troops, are
notions that any divisional commander must be familiar with.
One can only ponder the thoughts that must have passed
through Potts's troubled mind after receiving this signal.

The plain, simple and undeniable truth is that on 4 September, Brigadier Arnold Potts could muster no more than
400 soldiers with whom to defend Myola. The Japanese were
thrusting battalion after battalion against him. At 6 pm Potts
signalled Allen:

> Strong enemy attack driven in 2/16th Battalion one and a
> half hours Myola. Am supporting defence with 2/14th Battalion,
> but country entirely unsuitable for defended localities Regret
> necessity abandon Myola. Intend withdrawing Efogi. No
> reserves for counter-attack. Men full of fight but utterly
> weary . . . Will keep you informed.

Potts's initial decision to locate a position between Myola and
Efogi had been based on his inadequate maps which showed
the two Kokoda tracks; the old through Kagi, and the new,
passing near Myola, joining north of Efogi village. The
junction of those two tracks appeared to be the logical place

to hold the enemy advance, regardless of which of the two tracks the enemy might choose to advance upon. However, Potts's reconnaissance showed that this junction was no place to contest the Japanese advance—from the Mission Ridge spur rising southward above the village the junction was below in an open valley; it could be bypassed on either side to seize that very same commanding spur in its rear, cutting off withdrawal. There was no realistic hope of effectively holding any ground in the junction area or of escaping from the very likely resulting enemy trap. The heights of Mission Ridge offered the only local hope—hence Potts's change of plan from a point between Myola and Efogi (the tracks' junction) to Mission Ridge.

After having consumed as much of the supplies as their stomachs and time would permit, 21st Brigade abandoned Myola on 5 September 1942. The stage was about to be set for one of the most horrific confrontations of the Owen Stanley Campaign. For veterans of Maroubra Force alive today, it matters little which of the terms Brigade Hill, Mission Ridge and, indeed, Butcher's Hill is used. All are evocative of the desperate battle for Efogi Ridge.

11

A question of momentum

Wednesday—2 September

Spent an uncomfortable night—too cold to sleep well! . . .

I found a decent stick to help me along and hit on the idea of carrying my rifle and discharge cup over my shoulder which is more comfortable than slung . . .

Towards the end I was spelling every couple of hundred yards . . . I had to halt for a breather ten steps from the top. Gosh! I was done in, and never was a goal more welcome . . .

It was a terrible day's stage and took nine solid hours, and more for the stragglers.

Friday—4 September

Our planes came over and dropped stores. At first, it was a great joke watching their line and calmly dodging, but when five blokes were hit and injured—one killed—and a plane swerved in its swoop and seemed to follow me I deemed it time to get out, so I went back and cowered behind a big tree until the danger was gone . . .

We were sure done in when we reached the inevitable creek but from there U'Fogi was a mere ten minute climb and once again Ray and I and Big Mac were the vanguard—Roy came in a bit later.

There were some dead-beat A and B Coy blokes already at the village.[1]

Such were the initial impressions of one soldier, Corporal C. E. Edwards of D Company, as the third and final 21st Brigade battalion was committed to the Owen Stanley Range at the beginning of September 1942. The 2/27th Battalion from South Australia journeyed forth to battle with a fine Syrian Campaign record and a pent-up enthusiasm for action after having been forced into a passive defensive role as the divisional reserve at Port Moresby during August, pending a clarification of events at Milne Bay. The battalion was commanded by Lieutenant-Colonel Geoff Cooper.[2] Captain H. J. Katekar, 2/27th Battalion:

He [Cooper] was first of all courageous, no question of that. He was competent; he'd been well trained and he'd already shown his ability with the 2/10th Battalion over in the Middle East. He was compassionate; he had a great feeling for his troops, although he didn't show it.[3]

Sergeant J. Burns MM, 2/27th Battalion:

I rate Cooper as a top class bloke in every respect. Colonel Cooper is a man of tremendous heart and compassion.[4]

Lieutenant-Colonel Cooper and his A and B Companies arrived at Kagi on 4 September, with the purpose of assisting Potts's defence of Myola.

Prior to his forced abandonment of Myola, Potts had intended to use his fresh 2/27th to achieve two aims. His first intention was to deploy a company to approach Templeton's Crossing along the track via Kagi, and then fall upon the Japanese rear. That role was given to Captain Lee[5] and his

B Company. Potts's second objective was to reinforce the undermanned and exhausted 2/16th Battalion on the new track between Myola and Templeton's Crossing. Captain Sims and his A Company were despatched on that mission.

It was planned that the 2/27th would commit its C and D Companies, on their arrival at the front, to bolster the 2/16th and 2/14th Battalions' proposed defence of Myola. Major-General Allen's signal of 3 September regarding the need to hold Myola and push offensively forward towards Templeton's Crossing, clearly implied his concern that Potts's planning lacked sufficient aggression. And yet Potts's initial plan for the deployment of the 2/27th Battalion clearly portrays his continual endeavour to regain the initiative and reveals his consistently aggressive attitude.

It is significant that during the next two or three days the hurried occupation and defence of Mission Ridge and Brigade Hill by the 21st Brigade would be the first and only time that Brigadier Potts had the opportunity to command the three battalions of his brigade in action. Ironically, during most of that brief command, he was to be distracted, and his own personal safety was to be threatened, by enemy assault on his headquarters.

By this time, 21st Brigade was a mere skeleton of its normal strength. The savage fighting and severe conditions during the previous days had reduced the 2/14th and 2/16th Battalions to about 25 per cent of their usual numbers; a combined strength of about 400.

The incoming 2/27th Battalion, about 600 strong, had been fatigued by a forced four-day march from the base area. Total brigade strength was little more than that of a full-strength battalion. The 21st Brigade was also completely devoid of its normal supporting arms such as artillery and heavy machine-guns and of engineering equipment and had only meagre medical and supply services. Another worrying factor was that not only were Potts's numbers greatly diminished but, also, the physical condition of his force was causing both him and his medical staff increasingly grave concern. The military consequence of this state of affairs was that the battle for the Kokoda Trail had, for its defenders, become extremely fluid and hazardous and the tactic of the controlled and vigorous fighting withdrawal infinitely more difficult. It was into this precarious environment that the 2/27th Battalion, fresh though it may have been, was thrust.

The fluid nature of the battle manifested itself very quickly indeed. Having despatched his A and B Companies in compliance with Potts's orders, Cooper was forced to retrieve them after receiving the news that the Japanese had forced the 2/16th back to Myola, and that Maroubra Force was to withdraw to Efogi. Captain Lee's B Company was contacted and turned back. However Captain Sims and his A Company who had set themselves a gruelling pace over very rough country between Kagi and the Myola track, could not be contacted by a Papuan policeman who had been sent after them. These events were recorded by Captain Sims in his diary:

4 September:
. . . Brigade Commander ordered Coy to leave Kagi and make Myola by night fall, as a result Coy left Kagi at 1730 hours for Myola taking cross country track for the first one and a half miles to the main Myola track. The going was very treacherous owing to the rain and two men had to be left behind because of injuries sustained whilst crossing a creek. Coy reached main track and continued on towards Myola travelling until 2100 hours that night. They lay either side of that track in the undergrowth and spent a most uncomfortable night in the rain. It was found out afterwards that native police had been sent out to order our return to Kagi . . .
5 September:
Early morning A Coy moved off towards Myola. One hour distant they contacted Bde HQ withdrawing to Efogi. Brigade Major put the Company in the picture and Coy about turned and moved back to Efogi . . .[6]

The position chosen by Potts dominated the ground over-looking Efogi, which lay just to the north, and the village of Menari to the south. From Efogi the ground fell away to a creek just south of the village and then climbed steeply to a spur which ran southward to another steep hill. The spur was a mixture of timber and patches of kunai grass varying in height from six to eight feet. The only artificial feature on the spur was a derelict, roofless, Seventh-Day Adventist mission hut which was on the highest point of the spur. This spur, soon to be the scene of desperate fighting, became known as Mission Ridge. The hill dominating the rear of Mission Ridge became known as Brigade Hill and was also very heavily timbered. To the east and west of the Mission Ridge–Brigade Hill feature, the terrain fell away very steeply into dense, heavily timbered jungle. South from Brigade Hill the terrain ran down an extremely precipitous decline to the village of Menari.

On the night of the 4th Potts ordered Cooper and Honner to evacuate Kagi the next morning and establish defensive positions on Mission Ridge. Honner was the first away, recon-noitred defensive localities for both battalions and had his men in position before midday and partially dug in by the time the 2/27th arrived around 2 pm. With Cooper's last companies marching in from the south that afternoon, Potts was able to effect the long-awaited relief of the 39th. Its War Diary records:

> At about 1530 hours, 2/27th Bn commenced taking over 39th
> Bn positions with all 39th Bn's automatic weapons, grenades,
> rations, blankets, signal stores and medical supplies. In the
> afternoon 39th Bn marched to Menari.

A month earlier at Deniki, after losses in the first Battles of Oivi and Kokoda (including the battalion commander and the first of three company commanders to be killed) the 39th had a total strength of 470. At Efogi it had about 180 left, roughly a quarter of them convalescents and slightly wounded recently recovered from Myola, some of them still marching with, or being treated by, the R.A.P. Laurie Howson, Ack-Ack gunner turned Bren gunner, remembers:

> The Bn was paraded and the C.O. delivered a message of appreciation from Brig. Potts for the splendid service the Bn had given while under comd 21 Brigade.

Potts wrote in his official report:

> their efforts represented gallantry, courage and fortitude of the highest order, and their fighting prowess was an inspiration to all who saw it.

The afternoon rains of 5 September poured down on the four rifle companies of the 2/27th Battalion as they dug in within a well-linked but isolated perimeter on the northern end of Mission Ridge. The previous afternoon the 2/16th Battalion's skilful and savage withdrawal to defeat encirclement by the II Battalion of the 41st Regiment had precipitated Potts's decision to abandon Myola. On the 5th, at 7 am, Horii changed the composition of his pursuit force to include the II and III Battalions of the 144th Regiment with elements of the Mountain Artillery and a Pioneer Company. After the 2/16th, with its wounded, had passed through the 2/14th's holding position north-west of Myola—to which the hungry Japanese, hot on the scent of rations, were temporarily diverted—the unharried Victorian rearguard left for Efogi at about 9.30 am, arriving there seven hours later. The 2/16th had stopped at the creek crossing below Efogi village to cut the rotted socks from their pulpy, swollen feet, oblivious to the soaking rain. Both battalions sheltered at the village for the night.

On the morning of 6 September, Caro and Rhoden led their weary men through the fresh 2/27th Battalion to occupy positions to the rear. Some three-quarters of a mile to the south the 2/14th dug in with the exhausted 2/16th behind the Victorians' right flank. There Rhoden was rejoined by Lieutenants Pearce and Gardner—both wounded—and some of their men who, after the fall of Isurava on 29 August, had carried on the battle there for another two days.

On his movement back to Efogi Potts had left, to cover the withdrawal of the rest of his force through the junction of the tracks from Kagi and Myola, a standing patrol of one platoon from the company of the 53rd Battalion that had been stationed at Myola for carrying and guard duties. After reporting an uneventful night, the platoon commander, apparently in the absence of other instructions, withdrew his men at 7 am on 6 September. So that a position useful for observation, early warning and possible ambush and delay should not be relinquished, Cooper was ordered to provide a replacement patrol.

Lieutenant F. D. Bell, with his 8 Platoon, arrived at the track junction at about 2 pm, unaware of the previous patrol's earlier withdrawal and surprised to find no one to relieve. But he soon found action. He counted some seven Japanese platoons moving down the Myola–Efogi track at a distance of about 1500 yards. He was reconnoitring for a suitable ambush position when he was himself ambushed by a strong flank patrol scouting ahead of the vanguard. Heavily outnumbered, the South Australians fought back to hold their ground until mounting casualties and the threat of annihilation forced their withdrawal. The wounded Bell arrived back at the battalion at about 3.30 pm, reporting three others wounded, one killed, one missing believed killed and eight others missing.

During the same afternoon Potts re-examined the 2/27th Battalion positions and concluded that a tightening of the Brigade perimeter was imperative in order to reduce the length of exposed flanks. Accordingly the battalion was moved back on Mission Ridge to a higher position overlooking the earlier Brigade Headquarters at the old mission hut. That move reduced the length of the brigade's track-holding by approximately 800 yards. As the late afternoon passed the 2/27th had its B Company in the left forward position, its A Company in the right forward position, and its C and D Companies deployed in the left rear and right rear positions respectively. The task of digging in was a particularly onerous one as the 2/27th lacked entrenching tools, just as had its two sister battalions throughout the campaign.

Potts established his Headquarters on Brigade Hill with Langridge's D Company and a platoon of C Company 2/16th Battalion, approximately 200 yards north of his headquarters.

Dusk, and the night, brought with it an unnerving sight and a sense of frustration to the South Australians. Private A. A. 'Slim' Little, has a vivid recollection of that night:

> The night that we dug in at Efogi. I'll never forget that night as long as I live! We dug in, in a bit of open Kunai grass and we dug a hole with a bayonet and tin hat, and that's where we slept that night. And coming down the other hill towards the river were Japs, hordes of Japs with lanterns, and you could hear them jabbering and carrying on. And no noise! I mean there was us, no lighting a cigarette, no making any noise. We had to sit there watching them come up. It was pretty nerve-racking![7]

The eerie and long drawn-out lantern parade continued throughout the night as the Japanese concentrated a very large force in front of the 2/27th positions. The 21st Brigade had not one suitable long-range weapon with which to challenge the relentless Japanese advance. Brigadier Potts watched the steady and seemingly endless lantern procession with great chagrin. He took the only offensive course of action open to him; he signalled Port Moresby requesting a bombing and strafing operation from the previously unreliable air force. Efogi, Myola and the Efogi–Myola track were given as the priority targets.

At approximately 8 am on the 7th, the air force made amends for its blunders at Kokoda and Alola. As the troops of

Maroubra Force stood by in a state of awe, a succession of aircraft bombed and strafed Efogi and the Efogi–Myola track.

Captain Sims surveyed the early morning air attack from his right forward defensive position:

> The first one was good. That gave us great heart, everyone.
> This'll fix the little so-and-sos! It came fairly close. They blasted
> down over the river and up the track.[8]

Major-General Horii spent the remainder of 7 September probing for the Australian positions and sending out flanking patrols. Cooper pushed out similar patrols from his A Company positions. One under Lieutenant Johns[9] returned at 5 pm, its successful ambush of a Japanese patrol having resulted in the death of six of the enemy and the acquisition of a Japanese light machine-gun and a grenade discharger. Then, about 5.30 pm, the Japanese, using a quick-firing mountain-gun, again began to bombard the battalion positions, particularly those of A Company which lost two killed and five wounded during the action.

Tuesday 8 September will stand forever as the date of one of the most intense, bitter and, at times, confused actions seen during the battle for the Kokoda Trail. One day can be an eternity in war. This was to be one such day. And the long day and its aftermath were to become the focus of controversy as Potts and Maroubra Force grappled not only with a formidable enemy in front of them but also with an uncomprehending New Guinea Force Headquarters behind them—and, indeed, indirectly with a General Headquarters (moved from Melbourne to Brisbane by the Commander-in-Chief, South-West Pacific Area in July) which, even farther behind, began to panic in a fashion that history will record as ignorant and unprofessional.

Major-General Horii had been reinforced with 1500 freshly landed troops, including his sixth infantry battalion, and had at the Efogi front two complete regimental (brigade) groups with their own supporting arms such as mountain-gun and quick-firing-gun detachments (considered by General Blamey in a report to the War Council on 17 September[10]—after all their heavy losses—to total 6000) plus strong support units of engineers, mountain artillery and dismounted cavalry. Horii's front-line troops outnumbered the reinforced Maroubra Force by considerably more than six to one.

During the last cold but peaceful moments of moonlight before the dawn of the 8th, the Japanese propelled their enormous superiority in numbers and firepower against Captain Sims's A Company perimeter. At 4.30 am, a three-company assault attempted to shatter the Company's front in fighting which was reminiscent in its ferocity of the recent slaughter at Isurava. By daybreak the enemy was raking the whole 2/27th Battalion front with concentrated and relentless mountain-gun, machine-gun and mortar fire. Sims's company had had a very trying time the previous day as it was positioned in kunai patches exposed to the morning and early afternoon intensity of the sun and then the heavy afternoon rains. It relied on water, ration and ammunition replenishment from its rear but its supply operations had been continually disrupted by accurate Japanese fire. As the Japanese attacks mounted in both intensity and frequency, the disruption became continuous, and the conservation of ammunition critical.

Training, experience and fortitude answered the challenge, and in repelling some eight attacks during the morning, A Company wrought utter carnage upon their enemy. As wave upon wave of the Japanese attacked they were met with a concerted hail of small-arms fire and a liberal supply of grenades either thrown or rolled down the hill at them.

During this action the intensity of fighting was such that the company's 1200 grenades and 100 rounds of ammunition per man were expended in addition to the battalion's reserve supplies and the reserve company's stocks!

An attack upon B Company's front at approximately 7.30 am was met with the same resolute defiance; at no time during 8 September were the Japanese able to penetrate the A and B Company positions. However the price paid for steadfastness was high. Sims had six of his Bren guns knocked out and numerous casualties from both the infantry attackers and the artillery shelling of his positions. The area in front of A Company and B Company became a macabre scene of slaughter and destruction.

Potts heard the intense noise of battle that had erupted at daybreak from the 2/27th Battalion lines. After having received a report from Cooper he was in the process of making his way towards a latrine positioned on the edge of the jungle when the relative safety and early morning tranquillity of Brigade Headquarters were shattered by a rifle shot which killed Private Gill of the Guard Platoon. Only the marksman could have known why he selected that modest target. Potts himself could so easily have been the recipient.

That single shot heralded the climactic struggle for Brigade Hill which was to evolve into two brutally intense but distinct battles. During the previous day the Japanese had sent a major force around the Australian left or westward flank. That outflanking movement was nothing extraordinary in its basic conception, as the Japanese had employed that tactic from the outset of the campaign. However, the attacks on Cooper's front, on Potts's Headquarters and on the 2/16th Battalion lines were unusually well co-ordinated and synchronised. Major-General Horii had attempted his enemies' envelopment and annihilation at Isurava; having been frustratingly denied his goal there, he then all the more determinedly sought a final solution to this debilitating and time-consuming Maroubra Force fighting withdrawal.

Horii's outflanking movement must have been very wide as no contact with the far-ranging Japanese was made by the Australians, despite their constant patrolling. Thoroughness and boldness in planning were matched by determination and endurance in execution. Private Bert Ward, 2/27th Battalion:

> I must admit I had some degree of amazement as to how active they were, to be able to keep going. We were flat, absolutely flat out! Physically exhausted! And so they must have been! Still, when they encircled us at Efogi in an area like that . . . Well you'd have to be a qualified mountain goat to be able to do physically what they did—to be able to get right around the Battalion; around Brigade Hill.[11]

Brigade Headquarters, as was usual, represented a wide variety of occupations—staff officers and guards, signallers and intelligence gathers, clerks and runners, cooks and storemen, and a motley collection of others between 35 and 45 years of age. It was most unusual for such men to be called on to fight in action. On this day warfare in all of its Owen Stanley ferocity came to the men of 21st Brigade Headquarters, known universally as 'the old and bold', and 'the toothless and the ruthless'. Toothless some of them may have been, ruthless they all became on the day of the battle.

On a number of occasions the Japanese were able to press quite close to Brigade Headquarters. They came within fifteen yards of the perimeter on one such occasion before being driven back. Lieutenant Fraser, a Liaison Officer on Potts's staff, distinguished himself by his steady, disciplined fire and displayed an impressive aptitude for grenade throwing. A two-inch mortar was also used with gratifying results despite the fact that the nearness of the enemy made the trajectory of its bombs very precarious.

The primary Japanese objective however, was to block 21st Brigade's front and rear and then annihilate the three battalions. Had they decided to deploy most of their force which had cut the track to the rear of the 2/16th Battalion positions, against Potts instead of Caro, and moved in force

Brigade Hill, 6–9 September

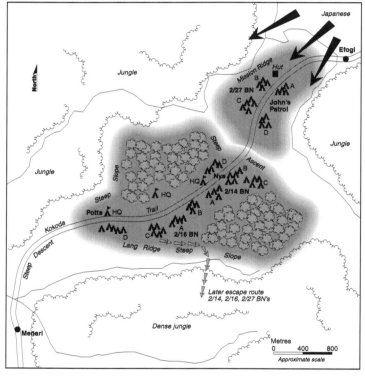

southwards, Potts and his Headquarters would almost certainly have been liquidated and the three battalions' one and only line of communication severed.

By 10 am the 2/27th Battalion was under heavy mortar and machine-gun fire, and its A and B Companies still under close attack. In addition, its water, ration and ammunition supplies, already having been very spasmodic for over 24 hours, were being further restricted. The 2/16th Battalion Headquarters, also without water and under fierce attack, was in grave danger and Potts and his Brigade Headquarters were besieged on Brigade Hill. As a consequence of the invasion of the track by the Japanese and of their digging in, in force, between Caro and Potts, the telephone cable had been cut, and the less reliable wireless communication between Potts and his battalions was only intermittent.

> Communications with the units was now a matter of great difficulty but, 2/14th Bn was contacted by W. T. [wireless transmitter] during two periods from 0830 hrs to 1030 hrs and 1345 hrs to 1600 hrs. Apart from this no communication was possible. In view of the probability that Brigade HQ would be wiped out Brigade Commander at 1000 hrs sent a message to commander 2/16th Battalion that in such an eventuality he was to take control of the Brigade and move back to Menari.[12]

As the gravity of the situation became extreme it was decided that Caro would mount a concentrated attack towards Potts which, it was hoped, would regain control of the one and only track, to restore the supply line to the forward positions and ensure the continuation of the Brigade's cohesive fighting withdrawal and the evacuation of the wounded. In accordance with these plans, a very significant contraction of the 2/14th and, more drastically, the 2/27th Battalion positions was put into execution. Corporal Edwards noted the 2/27th's withdrawal in his diary:

... after a warning order, we began to withdraw in earnest just after midday and it has been a nightmare journey. I was ordered to take a platoon up a rough path through the jungle to the left of the main path and that blinking 'tree-cutter' M. G. of the Japs chased us every minute of the way but miraculously we got up unscathed. Helping with a stretcher delayed us.[13]

Caro's attack back towards Potts involved his A Company attacking along the track with B Company in its rear, and his C Company on the eastern side of the track. To Captain Nye and his B Company, 2/14th Battalion fell the task of penetrating the western side of the track which the Japanese had used in their outflanking movement. As a consequence, Nye was extremely vulnerable to not only the force ahead of him but to a possible attack from his right flank. Nye and his men, in keeping with their battalion's magnificent performance in this campaign, went into battle again with great courage and aggression. The Japanese responded with a hail of fire from well-concealed and dug-in positions, and a later flank attack from the west. The battle raged with an awesome intensity for nearly two hours as the desperate men of 11 and 12 Platoons savagely mauled the Japanese barring their passage through to Brigadier Potts. But only eight of their number, bravely led by Warrant Officer Noble, forced their way through to him. Behind them lay seventeen dead comrades; amongst them, the gallant Nye. The loss of this resourceful, dedicated and respected young officer was most keenly felt by the men of the 2/14th.

The 2/16th fared a little better. As the usual heavy afternoon rains began, A and B Companies stormed the Japanese positions only to be met by a murderous wall of fire from Japanese machine-guns. For a fleeting moment the Japanese broke their lines and retreated. But a bugle call, heard so many times previously during the campaign, rallied the enemy. They concentrated and held firm. On the eastern side of the track, C Company although subjected to heavy fire and casualties, managed to push approximately a dozen men through to Potts.

In a last desperate endeavour to establish a pathway through to Brigade Headquarters, Caro requested that Potts send a force towards the 2/16th lines. To this end, Captain Langridge, positioned 200 yards north of Potts, was ordered to attack northward with one of his own platoons and another from C Company. Langridge passed his identity discs and paybook to a friend and then inspiringly led the forlorn foray. Affectionately known as 'Lefty' to the men of his battalion, Langridge, along with Lieutenant 'Bluey' Lambert[14] and some twenty of their comrades perished in the vain attack. That horrendous Brigade Hill action typified the spirit of Maroubra Force—not just blindly reckless but calmly brave, and faithfully accepting the duty that often meant death.

The only viable course of action open to 21st Brigade after their brave but tragic attempts to re-establish their line of communication was an immediate withdrawal to the next southward village—Menari. Potts's precarious position at Brigade Headquarters was eased by two important factors. The first was that Langridge's desperate surge towards the enemy, whilst failing and sustaining heavy casualties, nonetheless relieved some of the pressure upon Brigade Headquarters. The second was the extremely opportune arrival from Menari of the Brigade Major, Major Challen, and approximately 40 men of the 21st Brigade Composite Company, who were able to assist Potts in his withdrawal.

In the failing light Brigadier Potts and his headquarters were able to move back towards Menari with the knowledge that Caro, Rhoden and Cooper had a contingency plan for their withdrawal to Menari by a circuitous route.

The battalion commanders were faced with three critical problems. The first was time. All three units were cut off and could expect the Japanese to push forward to Menari with a great sense of urgency. The terrain was the second problem. The narrow alternative track to Menari confined by surrounding dense jungle was, even by Kokoda Trail standards, a desperately taxing campaign route. It would have been a very severe test of stamina for fresh, physically fit troops let alone men in the weakened physical condition of those in Maroubra Force. The final factor was the care of the wounded. The campaign was not an orthodox one in relation to the treatment of prisoners of war. Realistically, only one fate could have been anticipated for any Australian soldier abandoned and then captured on the Kokoda Trail—a savage, possibly tortured, execution.

It was agreed that the three units would move via the steep, narrow eastward track which, although through extremely rough, closed-in country, would offer the best cover and the most expeditious movement away from the area. It was hoped that the battalions, by following this route and then moving back westwards to cut the Kokoda Trail at Menari, would reach that village before the enemy. But Menari seemed a distant and difficult goal as the 2/16th Battalion commenced the arduous withdrawal from the Brigade Hill feature at 4.32 pm, to be followed by the 2/14th and, finally, the 2/27th as a rearguard.

> Meanwhile B and D Companies were moved downhill towards the enemy position and took up defensive positions astride the track. In the midst of this operation the enemy attacked on the right flank. B Company successfully repulsed this attack, and then at 1730 hours, as rearguard to the battalion, it made a short sharp counter-attack, causing the enemy to withdraw. This short clash was made with great dash and was particularly successful as contact with the enemy was effectively broken.[15]

Captain H. J. Katekar recalls the significance of Captain Lee's counter-attack:

That was a tremendous operation, a wonderful action by
B Company. They had to buy time some way or other and the
way they did it, they counter-attacked down towards the Japs.
The Japs were so shocked that they broke contact. We didn't see
them again that day. They had the impetus and they were hot
on our heels. We were withdrawing with our wounded; they
would have known that because they were in physical contact
with us, sniping at us and so on. And then B Company was
given this job to stop them. Instead of just standing there and
firing at them they counter-attacked and that must have
shocked them considerably.[16]

Squelching through the deluge into the deepening gloom of
the jungle proved not merely a sluggish journey, but a nightmare one. The track was very narrow, necessitating in places
some hacking of the vegetation to allow stretcher movement. Moving through unabating rain along this initial part
of the escape route, some men were in a state of utter
exhaustion as they bore the additional burden of their
stretchers. In places, as the gradients increased dramatically,
the stretchers needed to be handled slowly and passed carefully along the line, as individual movement had to be
undertaken on all fours. As soon as it became dark, the withdrawal ground to a halt and the men slept where they could
find a suitable position. It was not unusual for many men to
sleep with their feet against a tree or sapling to avoid
slipping during the night.

That they had a chance to sleep at all may well have been
due to Captain Lee's superb counter-attack which marked the
conclusion of the 2/27th Battalion's action in the Efogi area
with a fitting culmination to its splendid achievement. It had
not yielded one inch of its embattled territory and had, under
appalling conditions of heat, lack of water and rations, and precarious ammunition supply, upheld its own proud reputation
and that of its brigade.

In the two-day battle at the Efogi position, the battalion had lost 39 other ranks killed in action and 2 men were missing believed killed. In addition, 3 officers and 43 other ranks had been wounded. This was approximately 1 man in 6 and was a high price for such a relatively short action. It is an indication of the intensity of the action fought, particularly by A and B companies. The enemy dead later counted in the battalion area by the 25th Brigade exceeded 200, so that he was forced to pay a heavy price.[17]

The events and circumstances surrounding the withdrawal of the 2/27th Battalion from Mission Ridge, their subsequent failure to regain their comrades' lines at Menari and later Nauro, and finally, their horrific ordeal regaining their rear base area after nearly three weeks of deprivation and torment, are clouded in controversy. This controversy is embodied within two historical planes. Firstly, there is the controversy within 21st Brigade. Secondly, there is the controversy that erupted in all of its emotions, and indeed venom, at the infamous Koitaki parade which was held some time after 21st Brigade's withdrawal from the campaign. This second issue will be dealt with in detail later. The whole course of events brings under close scrutiny the performance of the 2/27th Battalion and its officers, particularly Lieutenant-Colonel Cooper, its Commanding Officer. There has been only one book which has attempted to examine the issue, *Retreat from Kokoda*, written by Raymond Paull.[18]

> The South Australians knew nothing about the reason for the withdrawal, until on joining the Victorians, the noise of heavy fighting in the direction of the track to Menari told its own story. Nobody seemed clear about the measures necessary to break free from the enemy's unexpected checkmate. The officers had nothing to communicate to their troops . . .[19]

Cooper himself, conscious of holding his first command, excluded all but the problem of extricating his unit to continue its fighting role. Reticent, sensitive, sometimes regrettably aloof,

Cooper did what he considered to be right, never bothering to justify his decisions to anybody, nor to promote a favourable impression except on behalf of the men he commanded. He was intensely proud of his men. His friends and colleagues admired and championed his integrity, while deploring his unwillingness to win popularity and success other than by the rigid standards he prescribed for himself.[20]

If Cooper had been less remote; if he had communicated his problem through his officers to the men, and described to them the plan for evasive action in the withdrawal from Brigade Hill, the criticism and uncertainty which disturbed the South Australians might have been allayed on the spot. Time and the enemy pressed too closely upon him.[21]

The clear implication here, is that Lieutenant-Colonel Cooper and his officers were unclear as to how to react to the Japanese penetration of 21st Brigade's rear positions and, as a consequence of this confusion, could not and did not relay the situation to the troops. The facts present a radically different story. Lieutenant-Colonel G. D. T. Cooper, MBE:

It's all rubbish really. I was a bit cross when I read that, because obviously your company commanders know what you're doing. The adjutant's there, your company commanders are there . . . they know what you're doing because the operation's been explained to them! You couldn't be reticent and tell nobody. This business, this soldier talk, you know; nobody knew what was going on, nobody was told what was going on; troops always talk that way. But then he's [Paull] talked to some private soldiers who didn't really know the full circumstances of what was going on.[22]

Captain Katekar, Cooper's adjutant is of the same mind: 'There was absolutely no breakdown in the line of communication; we all knew what lay ahead; what we had to do.'[23]

At dawn on 9 September, the weary troops of the 21st Brigade set forth, resuming their tortuous journey through the thick jungle towards Menari. The 2/14th Battalion history[24] is illuminating:

> Because the stretchers made the speed of the column very slow, it was feared that the enemy might be first into Menari. Lieuts. McGavin, Clements and Greenwood with B and C Companies, were therefore left behind, together with parties from the 2/16th and 2/27th, to carry the stretchers, while the rest of the 2/16th and 2/14th pushed on to Menari. The 2/14th reached Menari at about 11 am.[25]

The decision was based upon clear, precise and astute thinking. The leading men of the 2/14th and 2/16th Battalions arrived in Menari almost simultaneously with the beginning of the Japanese bombardment of that village. *The Report Into Operations 21 Brigade—Owen Stanley Campaign*, casts further historical light upon the subsequent events:

> At 1115 hrs enemy mortar, QF and L. M. G. fire began to fall on the village from North and NW and almost simultaneously the leading tps of 2/16th Bn began to arrive in the village . . .[26]

> The posn. at midday was, the Bde Comd had to decide at what time to evacuate Menari in view of the possibility of 2/27th Bn coming in. The village itself was extremely vulnerable and could not be held. The time given for the evacuation was 1430 hrs . . .[27]

The decision by the 2/14th and 2/16th Battalions to push their fit men forward with all haste was thus a critical one. They had only just recovered their stretchers and bearers before the final withdrawal from Menari was forced upon Potts. The 2/27th acted with similar judgment. Cooper sent Captain Sims with A Company and Lieutenant Sandison with two platoons of C Company ahead to Menari without the encumbrance of any of the wounded. It was hoped that these men could ascertain whether Menari still lay in Potts's hands. If this was the case, their force could bolster its defence and thereby increase Potts's chance of holding the village pending the arrival of the rest of the battalion.

It would not have been sensible for Cooper to send forward any more troops than he did. He had to retain a sufficient number of men to carry the stretchers to safety and, in order to keep them moving at a maximum speed, there had to be an equal number of replacements able to relieve those actually carrying.

In addition, he had to retain enough men to be an effective fighting force as a rearguard. At any minute he had to expect that the enemy could easily catch up with his slow-moving column, and try to destroy it. The enemy's failure to press the pursuit is surprising.

However, in hindsight, it might be assumed that Major-General Horii reasoned that such a force as Cooper's would be out of the battle, cut off from any chance of resupply of food and ammunition, and that he, Horii, should use all of his resources of manpower and supplies to hasten along the main track to Port Moresby.

Circumstances beyond Cooper's control denied him access to Menari. Firstly, his was the last formation out from the Brigade Hill feature. As a consequence of covering less ground before dark on 8 September, he had further to travel than the 2/14th and 2/16th Battalions but less time in which to traverse the ground into Menari before the withdrawal deadline. Secondly, his stretcher-cases, comprising men from all three units, made his progress unbelievably slow. During the action on Mission Ridge and Brigade Hill no native stretcher-bearers were available, as they were not expected to endanger their lives. It is all too easy to conjure up visions of two men carrying a stretcher along a jungle trail. The harsh reality was that the normal army stretcher was inappropriate for use on the Kokoda Trail. Long wooden poles with a humble army blanket lashed to it then comprised the Owen Stanley Range stretcher. These long wooden poles facilitated the task of the eight stretcher-bearers needed to carry a wounded man in this terrain. Thus, the stretcher-cases carried by the 2/27th Battalion away from Brigade Hill required 120 soldiers to carry them and an equal number to act as relief carriers. The third factor was the terrain. Movement along the Kokoda Trail itself was arduous enough. The jungle and gradients found to the east and west of the Trail between Efogi and Ioribaiwa made progress more difficult. The geographical position of Menari itself was the fourth factor. Menari lay at the foot of the massive incline which wound its way up to Brigade Hill. Not only did the Japanese now have the high ground overlooking Menari, but they still possessed the weaponry with which to bombard the Australian force there. Raymond Paull:

> If in spite of his insecurity there, Potts had known at Menari about the landing of Brigadier Eather's formation at Port Moresby, he might have been tempted to wait, gather up Sims' men, and fight to hold the village until Cooper came through. Lacking that knowledge, Potts had no choice but to fall back . . .[28]

Potts did know of the impending 25th Brigade arrival as he had been told by Allen of Eather's arrival by a signal on 3 September. Paull acknowledges this signal during the earlier part of his own narrative.[29] Potts also knew that Eather was subsequently delayed and that the 3rd Battalion was proceeding to Ioribaiwa as a supporting force. This signal reached Potts on 5 September. The truth is that Potts left Menari because he had absolutely no choice and that far from not knowing what force lay behind him, he actually knew that the 3rd Battalion would be at Ioribaiwa and that Eather's 25th Brigade would be ready to reinforce him from Port Moresby.

Captain Katekar is just as convinced in hindsight as he was then of the futility of any attempt by Potts to make a prolonged stand at Menari:

> But to comment on that man's theory . . . It's so much bull, because Menari was in no way a suitable holding position. You wouldn't think of staying there five minutes if you knew the enemy was occupying or coming down that track from the so-called Brigade Hill, because it completely dominated the Menari area.[30]

The 2/27th Battalion quite simply did not arrive at Menari in time; Brigadier Potts could stay no longer.

When Captain Sims and his A and C Company force found Menari occupied by the enemy, he was faced with a momentous decision. He could no doubt have surprised a significant number of his enemy by attacking them at Menari. He was not encumbered with stretchers, as were Cooper and the main body of the battalion. However, there were three very compelling reasons for his choosing not to do so. Firstly, his force was deployed in a position where he would have to commit his men over open ground in small numbers. In addition, he was behind the Japanese lines and facing an enemy of infinitely greater numerical strength. As a consequence he could not hope to regain his line of communication, the Kokoda Trail itself. Secondly, his force, and indeed the remaining 2/27th Battalion force with Cooper, was quite short of ammunition and rations; the 2/27th Battalion's ammunition supplies had run dangerously low at Mission Ridge. He therefore could not hope to sustain an operation of any significant duration. Norm George was the platoon sergeant of Captain Sims's 9 Platoon. He has vivid memories of the situation at that time:

> In my platoon, 9 platoon, after the seven or eight attacks in the couple of days before we came out of Efogi and went up the

hill, I went around and said, 'Well how much ammunition have we got?' We had very little, very little. Old 'Slim' Little . . . I know I struggled out from Efogi with Slim's Bren gun and I got up the top and said, 'There's your Bren back Slim.' And he said 'What's the use of that bloody thing! I've got no ammunition for it anyway!' So the stretchers weren't the only problem Cooper had. It was lack of food, and A, and possibly B Company, were practically out of ammunition.[31]

The third reason must surely have been the most compelling. If Sims either with his own force, or later in unison with Cooper's main body, had mounted an attack on Menari they would have sustained casualties; and each new stretcher-case would have required eight men to carry him out of the battle. For men already encumbered with stretcher-cases from the three battalions engaged at Brigade Hill, this additional burden of wounded would have even further weakened the force. Captain Katekar:

> There was only one option for Cooper, and the rest of us and that was to get our wounded out, and not create more. We thought of that; we thought of attacking Menari, that was deliberated on not only by Cooper but by all the senior officers that were there including myself. And the decision was clearly made; we would have been utterly foolish.[32]

Raymond Paull:

> It is easy, perhaps, to pass judgement on Cooper as the officer responsible for the 2/27th Battalion's prolonged ordeal, but to what extent can such criticism be justified?[33]

Lieutenant-Colonel Cooper and his 2/27th Battalion fought a copybook defence of their lines at Mission Ridge. Despite prolonged, concentrated bombardment, intense mortar and machine-gun fire, and repeated attacks upon their positions, the 2/27th Battalion gave no ground. Cooper at all times consulted and informed his subordinate officers of his considered decisions. The 21st Brigade withdrawal from Mission Ridge was a co-ordinated plan devised and adopted by Caro, Rhoden and Cooper. Its execution was flawless, and was assisted in no small measure by that gallant B Company 2/27th Battalion counter-attack led by Captain Lee. In addition, Cooper employed the same tactic as had Rhoden and Caro during the morning of 9 September. He sent an advance guard under Captain Sims forward to Menari to strengthen Potts's defence there and facilitate the 2/27th Battalion's main force arrival.

The plain and simple truth is that Cooper would quite possibly have arrived at Menari in time if he had abandoned his stretchers. Sergeant John Burns, MM, has a very forthright and indeed, sound argument:

> Where the hell would your conscience be if you'd left the wounded there? Geoff Cooper can go to his grave with a totally clear conscience and with the grateful thanks of quite a lot of wounded blokes, and also keeping alive a good name of a battalion. They can talk about us being lost and that sort of business . . . If you'd left your wounded behind and your sick and your lame who just couldn't have made it, how well would you sleep, tonight, tomorrow night or any other night? As far as I'm concerned it's a question of conscience and principle and morality.[34]

Lieutenant–Colonel Sir Arthur Lee, MC:

> I'd like to see their evidence. The withdrawal moved very quickly. I can't see any Battalion Commander doing it any differently to what Cooper did.[35]

Potts had once again eluded Horii's net of encirclement and annihilation. Although he had lost half of his force at Mission

Ridge and Brigade Hill, he had once again delayed his enemy by three crucial days and left him no supplies to sustain him. Brigadier Arnold Potts was, despite a host of factors working against him, fighting a magnificent, copybook withdrawal. Captain H. J. Katekar, 2/27th Battalion:

> It's all a question of momentum; who's got the strength and numbers. We were out-gunned and out-manoeuvred. When we gained the momentum at Imita Ridge, we just reversed the procedure.[36]

For the 2/27th Battalion, the ordeal of trying to survive despite unbelievable deprivation was about to begin.

12

92 this way

The story of the 2/27th Battalion's wretched journey to regain its base area after the battle for Brigade Hill emphasises the fact that the first Owen Stanley Campaign from July to September 1942 was in fact a campaign of two different wars.

The first was the obvious war against the most competent, aggressive and ruthless jungle fighter yet seen. The second was a tragic war against nature, against an environment that was almost totally unforgiving. That environment defied the exertions of the physically fit and then proceeded rapidly to weaken them. Its vegetation offered no life-sustaining food save the odd native garden of yam or taro. Its seemingly endless mountains and valleys restricted the withdrawal of the wounded, the weak and the hungry, and dramatically delayed, disrupted or destroyed communication. Through this hostile terrain ran one main narrow track, muddy and slippery, root-trapped and treacherous, but still the one vital lifeline; when it was lost the soldier was plunged into days or weeks of torment and deprivation.

From the very beginning of the campaign, groups of men varying in number from a section to a company found themselves denied the use of the Kokoda Trail itself. Templeton and part of his B Company 39th Battalion, had been cut off near Oivi; Symington and his A Company at Kokoda; Dalby and Pentland at Deniki; Sword, north of Isurava; and significantly the 2/14th Battalion, despite its truly magnificent efforts at Isurava, had lost its commanding officer, adjutant, intelligence officer and Captain Buckler, Lieutenants Treacy and Butler and 42 men from A, B and C Companies from the Isurava Rest House area. The subsequent loss of the 2/27th Battalion after Brigade Hill is thus only a more striking illustration of the persisting and increasing Japanese ability to cut off and thereby isolate varying groups of their enemy during the campaign.

When Captain Sims found Menari occupied by the Japanese and reasoned that an attack upon the village was out of the question, he sought to regain contact with Lieutenant-Colonel Cooper and the main body of the battalion. A and C Companies moved back along the Brown River in an attempt to discover the point at which Cooper might have crossed it in his southward movement. Captain Sims well remembers the experience:

> This icy cold water . . . There was no bridge or anything to get across on and you had to wade up to your chest and hold whatever weapons you had over your head. We were stuck down in this great canyon! The main track was well away to the right.
>
> I told them to look for any sign of a track coming down, but mainly leading up on our right hand side. And I said 'Well if you can see that, that's presumably where the rest of the battalion's gone. That's their advance party, going to establish a firm base somewhere on the left flank of Menari.'[1]

Sims and his advance party of approximately 75 men eventually found what appeared to be a track. Noting evidence of recent movement on it and assuming it had been cut by Cooper's men, Sims followed it. However, Lieutenant-Colonel Cooper and his main group had not yet journeyed that far; the track found by Sims must have been blazed by others. Captain Sims, MC:

> And at that stage, that day or the next day, we had stragglers coming in from the 2/14th from all over the place. Poor beggars! One bloke started off with half his behind shot away. He'd had a Jap grenade tossed at him. He had all the guts in the world, struggling along with two blokes helping him.[2]

After having thus spent the night of 9 September on the ridge above Menari, Sims and his men set out early next morning to catch up with Cooper. Knowing that Cooper, burdened with the stretcher-cases, could not be travelling as fast as his own smaller group, Sims soon deduced that Cooper must actually be far to his rear. As a consequence, he decided to press on to Nauro in the hope that he might yet rejoin the 2/14th and 2/16th Battalions and thus resume the battle.

Sims's group although very fatigued and having also had little or no food since the 8th, pushed on towards Nauro with surprising speed. On a number of occasions, blazing a new track as they went, they came perilously close to the main track. Japanese troops were heard moving forward along the Kokoda Trail. At approximately 5.30 pm they paused on the high ground overlooking Nauro. To their utter dismay they were able to hear the noise of the Japanese in the village itself, and also along the track approach. Potts and Maroubra Force had left only a matter of hours before.

None of the three alternative courses of action available to Sims and his men could have injected any real degree of enthusiasm into their exhausted bodies. The first alternative was an attack upon the enemy at Nauro itself. Captain Sims, MC:

> Well this would have been no good; we couldn't allow an attack on the L of C. We didn't have the ammunition, and

we only had rifles, no other support at all. We also had
people who were pretty well fagged out and some of these
walking wounded from other battalions.[3]

The second alternative was to attempt to relocate Lieutenant-
Colonel Cooper's main force and assist him with the wounded
and increase the strength of that force. This would have been a
foolhardy course of action. A search for him now would have
been an undertaking fraught with danger and an unrealistic
drain upon already diminished reserves of energy.

The last alternative was the only sensible and indeed viable
course of action to follow. Sims must regain his base area as
soon as humanly possible. It was now left to determine the best
means of doing so.

> So I got all the officers and said 'Well my thoughts on this now
> would be to divide into small groups, tactical groups' . . . So it
> was decided that we'd move off in these groups of eight or ten
> men. I gave them an indication with the points of the compass
> where Moresby was, what to look for; aircraft; the rivers
> running at right angles to the track and so on, and finally we
> said, 'Best of luck see you there!'[4]

And so approximately eight groups set out from that ridge near
Nauro, each man full of hope and determination and, above all,
confidence in his own self-reliance that all would be well.

There was little to distinguish one day from another during
their journey out from the ridge near Nauro to the country east
of Itiki. The terrain seemed never to change, nor did there
appear to be an end to it. Tortuous climbs up ridges and mountains were followed by the inevitable precipitous descents and
the numerous creek crossings which, despite Sims's instructions
as to navigation, contained a sameness that almost defied even
the experienced bushman. Corporal Norm George, A Company,
had been a stockman prior to his enlistment:

If you get lost in the country up around the Flinders Ranges, alright, what you do, you climb the nearest hill, get up there and have a look around. You can generally pick out where you are. But up in New Guinea in the jungle, the trees were so thick that when you climbed a hill, it was like looking through a two-foot window. It seemed as though it was all you could see![5]

The very few tracks that were encountered were eagerly followed until the realisation came that they led towards the Kokoda Trail and, therefore, the enemy. Because of the nature of the terrain each group almost inevitably zigzagged its passage through the jungle, occasionally meeting one or more of the other groups, or perhaps a small party from another battalion lost after Brigade Hill.

Having run out of rations by the end of 9 September, the men relied upon the very occasional native garden which yielded meagre supplies of yam or perhaps taro. These were gathered, cooked and consumed, and the night was spent by the still hungry men, sprawled out in the cold and the rain, wondering what the next day would bring. Sims had the rare good fortune to dine on something more substantial. On 14 September, a pig was shot which was shared with a number of men who had wandered into the camp site. Not a morsel of food was wasted. The eyes, brain, and intestines were consumed and the bones were broken up for marrow.

It's amazing what you do when you've got a bit of hunger! A knuckle of the old pig . . . because we drew lots and you'd have a bit of this and a bit of that, and I had a bit of his hind quarter with a bit of knuckle.[6]

A cockatoo was later shot with the result that every single portion of that bird was consumed, including the bones. As a result of the appalling diet and the strenuous passage through the jungle, the men's health underwent a very rapid deterioration. Captain Sims MC:

> I had dengue . . . high fever, slightly delirious, and you perspire and you sweat. I also had a tropical ulcer in my leg. You could see the bone and sinew because it ate it away. And I had pneumonia. Not a very happy mixture.[7]

On 17 September Sims's group met a mule team east of Itiki. The other groups all regained the base area within the next few days. Despite the comparative speed of its early movement (thus just missing Potts at Menari and Nauro) and its fortunate freedom from the encumbrance of stretcher-cases, this advance party had endured much.

When Sims had made his decision to push on to the base area after having ascertained that Menari lay in the enemy's hands, Cooper was in a position that no battalion commander could have contemplated even in his most horrific nightmares.

The historian is blessed with two vivid, succinct and wonderfully detailed documents concerning the subsequent plight of the main body of the 2/27th Battalion from 9 September, until its emergence at the base area fourteen days later. Corporal Edwards of D Company wrote a moving account immediately after the campaign, while Captain Katekar, the battalion's adjutant, committed his experiences to paper while in hospital in Queensland commencing 10 May 1943.[8] Interspersed with their accounts are interviews with a number of other participants.

Wednesday, 9 September 1942
Captain Katekar:

> In the meantime the rest of the Unit, Bn. HQ, HQ Coy, B and D Coys with 14 stretcher cases (300 men) and 60 natives heard the bad news about the fall of Menari where we had hoped to pick up rations and ammunition.

The only course was to continue to cut a separate track through the rough stuff, approximately 1 mile from and parallel to the main track. We hoped to reach the next village Nauro, ahead of the Japs.

So commenced our long, arduous, foodless and heartbreaking trek which finished 14 days later. On that night we dossed down wet and miserable in the undergrowth near Menari. Again we had to remain particularly alert and silent as we were so close to the Japs. Our stretchers were the limiting factor.

Thursday, 10 September
Corporal Edwards:

We didn't get a very early start despite being up at first-light and we chafed with impatience, but this horrible feeling of frustration was to increase as the day wore on, and a tortuous track had to be carved down toward a fairly large stream, (the same which flows past Menari) and as the pangs of hunger began to hit us in earnest we chafed even more at the inactivity . . .

Dysentery in a mild form has hit the lads and some of them, particularly Dave Sheppard, are in a bad way. The track on this side of the stream as it followed the ridge along, up and down and precipitous, was even worse than on the other, and we finally had to halt for the night at a place where I had to use my string to tie my gear to a bush to prevent it sliding downhill. I have only the tiniest of hip-holes in which to sleep.

Captain Katekar:

After struggling all that day, we only covered a couple of miles. We had passed through a native garden of sugar cane and sweet potatoes, but at that time the C.O. would not allow us to forage, as the garden was possibly under enemy observation and our whereabouts had to be kept secret . . .

I finished my rations that day, and faced the future foodless.

Friday, 11 September
Corporal Edwards:

> . . . commenced a long and stern climb—we are getting weaker
> and the effort to be expended on such a climb is growing
> greater and thus we found the spells ever more welcome . . .
>   We lay down tonight with a light head apiece.

Captain Katekar:

> Some of our aircraft flew overhead, but we could not attract
> their attention, so dense was the undergrowth. The men were
> feeling the strain and the natives were starting to complain
> about lack of food.

Saturday, 12 September
Captain Katekar:

> The column continued its snail's pace. It was very disheartening
> to have to move so slowly; the stretchers limited our pace to
> almost a crawl. By the afternoon the men were too exhausted to
> go on, so the C.O. sent back D Coy, along the trail to the native
> garden we had passed two days before . . .
>   Because of smoke possibly disclosing our position, we could
> not light a fire until after dark when the mist settled down to
> cloak us. Then we cooked the yams and had some sort of meal;
> a very tasteless one, but filling.

Corporal Edwards:

> Certainly when the issue came back of 3 cooked and about 4
> uncooked vegetables per man we had a reasonable feed and felt
> a little more secure as regards the future . . .

Since the improvement in the tucker situation the general morale is much higher.

Sunday, 13 September
Captain Katekar:

> The wounded, God only knows, were in purgatory, hungry and in great pain. Some of our natives began to desert, meaning that our men had to replace them as bearers. 'Doc' Viner-Smith allowed the maggots to remain on the wounds in order to eat the rotting flesh and so prevent gangrene. That night we were still short of Nauro. I found it a great mental strain and so did the C.O. and other officers, with that great responsibility of not only saving our wounded but of saving ourselves from starvation.

Doug Keane (Signals 2/27th Battalion):[9]

> One chap from the 2/14th Battalion had one straight through the throat and kept asking for water and as you kept giving him the water much of it ran straight out again. He didn't last. One day I thought, 'He looks better today'—and then he was gone.

Monday, 14 September
Captain Katekar:

> The 14th Sept brought us to the outskirts of Nauro. It is a memorable day . . .
>
> After struggling up a very steep incline to the top of a ridge, through our binoculars we could see far down in the valley ahead; the thatched huts of Nauro. We could hear no firing; we did not know if the village was ours or the Japs. So we moved down a long spur and by nightfall, when we halted, we guessed that Nauro was only a mile or two away.

Tuesday, 15 September
Captain Katekar:

. . . we hurried down the spur to the river—It took us some time to ford this deep swift flowing stream with the stretchers . . .

The men were absolutely exhausted and ravenous. Nauro was our hope . . .

Imagine our intense anguish and disappointment when the report came back that the Japs were occupying the village.

We considered the wisdom of attacking the village, in the hope of capturing food; but our better judgement prevailed, as we still had to consider our wounded and we didn't want to be encumbered with more. It was late afternoon when the decision was made to retrace our footsteps and attempt to find a suitable track around the village further to the east. By this time the men were desperately exhausted and it was a cruel blow to them to be told to about-turn. A couple of providential incidents occurred that day; it seemed as if God was taking a hand in the matter. While we were waiting outside Nauro it suddenly occurred to me that a lot of the food which had been dropped by our planes would be scattered far and wide in the undergrowth around the village . . .

I wandered off into the jungle in search of food. Something must have led me to the spot, for after a while I noticed that a branch of a tree had been broken off, as if by a fallen object, and so looking down I saw a bag-covered bundle. Almost tenderly I went down on my knees to tear away some of the bag, and lo and behold inside was a perfectly good tin of Arnott's Army biscuits. Some of the starving men were watching me, and it was as much as I could do to stop them from struggling to get a share. I managed to salvage some of the biscuits which were distributed amongst our wounded. In the meantime a flank guard patrol of B Coy had stumbled over a 25 lb tin of Crowe & Newcombe's dried apricots, and these provided a handful for each man in the company, standing them in good stead in the days to come.

Corporal Edwards:

> It's certainly a tremendous job for men weakened as we are but
> the lads stuck at it valiantly and took the stretchers down a long
> hill and across a large river which we recognised as the one
> which flows past Nauro. It was a most difficult crossing and our
> hearts fell to zero when, just as the last stretcher had crossed,
> orders came from the front to retrace our steps across the river
> and up the hill as quickly as possible because the Japs were
> sighted in the front. It was an awful grind up the hill with
> the stretchers . . .

Doug Keane (Signals, 2/27th Bn):

> Carrying those stretchers! That really taxed us right to the limit.
> You'd just stand up and hold yourself with your stick against a
> tree and stand there till your head stopped spinning enough to
> go pick up the stretchers again!

Captain Katekar:

> . . . the C.O. decided to leave D Coy to look after the stretcher
> cases and to push on unencumbered with the rest of the
> column with the idea of finding food and sending back
> sustenance to D Coy and the wounded. In this event the plan
> was for the main body to wait in that garden until D Company
> had carried them forward—then the stretchers would be left in
> the garden and the rest move back rapidly to Base for help.

Corporal G. R. Williss:[10]

> Absolute murder! Now I carried one every day. There were
> eight of us to a stretcher, and I being a Corporal was in charge
> of it. And it was almost agony to get those fellas, particularly
> older members of the section to take their turn. It was the

thought of getting nowhere that got at me. I mean, I was only a corporal, but I knew that while we were carrying them . . . I didn't want to just dump them and leave them, but I knew that while we had them we had no hope of getting out . . .

Lieutenant-Colonel Cooper:[11]

Now in this case the problem was this; the speed at which we were travelling with those wounded was so slow that we'd never get anywhere. The whole Battalion would (a) be collapsing through lack of food; not just the wounded but the whole Battalion, (b) we would never intercept the Japanese at the lower parts of the trail or get into the Moresby area fast enough to be of any use to delay them. So really the question was, which was the greater method, keeping the Battalion together, making it, getting it on to do its job, or having it just be dispersed and destroyed virtually through being bound down in the jungle looking after its wounded.

When we felt we were a fair way from the Japanese and they were not following us beyond where we were going, we had to find a quiet place back in the jungle a bit, and put them in there with a few volunteers, John Burns in charge of them; who were prepared to look after them until we could get down to wherever we would end up and send men back to look after them.[12]

Thursday, 17 September
Captain Katekar:

Sgt. Raftery and a small party had been despatched with a message stating our circumstances and to move to Base with all haste. That party got through 3 days ahead of us and as a result search parties were sent out with food and native bearers, but unfortunately we missed them. The thing that played on our minds a lot all these days was the deathly silence of the jungle;

no firing could be heard and we didn't know how far the Japs had advanced.

About midday that day we found succour in the shape of hundreds of yams and green paw-paw in a couple of native huts. We put out protective patrols and lit fires, cooking a stomach full of yams and roast paw-paw for each man. We sent back a message with a patrol of 3 men to Tom Gill O.C. D Coy, telling of our find, and after they had had their meal we despatched a party with food asking them to reach D Coy that night. The message carrying patrol was waylaid by a Jap patrol, and one of their men was killed. The food party also bore a message instructing D Coy to move the stretchers to this village, to leave them with attendants, and push on for base. In the meantime, the C.O. and party would proceed ahead. By that night we had climbed up a steep hill overlooking the river, lit some more fires and cooked a few more yams. We were now on a faint trail moving South East. Because of this discovery we decided to send back guides to Tom Gill's party.

Friday, 18 September
Captain Katekar:

> . . . a fine native garden of sweet potatoes and sugar cane . . .
> The cane was marvellous, so beautifully sweet and refreshing, and I chewed little pieces often during the next two days.

Saturday, 19 September
Corporal Edwards (D Company):

> Well about 8 a.m. we set off minus the encumbrance of stretchers and full of hope . . .
> At 11 a.m. we commenced climbing the long ridge and when we settled down at nearly dusk tonight we were still climbing but had made great progress though at the cost of

absolutely tired out bodies. A highlight of our trudge was the rifling of a native garden which was lousy with sweet spuds.

Sunday, 20 September
Captain Katekar:

> We struggled on that day across many steep waterfalls. In the afternoon we crawled on top of a high range from which we could see for miles ahead; range upon range of forest clad heights; we heard what seemed to be a tractor or bulldozer working in the distance. We could not gauge exactly what it was or where we were, but it raised our hopes.

Corporal Edwards, D Company, (1–2 days behind):

> The climb continued this morning until we judged we had drawn level at least with Ioribaiwa though 'tis hard to judge. Our track then lay along the top of a ridge which narrowed to a mere foothold in parts and towards evening began to descend sharply in places and ascend in others—a muddy and rough track which nearly jarred us out of our senses.

Monday, 21 September
Captain Katekar:

> . . . seemed endless, just plodding on wearily and seemingly getting nowhere . . .
>
> I felt very baffled and forlorn. I wondered if our troops were still at Itiki or even at Moresby.

Corporal Edwards:

> One of the hardest days we have yet put in for the track led us down many hills, across creeks, up steep and rugged hills and tested our every muscle and every ounce of our endurance.

We had no clue as to whether the track was leading us back to civilization or not and again we find ourselves cheering each other up.

Tuesday, 22 September
Captain Katekar:

> . . . we set out early and when our hopes seemed lowest, at about 1200 hrs a ray of hope beamed, for there at a point where 2 tracks met was a stick on which a piece of paper was fastened saying '92 this way'—that meant that Brigade HQ was along that track, somewhere. An hour later we got the thrill of our lives when we suddenly met a patrol of the 2/14th Bn at Nigabaifa. We were saved; we could get food at a camp 3 hours away. During those preceding days our only subject of conversation and our nightly dreams had been about food. We talked about apple pie and cream, roast lamb and vegetables, about all of our favourite dishes just like big kids.

Corporal Edwards (upon arrival at base area):

> We were only allowed 4 biscuits and jam for lunch plus a chocolate but it was a glorious taste. After lunch they supplied towels and soap and we all had a bath in the creek and I've never seen such a mob of wrecks in my life. I look so skinny that I frightened myself and my legs are in a shocking state with these sores.

The last paragraphs from both diaries:
Captain Katekar:

> Search parties, natives and food were sent out to bring in the wounded. In the meantime D Coy had left them in the garden with food and with Cpl Johnny Burns and a small party to

attend to them. No words of mine will be able to express the wonderful, unselfish, the tender way in which Johnny and Alf looked after those suffering men . . .

Corporal Edwards:

I can't possibly describe fully the hopes and fears, achievements, and disappointments, the sheer determination and will to survive which was all that kept us going during some of the harder stages. The longing for food was such that one would dream about it at night . . .

Each night I used to think of the mob at home and pray for them and myself, how I used to long for the old home comforts. And now we're safe—a feeling of security pervades my veins and I'm truly happy, thoroughly relaxed but above all, thankful to my Maker for His care.

13

The rabbit that runs

We came back along the track in the pitch black darkness. And the only way you could go back was by holding the sig. cable in your hand. We had one torch with us, and must have gone for about five hours I reckon. We had no idea where we were going, but just kept going down following the cable. So we thought we'd stop and put a phone on the line and ring up to find out whether anybody else was on the line. We contacted two people . . .

When we got up in the morning we tried to find where these people were and we'd all been on the phone within a hundred yards of each other! That was a terrible night, I still don't know how we did it.[1]

Corporal Thomson, a 21st Brigade signaller, was one of a number of Brigade Headquarters personnel who left Brigade Hill with Brigadier Potts on the night of 8 September, bound for Menari. While Potts and his staff made their slow and taxing night trek to Menari, Captain Hodge[2] and 60 troops acted as the rearguard to the withdrawal. Hodge's rearguard comprised a small number of troops from the 2/14th and 2/16th Battalions who had forced their way through to Potts during the battle of Brigade Hill, a number of Langridge's D Company 2/16th Battalion, and a number of Composite Company men who had arrived with Major Challen that day. Captain Russell[3] from the 2/14th Battalion, was left in command of the Composite Company detachment.

Early on 9 September, a reconnaissance party moved back to select the next holding position on the high ground south of Menari. It was very soon realised that no great stand could be made there because it was a razorback of little depth, and could therefore be readily bypassed by the enemy.

The truth is that Potts was now operating under impossible conditions. The terrain from Brigade Hill to Ioribaiwa offered not one suitable defensive position. To compound the problem, his force was greatly weakened by the endless fighting and the gruelling conditions and numbered a mere 300 men by 9 September.

As the main brigade force regained its lines at Menari its members were greeted with small gifts from the hands of a truly great man. To nearly all of the troops of Maroubra Force the name Albert Moore is symbolic of selflessness, compassion and, above all, simple kindness. Moore was repeatedly found during this campaign near the front line working beneath his Salvation Army banner, calmly and methodically dispensing small gifts or perhaps a hot mug of tea to the withdrawing men. Captain Bisset, that stalwart officer of the 2/14th Battalion, remembers assisting Moore at Menari:

> I remember well the last climb up from a creek crossing and coming onto a level piece of ground at Menari. The men were very battle and jungle weary, constantly wet, and lacking sleep and good food. Stationed at this spot was Albert Moore our Salvation Army hero, with a handout for each man—a packet

of cigarettes and a large block of chocolate. I was the first up and helped Albert with the distribution. The great variety of expressions on each individual face as he looked up and saw the two gifts; one would clutch for the cigarettes another would seize the chocolate. It was 'manna from heaven' to these men.[4]

Meanwhile, after a contact-free night, Captain Hodge had withdrawn his untroubled rearguard to Menari. Its task was done and, early in the morning of the 9th, the 2/16th Battalion men of the Composite Company left it to join their Battalion just south of the village; but the 2/14th component—Captain Russell, Lieutenant Rainey and seventeen others—were posted to hold the creek crossing half a mile forward of Menari. They had an action-packed day, forcing the Japanese to seek uncontested crossings to the east. The enemy build-up and infiltration increased through the morning and early afternoon, harrying Potts's positions with long-range fire from the dominant high ground and spreading, from their creek crossings, west to cut Russell's telephone line and south-east to close off the return route for the still missing 2/27th Battalion and the stretcher party of the 2/14th led by McGavin, Clements and Greenwood.

The main body of the 2/14th, after swinging under cover around the east of the bullet-swept village, passed over the 2/16th's ridge to the south and pushed on through rain and mud to reach Nauro by about 5 pm. With no word from Cooper, Potts reluctantly withdrew from the Menari area at about 2.30 pm.

Back on the north side of Menari, Russell, in accordance with his early orders, began his withdrawal at about 4.30 pm, moving in short spurts towards the village. But his small patrol was ambushed, losing two men killed, and was forced to leave the track. He then divided his men into two groups; the first, under Sergeant Thorne, came in at Uberi after nine days; his

231

own, having left at dusk, regained the 2/14th lines at Ioribaiwa after seven days.

The morning of 10 September saw Caro's 2/16th Battalion fight a rearguard action just north of Nauro which inflicted about a dozen casualties upon the Japanese. Reducing the size of their rearguard as they fell back, the 2/16th rejoined the 2/14th on the Maguli Range south of Nauro by late afternoon. The 2/16th and 2/14th Battalions were still repeatedly ambushing the Japanese, inflicting heavy casualties upon them and, crucially, always delaying, harassing and frustrating their push towards Port Moresby. At no point on the Trail between Menari and Nauro was the mud less than ankle deep, while at some points the men sank almost to their knees—a gruelling experience for already exhausted troops.

As a result of the failure to hold Myola and then Efogi and of the loss of the 2/27th Battalion, Rowell and Allen decided to recall Potts to Port Moresby to report to them concerning the battle and the conditions. Brigadier Porter was sent up with orders to command all troops forward of Uberi, to stabilise the battle prior to the arrival of Brigadier Eather and his 25th Brigade and to gain what ground he could. The 3rd Battalion under the command of Lieutenant-Colonel Cameron (who had commanded Maroubra Force in early August and, subsequently, the 53rd Battalion) had been ordered to Ioribaiwa and was deployed there when he arrived.

> . . . At 1430 hrs Brig. Potts handed over to Brig. Porter who then had 3rd Bn under comd, and proceeded back to 7th Aust. Div. At this stage it was decided to combine 2/14th and 2/16th Bn into one bn. under Lt-Col. Caro. The strengths were approx. 100 and 200 respectively. The disposns. at nightfall were, 2/14th Bn. elements holding F.D.L.'s, Bde HQ and two coys. 3rd Bn approx. 3/4 hr along the track towards Ioribaiwa. The plan was to hold this position for as long as possible to allow 25th Bde which was moving up to

commence offensive ops. from a suitable jumping off place. In view of the incidents 8/9 Sept. Bde Comd decided it would be impossible to counter-attack along the track in the event of the Jap. getting behind 2/14th, 2/16th Bn psn. He decided therefore to withdraw to the high ground at Ioribaiwa which offered far more tactical possibilities.[5]

It is of more than passing interest that upon his assumption of command of Maroubra Force, the first move Porter made was a withdrawal to a better defensive position, despite having the fresh troops of the 3rd Battalion available to join in the battle and the prospect of more to follow. He was forced to withdraw as a result of the same two dominant factors that had continually influenced Potts during the whole campaign. Firstly, he was forced to react to the fact that the terrain offered few prime defensive positions. Secondly, he was forced to react to his having a drastic inferiority in numbers of troops with which to fight the battle. As a consequence, the Japanese were always in possession of the military initiative. Therefore, to require Porter to stabilise the position was one thing; to direct him to gain what ground he could was an order stemming from considerable ignorance.

By the early morning of 11 September, the 2/14th elements held the rearguard post while those of the 2/16th had passed through the 3rd Battalion and had set up ambush positions in considerable depth on a ridge approximately 45 minutes' march north of Ioribaiwa—21st Brigade ambushes continued to be lethal experiences for the advancing Japanese:

The withdrawal was carried out successfully, 2/16th moved back leaving C Coy and A Coy in extricating posns. about 20 mins and an hour respectively along the track. Remainder of Bn. passed through 3rd Bn which was in posn. further back and took up another extricating posn. to cover the withdrawal of the 3rd Bn. 2/14th Bn elements moved back direct to the slope fwd. of Ioribaiwa and took up posn. Immediately on their heels a strong Jap patrol coming from the Eastern Flank behind the posn which had been occupied ran up against C Coy 2/16th posn. and were shot up severely, and they lost 22 casualties. Without further incident the rest were leapfrogged back to the Ioribaiwa posn. leaving an ambush party of 2/16th Bn right on the crossing. This party late in the afternoon sighted a large party of the enemy on the other side of the creek moving down to the water's edge. The ambush party withheld their fire until the Japs were grouped in the Xing, then opened fire and killed approximately 25, wounding others, then withdrawing into the bde. posn. At 1845 a further Jap patrol of 5 working up the track were also killed by a small ambush party fwd. of our F.D.L.'s. Further Jap activity for the night was limited to a noisy patrol which worked up on the right flank of the spur calling on our men in good English to withdraw. The attempt met with no response, and the Japs themselves withdrew.[6]

On 12 September, the Composite 2/14th and 2/16th Battalion and the 3rd Battalion positions were sited on the spur just north of Ioribaiwa, pending the arrival of 25th Brigade. During 12–13 September the Japanese concentrated upon repeated mortar, mountain-gun and machine-gun fire on the Composite Battalion positions, whilst also probing their defences with patrols. While booby traps were used with telling effect against those patrols, the Japanese in turn inflicted tragic and ever-mounting losses on the 21st Brigade with their supporting fire.

But still the enemy could make little ground—and he was made to pay a heavy penalty for each yard. His attempt to cross the creek in front of the 21st Brigade position was met with a savage wall of fire, and short, sharp counter-attacks blunted his desperate attempts to pierce the Australian lines. The exhausted defenders lost eleven men killed and 29 wounded in their last actions near Ioribaiwa.

> This evening in the twilight I buried two Headquarter
> Company chaps. A very sad business, as they had been terribly
> knocked. A shell had caught them in their slit trench. One of
> the chaps lending a hand fainted for a moment or two at the
> graveside. No one said a word—we just helped him to his feet.
> I noticed tears in the eyes of quite a few of the troops.[7]

If ever New Guinea Force Headquarters or for that matter
General Headquarters, South-West Pacific Area had required
some strong and obvious testimony to the superb efforts of
Potts and Maroubra Force then such evidence was immediately forthcoming with the initial deployment of Eather's 25th
Brigade at Ioribaiwa. It is worth noting that Eather was in a
position to commit all of his three battalions to the battle at
the one time and, in addition, had the 3rd Battalion and the
composite 2/14th–2/16th Battalion at his disposal. Further, his
line of communication and supply was quite short in relation
to that of his adversaries, whereas Potts had begun his battle at
faraway Isurava, forced to commit his troops company by
company upon arrival, and suffering under an appalling supply
debacle in the process. And, importantly, Eather could not have
encountered Japanese soldiers in anything like the physical
condition that they must have been in at Isurava, for their
protracted and bloodied battle from Isurava to Ioribaiwa had
taken them over some of the worst terrain in the world, with
a lengthening supply line and almost three exhausting weeks
of fighting against Maroubra Force, incurring both battle and
sickness casualties as they moved southward.

Eather's plan envisaged a right flank movement by his
2/33rd Battalion through the 3rd Battalion; a thrust through
the Composite Battalion positions northward along the main
track by his 2/25th Battalion, and a left flank thrust by his
2/31st Battalion. Two events caused his undoing. Firstly, his
2/31st Battalion men moving on the left flank, became disorientated and briefly lost, trying to outflank and encircle the

Japanese positions. Secondly, the inexperienced 3rd Battalion were routed from one of their positions on the high ground to the east of Ioribaiwa when surprised by a strong and aggressive Japanese patrol; these soldiers were digging weapon-pits out of reach of their weapons and with less than alert sentries. Eather's offensive suddenly became a worrying instability of control of the Ioribaiwa feature. Despite counter-attacks he could not remove the Japanese, who had positioned themselves between the 3rd Battalion and the 2/31st Battalion. The enemy had acquired the high ground—a familiar Owen Stanley scenario.

It is at this point that a degree of controversy enters the story. Raymond Paull writes:

> . . . neither Eather nor Porter believed that they could devise any immediate remedy capable of snatching the initiative from Horii in the prevailing circumstances.
>
> Porter, too, retained little confidence in the value of the composite battalion. He detected amongst its troops a growing restiveness resulting from their mounting casualties, a distaste for the enemy's mortar and gunfire, and the frustration of being always unable to retaliate. In subdued tones, the remnants of 21st Brigade did not hesitate, either, to inquire when they could expect to move from front to rear of the five battalions now in the area. When Captain Steward, Caro's medical officer, diagnosed several cases of physical and nervous collapse Porter regarded this as a symptom of a general demoralization—words he chose to use subsequently in his report to describe the battalion's condition.[8]

Captain Steward collaborates this evidence:

> My considered judgement, and I said it, was that they 'had almost had it'. Porter's opinion was that they were in a state of 'general demoralisation'. It was a verdict deeply resented by us all . . .

He simply had not been present and didn't know what he was talking about.[9]

Porter's assessment is a difficult one to understand. He had previously served with the 7th Division in Syria and consequently must have had first-hand knowledge of the superb showing that 21st Brigade had made there. Further, he could have been under no illusion as to the quality of its leadership for exactly the same reason. His assessment was therefore strangely out of character for a soldier of his ability, and his choice of words a grave error of judgment and diplomacy. The truth is that Maroubra Force were down to their very last physical and mental resources at Ioribaiwa, but never demoralised.

However the really momentous outcome of Porter's summation of the 21st Brigade at Nauro and Ioribaiwa is the fact that his report must have been read by higher authority and therefore it must have had some effect upon subsequent events at Koitaki.

By early morning on 16 September, Brigadier Eather felt sufficiently concerned about his position to contact Allen:

> Enemy feeling whole front and flanks. Do not consider can hold him here. Request permission to withdraw to Imita Ridge if necessary. Porter concurs.[10]

Eather moved his force back to the Imita Ridge and had completed the deployment of his force by 11 am on 17 September. This action was a sound military decision. The Japanese had the momentum and the initiative. By withdrawing to a better defensive position and, as a consequence, further extending the Japanese line of communication and supply, Eather was merely placing himself into a position of strength where he could create a reserve and whence he could push aggressive fighting patrols forward and decisively wrest the initiative from Horii.

By 12 September, the 14th Field Regiment had manhandled two 25-pounder artillery pieces through the mud to the high ground between Ilolo and Uberi. The belated entry of Australian artillery into the Owen Stanley Campaign was in fact an anti-climax. The Japanese veterans of Malaya and the Philippines, of Java and Borneo, whose triumphs had apparently known no bounds, had reached the end of their tether and were about to turn back along that jungle track that had carried them so close to, and yet left them so far from, the strategic prize of Port Moresby. Judging that the defeat at Milne Bay had placed their intended capture of Port Moresby at great risk and fearing, as a consequence, an Allied attack upon Buna, the Japanese high command recalled Horii to the Gona–Buna beach-head.

It is not the purpose of this work to examine the subsequent exploits of the 25th and 16th Brigades on the road back. However three points are worthy of mention. Firstly, because of the Japanese force's general debilitation and insecure line of communication, caused in no small part by Potts and Maroubra Force, it was not until they had journeyed far back to Templeton's Crossing that the Japanese offered a determined resistance. Secondly, the Japanese force was so cruelly weakened and starving that evidence was found of its having resorted to cannibalism.[11] Although much of its plight can be fairly attributed to the newly aggressive and very potent Allied Air Force's harassment of their line of communication and supply, very significant credit is due to the disciplined, tenacious and, above all, time-consuming Maroubra Force fighting withdrawal from Isurava to Ioribaiwa. The fact is that the Japanese force that swarmed over the Ioribaiwa feature was a grievously debilitated one, having fallen far behind its ambitious timetable and having been denied expected captured stores. It had suffered still further by its neglect of basic standards of hygiene. Thirdly, Allen's new force was to suffer under limitations of supply and concentration of force similar to those which had bedevilled Potts.

The magnificent efforts of the native carriers were vitiated by exhaustion and desertion, by sickness and death, due to the prolonged ordeal of the unending campaign and the increasing carrying demands of the lengthening line of supply; and, in addition, air supply was still hampered by inaccuracy of dropping and, until the occupation of Myola, the lack of any suitable dropping ground. In short, despite an infinitely greater concentration of force, the possession of the initiative, and a greatly weakened enemy—advantages all denied to Potts—Allen (who to a large extent was responsible for the administration, supply and orders to Potts), Eather and Lloyd were faced with a gruelling, slogging reacquisition of ground before a deserted Kokoda could be re-entered.

After having been in reserve since 16 September near Uberi, where they had resumed their separate identities, the 2/14th and 2/16th Battalions were relieved by the 14th Brigade on the 26th and then moved to Koitaki. Their ordeal was finally over. Gone were the cold, wet, sleepless nights; the soul-destroying, mud-ridden climbs and steep, slippery descents; the monotonous and meagre diet; the filthy, stinking clothes; and, above all, gone was the seemingly endless slaughter of their mates. Gone too was the tragic sight of the wounded often literally dragging themselves and sometimes each other for days along the track, rather than face their enemy's maltreatment and butchery—spurred by some almost superhuman spirit to grotesque and incredible feats of movement, endurance and survival that belied their listing as 'walking' wounded.

Since the 2/14th had begun its trek over the Trail on 16 August, closely followed by the 2/16th, until the survivors were relieved some six weeks later, the soldiers of the two battalions had endured more than three weeks of actual contact and fighting.

Koitaki was not an ideal place to rest, recover and recuperate, for there were no nightclubs, bars or dances as had enlivened

Tel Aviv and Beirut; only the much savoured simple and previously taken for granted pleasures of life—a thorough, unhurried wash; a welcome change of clothes; jam, biscuits, butter, chocolate; a letter home; and sleep, hours of uninterrupted sleep.

It is a tragic and damning story indeed that the sheer magnitude of the performance of Maroubra Force and its commander in the Owen Stanley Campaign to save Port Moresby was at its conclusion known only to the participants themselves, for the chaos of ignorance, bungling and panic in September 1942 both at Port Moresby and in Australia was culpably characteristic of the Australian nation's totally inept military and political preparation for, and initial conduct of, a South-East Asian war in which the very survival of the nation was at stake. From an Australian historical perspective much is to be learnt from a survey of the inactions and reactions of our own leaders.

The key backdrop, against which any presentation of the roles of the Australian political and military leaders in the Owen Stanley drama must be viewed, must be dominated by their almost total ignorance of the battlefield and, as a consequence, their belated, disjointed, hurried and therefore inept reaction to the enemy thrust over the Owen Stanley Range as it occurred, without even a token gesture of forward planning. Four events during July to September 1942 sent shock waves through both the army and the Australian government that were reminiscent of those registered immediately after the fall of Singapore.

The first was the titanic battle at Isurava. That a little known and poorly trained militia battalion had been pushed back from Awala to Isurava was one thing; that a crack AIF brigade was forced to withdraw from Isurava after its brigadier had been ordered to advance beyond it to retake Kokoda was unfathomable to higher authority. The fact that Maroubra Force had achieved one of the most tenacious and magnificent feats of arms in Australian military history was therefore not only beyond comprehension; it was not recognised, or even apparent to such authority.

Myola's loss was the second event. This most important supply depot with its dry lake-bed had enabled Allied transport planes to drop large quantities of supplies to sustain Maroubra Force. If Myola's loss stunned Major-General Allen who, incredibly, had enquired as to when Potts intended further offensive operations, then it must have plunged General Headquarters in Brisbane into considerable panic. The tragedy is that it was New Guinea Force Headquarters and General Headquarters which had failed to supply Potts adequately upon his arrival at Myola, and had therefore severely restricted his ability to fight the battle at Isurava.

The third event was the intense and bloodied battle at Brigade Hill. New Guinea Force and General Headquarters could not appreciate why or how Brigade Headquarters could have been in grave danger of annihilation; how three AIF battalions could be cut off from their line of communication and, above all, how one of those battalions could have been lost from the battleground after only a few days of fighting. Hence, the fact that Brigade Hill had seen the second titanic and sustained infliction of significant casualties on the Japanese, and a further delay in their movement towards Port Moresby, was also lost on those in higher command.

If Isurava, Myola and Brigade Hill induced confusion and panic in Port Moresby and, to an even greater degree in Australia, then the withdrawal of Brigadier Eather's force to Imita Ridge came as a monumental shock which initiated a chain reaction of events during September–October 1942 that brought little or no credit to the military and the government. Those events are now examined in detail.

After the 1940 federal election the then Prime Minister, Mr Menzies, had founded the Advisory War Council, composed of members of all parties in the parliament, to debate and formulate advice with regard to the Australian war effort. As a direct reaction to the events at Isurava and Myola and to the continuing withdrawal of Maroubra Force, the Advisory War Council thought it desirable that the Commander-in-Chief of the Australian Military Forces journey to Port Moresby to examine the military situation there and then report back to the Council. This was an Australian initiative and one the politicians were certainly entitled and, indeed obliged, to take. General Blamey duly flew to Port Moresby, satisfied himself as to the Allied conduct of operations and then returned to report to the nation on 16 September, by means of a radio broadcast, and to the Advisory War Council on the 17th. Blamey's report to the Council contains some noteworthy points:

> On the 17th of August the Japanese made a heavy air raid on Port Moresby and destroyed Allied land transport aircraft. This disorganized our forward supply arrangements, with the result that supplies could only be made available for 1500 men in the forward area.
>
> The 53rd Militia Battalion was infiltrated by the Japanese, and the 39th Militia Battalion was attacked. The Commander, 21st Brigade, A.I.F., was unable to deploy his Brigade to make a fight, as he had to extricate the Militia Battalions . . .[12]

The fact that the Commander-in-Chief of the Australian Military Forces could have been so grossly misinformed is striking testimony to his own and the nation's total ignorance of the military operation in the Owen Stanley Range. Further, the report is but one of many noted in the Advisory War Council minutes wherein General Blamey chose to disparage the militia as a means of providing answers to questions as to the higher army command's conduct of the Owen Stanley Campaign. The fact is that the 39th Battalion was a vital part of Potts's force at Isurava. Far from prohibiting his deployment of 21st Brigade at Isurava, it had facilitated it. Potts was unable to satisfactorily deploy his force at Isurava because of a lack of supplies that were to be flown to Myola, but mysteriously disappeared in transit. Further, Potts defended Isurava against a Japanese force approximately five times greater than American Intelligence had ascertained—defended it too, without adequate supplies of more essential equipment such as maps, supporting-fire weapons and entrenching tools.

> The 25 A.I.F. Brigade, which recently arrived at Port Moresby, and the A.I.F. Pioneer Battalion were sent forward on the 15th September and deployed for an attack on the Japanese. The attack began yesterday, but no great progress has been made . . . [13]

The attack referred to by Blamey occurred on the 14th not on the 16th of September, and resulted in Eather's withdrawing to Imita Ridge on the 16th.

> Lieut-General Rowell, Major-General Allen and the troops are confident that the Japanese will not be able to take Port Moresby from the land. General Blamey shared their confidence. The Air Force has improved 100% and there are adequate landing grounds and sufficient aircraft, while Military Forces were there in sufficient strength to render the capture of Port Moresby a very difficult operation. [14]

Although not a totally accurate portrayal of events, Blamey's report to the Advisory War Council was thus essentially a defence of Rowell and his troops. The whole issue should have, and could have, been buried with his report—Blamey's loyalty in this instance was commendable.

It is ironic that one day before Blamey's report to the Advisory War Council, Eather's withdrawal to Imita Ridge occurred. On the evening of 17 September, General MacArthur contacted Prime Minister Curtin and suggested that General

Blamey proceed immediately to Port Moresby to take personal command of operations there—that he should 'energise the situation'. MacArthur claimed during this conversation that the Australians greatly outnumbered the Japanese and had withdrawn to Imita Ridge because of a 'lack of efficiency'.

Without demur Curtin acted on MacArthur's suggestion. A warning letter to Rowell preceded Blamey's return to Port Moresby:

> The powers that be have determined that I shall myself go to New Guinea for a while and operate from there. I do not, however, propose to transfer many of Adv. HQ Staff and will arrive by aeroplane Wednesday evening, I hope with Hopkins . . .
>
> I hope you will not be upset at this decision, and will not think that it implies any lack of confidence in yourself. I think it arises out of the fact that we have very inexperienced politicians who are inclined to panic on every possible occasion, and I think the relationship between us personally is such that we can make the arrangement work without any difficulty.[15]

In his book *Full Circle*, Rowell wrote:

> Blamey arrived in Port Moresby on the 23rd September. During that evening and on each of the two days following, we had a full and frank discussion of my position as general officer commanding in view of his arrival. At times the discussion was pretty acrimonious as I believed, and said, that the confidence he had expressed in me in his national broadcast a week earlier no longer existed. On several occasions he said that this was the first 'bump' I had had in my service, and this clearly indicated to me that, for all practical purposes, I was being supplanted in command.
>
> The main theme of these discussions, apart from the question of loss of confidence, was an endeavour to find a

working arrangement suited to the circumstances. Blamey had no staff, so inevitably sooner or later my own staff would be called on to serve two masters, and I would merely become a figurehead.[16]

From 23 September until the evening of the 27th, both Blamey and Rowell strove to make an appalling command situation work. Rowell, highly principled and keenly aware that the military situation would improve at literally any time, failed to appreciate the position into which Blamey had been manipulated by MacArthur and Curtin. For his own part, Blamey found himself in a predicament that he did not relish and, also, he keenly sensed that his own position was under intense scrutiny in Canberra.[17] This unfortunate episode was caused by the Australian Government's grave error of judgment when it handed over its military power to General MacArthur in March, 1942. The Australian Army had experienced a long, frustrating, and, at times, bitter struggle during the early Middle East campaigns of 1940–41 in its attempts to keep its military formations together and, above all, to have some degree of power and autonomy over their destiny. After Australia had secured this hard won autonomy, the inexperienced Curtin Government, which had taken office just two months before Pearl Harbor, proceeded to surrender it unconditionally to the Americans. General MacArthur, the recipient of this power, did not always base his decisions upon Australia's interests, but instead frequently formulated them with American and very often his own aspirations foremost in his mind.

On 28 September, General Blamey informed Rowell that he had relieved him of his command of New Guinea Force and had sent an adverse report on him to Curtin and MacArthur. Blamey's pursuit of Rowell's further downfall continued with an unnecessary passion, urging his retirement, or demotion to the rank of Colonel. Only political intervention by the likes of Menzies, Curtin and the Minister for the Army, Forde, allowed Rowell to continue his career in exile in the Middle East and, later, England. There is little doubt that Blamey's vindictiveness cost the nation the services of a talented and honourable soldier. The fact that Rowell was to later rise to the position of Chief of the General Staff in April 1950 is ample testimony to his talents.

If onerous circumstances had conspired to impel Blamey to remove Rowell on the 28th, then his subsequent treatment of the 21st Brigade during October and November 1942 brought his competency and judgment as Commander-in-Chief, Australian Military Forces, into sharp and condemnatory focus. Brigadier Potts had returned to his command of the 21st Brigade, then at Itiki, on 23 September. Wrongfully, tragically, and above all acting in unforgivable and almost unbelievable ignorance, Blamey relieved Potts of his command on 23 October. Raymond Paull writes:

> Potts remained one day short of a calendar month in his command. On the 22nd of October, he went to the telephone to hear Blamey's clipped tones at the other end of the line. The Commander-In-Chief made no attempt to soften the impact of the impending blow. 'Change of climate for you Potts', he said. 'You go to Darwin. Your successor, Dougherty, will meet you tomorrow and take over.'[18]

This account is inaccurate. Lieutenant-Colonel J. K. Murdoch[19] had only recently been promoted to Staff Captain 21st Brigade at the time of Potts's removal from his command. After Brigadier Potts's death in 1968, Murdoch saw fit to bring to light previously unrevealed evidence. The first publication of his account of Potts's removal from his command was in *Pigeon Post*, the official 2/16th Battalion newsletter. It is recorded here with Lieutenant-Colonel Murdoch's approval:

Brigadier A. W. Potts should be recorded in history as the man whose fortitude, courage and inspirational ability to the troops under his command saved Port Moresby from being overrun by the Japanese—what this did to save Australia from land invasion is anybody's guess or assessment.

Shortly after the 21st Brigade had reached Koitaki plantation area—even before the scattered parties of the 2/14th and 2/16th Battalions had made it to base, a parade was organized to allow an address to be given by Major-General 'Tubby' Allen, the then commander of 7th Australian Division. At this parade the G.O.C. gave the commander, the officers and men of the 21st Brigade, a personal message from the Prime Minister extending the nation's thanks to the brigade for 'saving Port Moresby and thus Australia'.

What a fillip this was for the troops—despite the difficulties and turmoil of the time the morale was high—it was tops, the veterans of the Middle-East had shown their worth under terrific odds and the Kokoda Trail must always be remembered with pride in the annals of their families.

Shortly after this episode and with little warning to the Brigade Headquarters, a visit by the Commander-In-Chief was announced. At the time I had just been appointed Staff Captain of the brigade, taking over from that inspired logistics wizard Peter Smith whose tremendous efforts on the Kokoda Trail were to be surpassed only by his amazing organization from Divisional Headquarters of the Nadzab, Lae and Ramu Valley Operations.

The above is explained to create the atmosphere of the time. The Commander-In-Chief's arrival was heralded by the arrival some minutes before of his personal assistant and some aides including, if I recall correctly, some military police. Unknown to me at the time, the personal assistant issued instructions that the headquarters was to be vacated by all ranks except Brigadier Potts. At that time the Staff Captain's job was reasonably onerous with a reorganisation of the brigade and other problems, time was precious—I recall I kept working not having nominated my presence to any of the visitors—before I could move out the Commander-In-Chief was present in the adjacent room having been welcomed at the front door by Brigadier Potts. The C in C's first words were— 'Is everybody out?' As the Brigade Commander was not aware of my presence, he answered in the affirmative. My position was delicate—I could not move and thus I became an unwilling eavesdropper. I was trapped. The conversation, with both officers standing, was completed in a matter of a few minutes.

I am of the belief and remain to this day that Brigadier Potts thought the C in C was visiting to extend congratulations to him for the efforts of the brigade. His first remark of substance after the greeting was to the effect that the men were wonderful—there was no doubt that their spirit and showing would bolster up the morale of the whole of Australia. The C in C replied that he was on other business—he pointed out that the Prime Minister and War Cabinet had instructed him to say that failures like the Kokoda Trail (it was the Owen Stanley's Campaign then) could not be tolerated—the men had shown that something was lacking—the C in C blamed the leaders— he further stated that he was relieving Potts forthwith. Naturally Brig. Potts expostulated—he said that if any blame was attachable to anybody then it was to him and him alone. The battalion commanders were not at fault—the officers and men were exceptional as had been shown.

The C in C was adamant and said that Potts was to leave the brigade forthwith and move to Darwin—a plane would be made available. Potts asked could he stay to meet his successor—this request was denied—the C in C said Potts was to hold himself available for immediate movement. Brigadier Potts did not have time for further remarks, the C in C departed abruptly—in fact, the Brigadier did not accompany him past the front door.

On the return of the Brigadier to the main room I made my presence known. The Brigadier expressed his personal feelings, but, ever the soldier, he said he accepted the position. As his movement was pending he said he would see the Battalion Commanders and the Brigade Major but other than that he would leave quietly, without any farewell parade or review. He asked that an order of the day be prepared for his signature—to thank the troops and to ensure that they continued their loyalty and support to his successor.

From memory, the time of the visit was approaching noon. The word spread rapidly throughout the brigade—many questions were asked—then came the resignations—most of the brigade staff paraded to 'Pottsy' and requested that they go with him—officers of the units tended their resignations in writing—almost certainly emotionally overlooking that in war the gesture was meaningless. Within hours, as staff captain, I received resignations from a large number of the unit officers—I advised the brigadier and also made a request to go with him. He was very overcome by the loyalty of his officers but insisted that no resignation be handed to him—I was to tell all officers that the papers were not acceptable—as many had said at the time of handing in their resignations— 'they had volunteered in—they were now volunteering out.'

The morale of the brigade hit a very low level and remained that way for some time. From memory again (much water having passed under the bridge) Brownie, Pottsy's batman accompanied him on the move. He, like Brigadier Potts and the C in C have now gone to their higher reward.

I need swear no affidavits to the above, none can deny what I have said, none can confirm my recollections of the day. I state simply that they are correct . . .[20]

Indeed, none can confirm or deny Lieutenant-Colonel Murdoch's account. There are, however, two very compelling reasons for considering his account accurate. The first is the integrity of the man himself: Lieutenant-Colonel Sir Arthur ('Mert') Lee MC: 'Ken Murdoch is a man of integrity and anything that Ken Murdoch stated and put down on paper, I'd take it as gospel.'[21]

Lieutenant-Colonel Lee's reaction to Captain Murdoch's document is typical of that of a large sample of 21st Brigade officers.[22] The second reason is that the attitude revealed by Lieutenant-Colonel Murdoch's account of Potts's removal from his command is closely aligned with that manifested in events at Koitaki.

It is staggering to contemplate that an Australian brigade commander could be thrust into a campaign with such a damning inadequacy of military intelligence, support and equipment and yet fight a near flawless fighting withdrawal where both the military and political stakes were so terribly important, and that he could then be relieved from his command as a reward.

Denied the right to address his men personally, Potts left them an emotional farewell, the contents of which are reminiscent of the man and the magnificent troops whom he was privileged to command:

Special Message To Officers, N.C.O.'s and men.

HQ 21st Aust. Inf. Bde.
23rd Oct. 42.

On relinquishing my command of the 21st Bde, it is impossible to express my feelings adequately to all its members.

Though in comd of you for only six months, my association has been for the full period of service of the Bde. It has so grown to be part of my life, that even when not facing you or speaking directly to you, the task of saying goodbye is the hardest job in my life and one I funk badly.

This much I can say—that I regard this Bde. as the best fighting formation in the A.I.F. and second to none in this war or the last. Your new comd. will be proud of it. Its discipline and tone is obviously high and that is not meant as praise—it is as it should be.

Be loyal to all the ideals we have built up around this Bde. of three hard-hitting, hard-marching and hard-living Bns, and nothing in your lives will ever give you half so much pleasure as belonging to it or so much pain as leaving it.

Thanking you for your loyalty and cooperation; you are a great team and I'm proud that I was one of you. Thanking you and goodbye.

A. W. Potts[23]

If General Blamey's removal of both Rowell and Potts from their respective commands was a determined attempt by him to demonstrate his ability to 'energise the situation' in New Guinea to those in power, whether in military or in political circles back in Australia, then the subsequent events at Koitaki on 9 November, portray General Blamey as a soldier-bureaucrat who reacted to the campaign under two very distinct and obvious handicaps. Firstly, he was quite obviously almost totally ignorant of the campaign and its complexities. Secondly, he was reacting to enormous pressure from MacArthur and the government to redress a perceived military failure in the Owen Stanley Range. By removing various commanders and addressing their troops he was firstly seen to be decisively reacting to that perceived failure and, secondly, also protecting his own now precarious position as Commander-In-Chief of the Australian Army.

The soldiers of the 21st Brigade were paraded at the Koitaki plantation sports field on 9 November. They were informed that Blamey would both address and inspect them. Believing as Potts had done, that Blamey was coming to offer his congratulations to them for their magnificent performance during the campaign these officers and men turned out on parade with justifiable pride and soldierly bearing—this was no tardy, undisciplined collection of untrained recruits, but rather troops who were among the nation's military elite, the veterans of the Litani River, of Sidon, Damour, Isurava, Abuari,

Iora Creek, Brigade Hill and Ioribaiwa. Their immaculate presentation and proud military deportment were obvious for all to witness. Drawn up in battalion formations near the dais, these men were in no way aware of, or prepared for, what was forthcoming. A true and comprehensive perspective of their outrageous disparagement may be obtained from corroborating impressions, deeply felt and keenly remembered, recorded by soldiers of the three battalions insulted on that infamous day. Captain H. D. Steward, 2/16th Battalion Regimental Medical Officer:

> I suppose few of the shocks I have had in my lifetime could be greater than the one I got that day, with all the surviving members of the Brigade drawn up in splendid order under the hot sun at Koitaki. Blamey showed no sign of nervousness. He spoke from a wooden platform in a clear, strong voice. He was no further than, say, two cricket pitches' length from where I stood, hands clasped behind my back in the 'at ease' position.
>
> The troops could have withstood the Japanese mountain gun more easily than what they received. Blamey got them on edge almost at once by saying that they had been beaten by inferior troops in inferior numbers. Then he made his famous remark to the effect that 'the rabbit that ran away was the rabbit that got shot'. The entire parade, officers and men, were almost molten with rage and indignation . . .[24]

Captain S. Y. Bisset, MC, 2/14th Battalion:

> The account of Blamey's address at Koitaki as given in 'Blue' Steward's book is in my opinion correct. As Adjutant I had a front position. He also stated that we had been defeated in spite of having superior numbers to the enemy. I knew so well the tremendous performance of the Brigade, particularly the 2/14th and 2/16th Bns, and my own brother's Platoon withstanding

some thirty attacks by one and two Coy. assaults, killing over 300 and wounding more.[25]

Sergeant (later Captain) R. N. Thompson, 2/14th Battalion:

Yes I was present. We were on parade anticipating congratulations for a job well done. What we received was the greatest dressing down of all time. His term, 'it is the rabbit that runs that gets shot', was taken as a charge of cowardice and an insult to men who had stood up to a numerically superior, better armed enemy and fought him to a standstill.[26]

Lance-Corporal J. A. Hocking, 2/16th Battalion:

As he [Blamey] proceeded the parade became more restive and began to vent their feelings. My impression watching General Blamey as the noise from the ranks of the parade became louder was that he was non-plussed—he couldn't believe that anyone would interrupt his address. For my part, the more I thought about what he said the angrier I became, and I still feel anger.[27]

Lieutenant-Colonel G.D.T. Cooper MBE, CO 2/27th Battalion:

He said something off the cuff, quickly, that might have been a joke in his boyhood or something like that, but it was dynamite under these circumstances. He simply said, and I've forgotten the precise wording of it, 'And don't forget it's the rabbit that runs that always gets shot' or words to that effect. And to people who'd been let down by lack of supplies, lack of air support; a carrying train behind them that had collapsed; that died away and slipped away into the scrub; who found themselves in a position where they had many, many casualties that they themselves had to carry back . . . Radio sets that were nearly all out of action because of moss or moisture ... Fighting! They kept on fighting and they went on fighting under the most difficult circumstances. Then when they'd been forced back by being flooded around by advancing Japanese . . . It was just a stupid thing to say![28]

Sergeant John Burns MM, 2/27th Battalion: (Burns had cared for the wounded with Private Zanker after the 2/27th Battalion had been cut off.)

> If you're getting to the point of what he said, I bloody well did hear what he said! I was disgusted because I had only just come out with the stretchers, give or take x number of days. I was weak; I was tired; I was sore and I was scarred all over from bites and scratches from the jungle, because we had no bandages. We had torn up what was left of shirts that had been worn and boiled to tie up wounds; the arse was out of my pants . . . And to have to stand out there and listen to that drivel! He was not only having a go, he was putting us down in no uncertain manner.[29]

The emotion, anger and frustration felt by the survivors of the 21st Brigade ran to almost immeasurable proportions on that hot, unforgettable day at Koitaki.

Imagine being amongst the assembled soldiers of the 2/14th Battalion. Their thoughts must have journeyed to faraway Isurava and to the remarkable deeds of the likes of Kingsbury, 'Butch' Bisset, Moore, McCallum, Treacy, Bear, Butler, and Key; or perhaps to Nye at Brigade Hill—and to so many other men, the names of whom the historian and the nation will never know.

Of all the soldiers who felt the anger of that day, the 2/16th Battalion must have been particularly incensed, for Brigadier Arnold Potts had been, and was considered still, one of them. Corporal Les Thredgold, 2/27th Battalion:

> That hurt the 16th! They were ropable! It hurt the whole brigade. The 16th, they were good fighters in the front line

and good fighters out of the front line. They were wild tigers but they were good fighters, and they thought the world of Pottsy.[30]

The thoughts of the 2/16th Battalion must have also been focussed upon Brigade Hill and the massive casualties suffered in that brave, determined attack back towards Brigadier Potts; and upon Langridge and Lambert and a multitude of men who had performed so magnificently in rearguard action after rearguard action along the Kokoda Trail.

The anger and frustration of the 2/27th Battalion was likewise immense, for they had wrought utter carnage upon the Japanese at Mission Ridge and had then been subjected to a form of torment and deprivation of enormous magnitude before regaining their base area.

The truth is that it was only the relatively calm and disciplined behaviour of the officers, particularly important amongst the 2/16th Battalion ranks, that prevented a very ugly and tragic reaction to Blamey himself on that infamous day.

There was one outsider at Koitaki who was in a special way very much an insider. Lieutenant-Colonel Norman Carlyon OBE, was General Blamey's ADC, 1940–42, Personal Assistant, 1942-44, and Military Assistant, 1944–45. In *I Remember Blamey* he records:

I was there when those fine soldiers formed up, not far from what had been the start-line for their thrust against the enemy. New Guinea's stormy temperatures being what they are, it may seem absurd for me to say that I was in a cold sweat. Standing beside the small platform from which Blamey was to address the troops, I realized that he was in a most aggressive mood. He was soon expressing this in harsh words.

He told the men that they had been defeated, that he had been defeated, and Australia had been defeated. He said this was simply not good enough. Every soldier here had to remember that he was worth three Japanese. In future he expected no further retirement, but advance at all costs. He concluded with a remark which I think was particularly ill-chosen and unfair. 'Remember' he said, 'it is not the man with the gun that gets shot; it's the rabbit that is running away'. It amazed me that Blamey should deal so insensitively with the men of such a well-proven brigade.[31]

After finishing his diatribe to the troops, Blamey addressed the officers separately. While some of the officers refused to attend because of the criticism that had been so unjustly levelled at them, most were present. Blamey made it clear that he considered that some of the brigade's officers had failed to perform adequately in the execution of their duties and had, in addition, failed to share the hazards of the campaign with their men. Lieutenant-Colonel Cooper was present at that address:

> The things that were said to the officers at Koitaki were generally speaking I feel, very irritating, terribly annoying, because after all, they should have been given some commendation, compliments on what had been done. The thing at the time was not being seen in perspective . . .
> . . . Those with the quickest tempers showed the most fire; of course you would understand that![32]

Lieutenant-Colonel Cooper's adjutant, Captain Katekar, was also present:

> He was displeased with the performance of at least some of our officers [21st Brigade]. He felt that they hadn't led their men properly; in other words 'you've got to pull your socks up!' Which officers was he referring to, and what knowledge did he have of any officers who hadn't? Blamey's inference left us dumbfounded, as it was so distant from the truth.[33]

Controversy concerning the Owen Stanley Campaign did not end with the Koitaki parade. Shortly after General Blamey's address at Koitaki the new New Guinea Force Commander, General Herring[34], in an attempt to efface the bitter resentment caused by Blamey's speech, added groundless insult to grave injury; he informed the Brigade that 'soldiers must not be afraid to die'. This was too much! Very many of the men actually broke ranks and the startled general was provided with a booing and jeering exit for him and his driver.

Within weeks of the Koitaki parade, Chester Wilmot had his accreditation as a war correspondent to report on operations in the South-West Pacific Area withdrawn, as a result of his succinct and first-hand observations of the campaign which he had written in a report that had subsequently been sent to Brisbane by Lieutenant-General Rowell prior to his removal. Major-General Allen was relieved of his command of 7th Division by Blamey after having been repeatedly accused of a lack of aggression and progress during the Australian thrust back over the Owen Stanley Range. It is ironic that, just as the fortunes of war were about to favour Allen with the imminent reoccupation of Kokoda, he was replaced by Major-General Vasey.

Previous historical analysis of the events at Koitaki has been of a very limited nature. In fact in one case it was prevented. Shortly after the Second World War, the battalion associations were encouraged to record their histories by the Australian Government and by the Australian War Memorial. Grants of money were made available to assist them in their labours. It is a sad fact that a 21st Brigade Battalion historian was dissuaded from recording the events at Koitaki and that the War Memorial grants were used as a means of enforcing this policy of selective censorship. Sergeant John Burns MM, 2/27th Battalion:

He alluded to the story that the rabbit that got up and ran was the rabbit that got shot and I quoted that in that (pointing to his copy of the 2/27th Battalion unit history) and Gavin Long[35] wouldn't pass my history, or wouldn't approve the grant unless I deleted that, because General Blamey had denied it![36]

And to this day there are those who deny it.

As far as 21st Brigade was concerned this feeling about Blamey was due to a very specific misunderstanding. On the 9th of November, 1942, when the brigade had been withdrawn after its heroic fighting in the Owen Stanleys, Blamey addressed them and referred to the manner in which the Japanese dug themselves in to almost impregnable defensive posts, but, he said, when brave soldiers force them out of those dugouts, they run like rabbits out of a broken burrow and that is when they can be picked off and destroyed. For some unaccountable reason some members of the brigade, probably not hearing his remarks properly, as the acoustics on parade grounds are usually very poor, thought he was suggesting that members of 21st Brigade had run. It took a long time for this error to be corrected. Blamey addressed the officers of 21st Brigade again at Ravenshoe in 1943 when they were re-organizing and very soon there was not criticism of General Blamey within the ranks of 21st Brigade or in other units.[37]

There must be a credibility cloud over the inventive authors who present a Blamey imagining the ever attacking enemy pushing their relentless assaults forward while 'dug into almost impregnable defensive posts'. Could Blamey have been so ignorant? Could they plead truth in reporting? They—or Blamey—might just as well have pictured, with equal authenticity, those Japanese military geniuses from the north advancing in impregnable, portable Eskimo igloos. The truth is that at no time during their aggressive thrust across the Owen Stanley Range were the Japanese engaged in constructing 'impregnable defensive posts', for they were in possession of the military initiative and were therefore busily engaged in offensive operations.

Odd absentee authors may fantasise but the veteran hundreds who smouldered under the Koitaki sun reliably remember what was said to them and in what context. They may have been censored but they have not been silenced; and no propaganda will persuade them that they were in 'error', that the 'error' was 'corrected' and that 'very soon there was not criticism of General Blamey within the ranks of 21st Brigade or in other units'. His subsequent remarks to the officers of 21st Brigade after the Koitaki parade only serve to reinforce this evidence. It is also worth remembering that the Commander-in-Chief removed the Commander New Guinea Force, the divisional commander, the brigade commander and a war correspondent from the campaign—hardly a demonstration of commendation and/or appreciation. And the ramifications of the Koitaki parade were to eventually journey even farther beyond a totally unjust condemnation of officers and men who had fought a magnificent battle in the Owen Stanley Range.

Meanwhile, after Brigadier Potts had been removed from his command of the 21st Brigade, Brigadier Ivan Dougherty[38] was flown from Darwin to assume command. Dougherty brought with him a distinguished record of service in the Middle East. He had originally journeyed to war with the 6th Division and had fought in Cyrenaica, Greece and Crete. He had commanded the 2/4th Battalion. Upon his return to Australia he had been promoted to Brigadier and given command of the 23rd Brigade in the Northern Territory. Lieutenant-Colonel J.K. Murdoch, then Staff Captain 21st Brigade:

> His tremendous personal attitude; aptitude towards the officers and men of the brigade and his perspicacity, his patience and his fairness in overcoming the difficulties and the feelings of the officers and men, welded the brigade once again into a fighting machine.[39]

Sergeant C. E. Edwards, 2/27th Battalion: 'You couldn't help but be impressed with that bloke! A first class soldier and first class man.'[40] Lieutenant-Colonel F.H. Sublet, 2/16th Battalion:

> He commanded 21st Bde from Gona to war's end. When I commanded the 2/16th Bn, I found him very supportive while also being very decisive. His responses were calm and measured and he was always ready to explain his decisions. Though quiet and unobtrusive, he seemed to have the capacity to absorb 'atmosphere' and spot strengths and weaknesses.[41]

When Dougherty assumed command of the brigade he was immediately conscious of the situation confronting him:

> When I got to 21st Brigade I realized that I'd supplanted someone who was a hero among the troops, and rightly so, in Arnold Potts. I knew how they liked him. My job was to overcome anything that was there. They were intensely loyal to Potts. I knew I wasn't going to be welcome. There was later some point, I don't know when, I think it might have been on the Sanananda Road, that the Brigade seemed to swing behind me, and for the next three years I could never have wished to have better support from that Brigade.[42]

Thus, Dougherty was placed in a most unenviable position which he handled with great tact and diplomacy. However, one important point arose which was later to have grave repercussions; Dougherty was made acutely aware by Herring that a doubt existed, in a high command view, over the performance of 21st Brigade and a number of its officers. Sir Ivan Dougherty remembers that period and the doubts which existed:

> When Potts was taken off from command of the Brigade and Allen the division; leave Rowell out of this, it's a separate issue,

there were other factors in it; now the only story I heard was a story Herring told me. There was criticism within New Guinea Force and Supreme Allied Headquarters, concerning the leadership of 21st Brigade. Much of this criticism arose from that particular withdrawal from Efogi. [Brigade Hill[43]] And I know at the time I was summing things up.[44]

Dougherty would have been negligent in the exercise of his command of the 21st Brigade had he not been 'summing things up'.

The outcome was that the doubt over leadership was to become a grave issue when the soon to be fought battle by 21st Brigade at Gona reached its bloodied climax in early December 1942. It will be shown that higher command was to assume the failure to secure Gona's early fall to be in part related to a perceived lack of aggressive leadership. That perception had had its genesis in the panic of the powerful, oblivious of the realities of the Owen Stanley Campaign and blind to the achievement of those who had endured it. In the delayed but eventual victory of Maroubra Force, they saw only the mirage of defeat; and they sought scapegoats for their own incompetence. And it was not only the leaders they condemned. Major Katekar, 2/27th Battalion, has a vivid recollection of the aftermath of the Blamey diatribe at Koitaki:

> And they were absolutely ropable! Incensed! In fact I claim to this day that some of the officers whom we lost at Gona did so because of the effect of Blamey's unfair criticism. He was sheltering, trying to in effect pass the buck to our officers instead of accepting it himself.[45]

Lieutenant-Colonel F. H. Sublet DSO, MC 2/16th Battalion:

> Well I'd tackle it this way. Many of the young officers who were killed at Gona weren't on the Owen Stanley track anyway. But

those officers who were at Koitaki and heard Blamey's speech were very, very incensed and they were really carrying on about it. Almost mutinous in their feelings! What I did see at Gona was that a number of the young officers and sergeants who had not taken part in the Kokoda Trail were determined to show their mettle at Gona, because they knew what the battalion had gone through on the Kokoda Trail and they'd been left out of battle; they were determined to redeem the battalion; put the battalion back on its mantle.[46]

Lieutenant–Colonel Sublet's observations were not limited to his own battalion. He was aware of a similar attitude throughout the brigade:

I can quote one! Stan Bisset used to jump up and down with rage every time he talked about it. Stan was absolutely ropable because his own brother had been killed up there. And a great bloke, Stan! A strong man, strong in will; strong in resolve; strong in every way. Actually the whole brigade was in the mood to show the Commander-in-Chief. And of course the opportunity arose at Gona.[47]

The events at Koitaki and the removal from command of Lieutenant-General Rowell, Major-General Allen and Brigadier Potts, bring into critical focus both the leadership and the judgment of General Blamey during the Owen Stanley Campaign.

Blamey had had an impressive and distinguished military career. His service during the Great War, particularly as General Monash's Chief of Staff during the fighting in France, had brought to notice his enormous ability as a staff officer. His early Second World War achievements had also been impressive; he had capably administered command of the AIF in the Middle East and had shown resolve and judgment in his successful attempts to retain it as a unified formation with some degree of autonomy. And his achievements in the reorganisation of the Australian Military Forces upon his return to Australia in early 1942, had provided further evidence of his special abilities.

However the Australian Government did not bring anything other than great discredit to itself during March 1942, by its total surrender of military power to General MacArthur. It had not done anything to secure any power for General Blamey nor had it actively sought positions for Australian soldiers on MacArthur's staff. Such abdication of national responsibility and interest had undoubtedly been a very great error of judgment by the Curtin Government as the Australian Army possessed officers with infinitely greater war training and operational experience than could be claimed by MacArthur's staff. Subsequently it was the same Curtin Government that panicked in early September 1942, and, as a consequence, ordered Blamey to New Guinea. Having satisfied himself that the military situation was being handled satisfactorily, and seeing no cause for panic, Blamey returned to Australia. And after that it was not any decision by General Blamey to return to Port Moresby on 23 September, but General MacArthur's request to Prime Minister Curtin that he return, which unleashed a series of tragic events during the ensuing months.

However, Blamey's subsequent removal of senior officers of New Guinea Force and his address at Koitaki constituted a grave error of judgment on his own part which was based upon an inexcusable ignorance of the conditions in which troops under his ultimate responsibility were fighting. Further, his failure to recognise the potential for a major battle in the Owen Stanley Range, his failure to facilitate the adequate logistical support of his force and his failure to seek out and apply the lessons of the Malayan campaign amounted to gross negligence. The culpable neglect continued. There is absolutely no evidence that the Australian Army sought out or learnt more than a thread of information from Rowell, Allen or

Potts. In fact the lengthy and astute *Report Into Operations—21 Brigade Owen Stanley Campaign* was sent to Army Headquarters in Brisbane shortly after the campaign. It was sent back with orders to condense its contents and emphasis.[48]

Lieutenant-Colonel Frank Sublet DSO, MC:

> . . . when politicians and theatrical generals like MacArthur are embarrassed or frightened, all steps must be taken to divert critical gaze from them; the usual device is to produce a scapegoat . . .
>
> I believe the interlude of arms which disposed of the only threat to Australia in our history should be memorialised as an illustration of the exercise of flexibility for which Australian troops have always been renowned.[49]

In the final analysis, when the Australian nation, through its own lack of preparedness to defend itself in a Pacific war, lay so tragically vulnerable to invasion in July 1942, it played its last desperate hand. Into the Owen Stanley Range it plunged a force of poorly trained militiamen and an only recently arrived home AIF Brigade. When all could have been lost, and indeed should have been lost, the nation had its heroes. And to this day they remain unsung heroes— 'Those Ragged Bloody Heroes' of Maroubra Force. Major-General Sir F. K. Norris:

> Time and rain and the jungle will obliterate this little native pad; but for evermore will live the memory of weary men who have passed this way, ghosts of glorious men that have gone, gone far beyond the Kokoda Trail.[50]

14

To the beach-head

In early October 1942 the opposing strategic positions in the Pacific War were still most delicately balanced. As a result of Coral Sea and Midway, the American Navy had to a large degree redressed the balance of naval power in the Pacific Ocean. However the situation in October was still a matter of grave concern.

Coral Sea and Midway, yes; our naval air fought those and it covered itself with glory. The submarines were doing well. But the rest of the Navy, in fact the Navy as a whole, had not looked good. 'Oklahoma' and 'Arizona' had left the fleet forever at Pearl Harbor; 'Lexington', 'Yorktown', and 'Wasp' were gone, 'Saratoga' and 'North Carolina' were in for repairs. In the Java Sea we had lost a heavy cruiser and a whole division of destroyers; at Savo three cruisers more, and our destroyer loss now stood at fifteen ships. What had the Japs paid for this? The carriers of Midway, another one at Coral Sea, two cruisers downed by submarines and a few destroyers—not a Jap ship was sunk by the surface Navy. They were ahead.[1]

In order to wrest a degree of the initiative from the Japanese, the American Navy embarked upon an ambitious invasion of the Solomon Islands on 7 August 1942. Using their crack marine troops under Lieutenant-General Vandergrift, the Americans effected a crucial landing at Guadalcanal Island.

The protracted Guadalcanal battle greatly influenced the campaign in New Guinea. The Japanese sought a decisive victory at Guadalcanal in order to concentrate a key reinforcement of their existing New Guinea forces. Thus, while the Japanese had been denied the acquisition of Port Moresby due to their telling defeat at Milne Bay and their grinding and debilitating halt at the hands of Maroubra Force on the Kokoda Trail, they still had not abandoned all hope of a favourable result at Guadalcanal and, as a consequence, a fresh attempt to seize Port Moresby. To this end, fearing that General MacArthur might embark upon a landing at Buna, thereby isolating their Owen Stanley Force, they determined that General Horii must be ordered to stage a fighting withdrawal from the Owen Stanley Range and concentrate his force together with limited fresh reinforcements, at the Gona–Sanananda–Buna beach-head.

It is against this strategic background that General Mac-Arthur sought to secure his positions in New Guinea and, by pushing forward with a great sense of urgency, reduce those Japanese beach-head bases.

In the pursuit of the Japanese over the Kokoda Trail during October 1942, the Australians employed Brigadier Eather's 25th Brigade (3rd Battalion, 14th Brigade attached), and Brigadier Lloyd's[2] 16th Brigade. In addition, it was decided in early October that a special force would be raised for the purpose of harassing the Japanese line of communication between Kokoda and Buna. To this end Chaforce was raised, under the command of Lieutenant-Colonel Hugh Challen from the 2/14th Battalion. The members of Chaforce were volunteers from the 21st Brigade. Major Sublet from the

2/16th Battalion was chosen as Challen's second in command and each of the three 21st Brigade battalions supplied a company of officers and other ranks.

The Japanese had decided that spirited, set-piece resistance would not be offered much forward of Templeton's Crossing. They had two very sound reasons for their decision. Firstly, their line of communication had become far too long. Allied bombing of the Wairopi bridge which spanned the Kumusi River and a general air force harassment of their Buna–Kokoda supply line had placed enormous pressure on the maintenance of their troops. Secondly, by withdrawing to Templeton's Crossing, Horii would be able to send significant numbers of his troops back to the beach-head to assist in the construction of defensive positions at his rear, and to ease the supply situation at his front.

A sobering and grim testimony to both the resolute Maroubra Force fighting withdrawal and the Japanese military and moral code awaited the advancing Australians. As the leading Australian troops pushed unopposed through Nauro and on to Menari they found evidence that the Japanese supply line had been near total collapse. The 3rd Battalion found a number of Japanese bodies which bore no sign of death through combat. Evidence of severe dysentery was found. As the advance progressed, contact was made with the local natives. Their story was a tragic one—the Japanese had driven the carriers to the point of death, had beaten them and, when they could go no farther, had executed them. They had interfered with their women and pillaged their gardens for food. The end result of such treatment was that the natives were eager to join Kienzle's carrier lines as a means of retaliation.

Brigade Hill provided a macabre scene. As the advancing troops reached its summit, and the spur which had become known as Mission Ridge, it appeared as if time had stood still. The air was tainted by the smell of death and decay—miasmal evidence of a titanic struggle. There was no evidence here of 'running rabbits' but grim relics of men who had gamely stood their ground against monumental odds, who had not yielded, who had stayed to die. Contorted corpses and skeletons still guarded their weapon-pits or covered the ground of their desperate counter-attacks. Rusted weapons, ammunition and equipment littered the area. To the men of Chaforce came the heart-rending task of laying their comrades to rest and of gathering their personal effects.

It is noteworthy that, finally, a senior army commander had journeyed forth to take charge of the battle and thereby see for himself the terrain and the conditions in which his troops were operating. Major-General Allen was soon to face the problems of supply, and of concentration of force in the almost unique Owen Stanley theatre of war, and, even more importantly, the misinformed and ignorant pressure from superiors that Brigadier Potts had endured during August–September.

As a consequence of the unimpeded progress of the Australian advance prior to Templeton's Crossing, Generals MacArthur and Blamey mistakenly concluded that the enemy were now unable to conduct a spirited defence of the Kokoda Trail and that their numbers were relatively small. From 11–27 October, the Japanese, using well-sited and well-concealed weapon-pits, concentrated firepower and grim determination, ground the Australian advance to two key halts at Templeton's Crossing and Eora Creek. The signals exchanged between Allen, Herring and Blamey bear striking witness to Allen's enormous problems, and the continuing attitude of higher command.

17 October, Allen to Herring:

> Implementation of air-dropping programme causing gravest concern. Under present system it would appear that air force cannot supply planes necessary to assure dropping of 50 000 pounds daily weather permitting. (2) 50 000 pounds daily covers

maintenance only and does not repeat not provide for building
up a reserve. It does however allow for 30 per cent wastage due
to destruction by dropping. Actual daily requirements for
delivery to units etc. for maintenance is 35 000 pounds. (3)
Understood it is intention to build up 21 days' reserve supplies
ammunition etc forward under existing system. This is quite
impossible as supplies etc dropped during first two days of
programme less than 50% of requirements for daily maintenance
only. (4) Unless supply etc. dropping of 50 000 pounds daily
plus additional to build up a reserve is assured complete revision
of plans will have to be made and large proportion of troops
withdrawn to Imita Ridge position . . .

11 October, Blamey to Allen:

Your order definitely to push on with sufficient force and
capture Kokoda. You have been furnished with supplies as you
requested and ample appears to be available. In view lack of
serious opposition your advance appears much too slow. You
will press enemy with vigour. If you are feeling strain personally
relief will be arranged. Please be frank about this.

12 October, Allen to Blamey:

My outline plan . . . is designed to capture Kokoda as soon as
possible. Apparently it has been misunderstood. Nothing is being
left undone in order to carry out your wishes and my brigade
commanders have already been instructed accordingly. The most
serious opposition to rapid advance is terrain. The second is
maintenance of supplies through lack of native carriers. Reserve
supplies have not repeat not been adequate up to the 11th Oct.
Until information of recoveries today am unable to say whether
they are yet adequate. Rate of advance does not entirely depend
on air droppings. Equal in importance is our ability to carry
forward and maintain our advanced troops. Notwithstanding

that men carry with them up to five days' rations maintenance forward of dropping place is still necessary. This country is much tougher than any previous theatre and cannot be appreciated until seen. From all reports the worst is north of Myola. The vigour with which we press the enemy is dependent on the physical endurance of the men and the availability of supplies. Our men have pressed so far with vigour consistent with keeping them fit to fight.

17 October, Blamey to Allen:

General MacArthur considers quote extremely light casualties indicate no serious effort yet made to displace enemy unquote. You will attack enemy with energy and all possible speed at each point of resistance. Essential that Kokoda airfield be taken at earliest. Apparent enemy gaining time by delaying you with inferior strength.

17 October, Allen to Blamey:

25th Bde has been attacking all day and enemy is now counter-attacking. Will advise when situation clarifies. Serious efforts have been made to dispose of enemy and energetic steps have been taken at each point of resistance. This action will continue . . . I respectfully submit that the success of this campaign cannot be judged by casualties alone. Until dropping ground further north is established possibly Alola there is no alternative once Lloyd's brigade is forward but to base Eather on Myola and Efogi North. In short with the carriers available I can only maintain three battalions forward in contact with the enemy . . .

21 October, Blamey to Allen:

During last five days you have made practically no advance against a weaker enemy. Bulk of your forces have been

The 2/27th Battalion R.A.P.—Gona

Lieutenant Bob Dougherty at Gona—K.I.A.
Haddy's Village *Above left:* Private Jack Breakey,
h Battalion *Above centre:* Lieutenant Hugh
39th Battalion *Above right:* Captain Stan
at Gona

A tragic example of the gallantry sacrifice of the 2/14th Battalion *L-R:* Lieutenant Moore, K.I.A. Isurava, Lieutenant H. Bisset K.I.A. Isurava, Captain Nye K.I.A. Brigade Hill, Lieutenant L.F. Mason Wounded 29th September 1942 Lieutenant Treacy K.I.A., Gona. Photo taken just prior to 2/14th climbing Trail August 1942

2/27th Battalion veterans after Gona's fall

2/14th Battalion veterans after Gona's fall

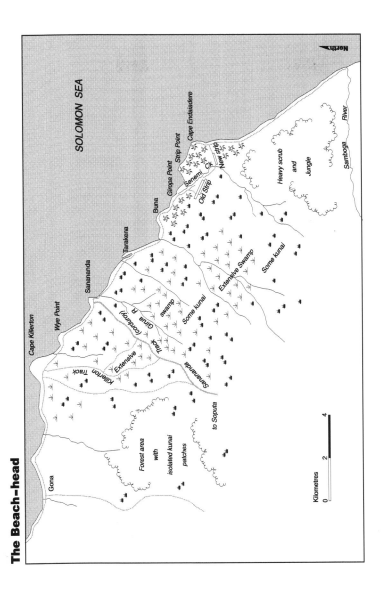

The Beach-head

However, his most important contribution to the campaign had probably been his skilled and tireless raising and deployment of the carrier lines which were so essential to its success. But even the energetic Kienzle had failed to execute one of his July orders—to build a road from Ilolo, outside Port Moresby, over the mountains to Kokoda before the end of August. The road has not yet materialised from its vanished military dreamland.

The reoccupation of Kokoda gave General MacArthur an opportunity to consider his strategic position afresh. Having acquired Kokoda as a forward supply depot and, as a consequence, forced the Japanese towards the Kumusi River, his thoughts naturally concentrated upon his tentative plans for a three-pronged attack on the Gona–Sanananda–Buna beach-head around mid-November. But events at Guadalcanal were still a source of grave concern.

After nearly three months of intense fighting and ever fluctuating fortunes, Guadalcanal still hung precariously in the balance. As Vasey prepared to push on with all haste towards the beach-head, the protracted Guadalcanal battle was about to reach its climax in the early weeks of November.

Why Horii chose to recontest Vasey's advance to the Gona–Sanananda–Buna beach-head at Oivi–Gorari rather than on the eastern side of the Kumusi will always remain a tactical mystery. The Kumusi is a fast-flowing, wide river which he could have used as a natural barrier. By the use of fighting patrols Horii could have significantly hampered the Australian crossing of the river and could have bought valuable time to find a suitable defensive position to the east and deploy his force there.

With the debouchment of his troops from the mountain terrain, Vasey had gained freedom both to concentrate his forces against enemy lines and to move them around enemy positions with a strength, speed and flexibility impossible for Allen to achieve in the confines of the Owen Stanleys.

An encircling onslaught between Oivi and a position east of Gorari killed approximately 600 and ensured that no effective opposition could be offered by the enemy between the Kumusi River and the beach-head defences. The chaotic crossing of the Kumusi swelled their losses, many fugitives being overwhelmed in the turbulent waters that swept their rafts away. Their most notable casualty was Major-General Horii himself.

With ample justification, the Allied high command and the Australian Army gave high commendation by way of publicity and awards to the men of the 25th and 16th Brigades. This was thoroughly deserved; their fighting prowess was formidable, the conditions under which they fought were arduous and their achievements were indeed great. However the statistics of the Owen Stanley Campaign[3] provide some stark reminders of the desperate travail of Maroubra Force, enhancing an appreciation of the sheer magnitude of its achievements. The battle casualties of 21st Brigade on the Kokoda Trail were higher than those of either of the other two AIF brigades to cross the mountains. When it is remembered that the 2/27th Battalion casualties were sustained within a few days at Brigade Hill, the extent of sacrifice of the 2/14th and 2/16th Battalion becomes clearer. Further, the 2/14th Battalion suffered losses quite markedly higher than those of any other battalion involved in the campaign—strong testimony to the terrible toll taken of its unflinching courage, particularly in the inferno of Isurava. Such statistics are at great variance with the publicity conceded to Maroubra Force, and they prompt an accusatory questioning of the removal of the brave Potts and the shame of Koitaki. Glory may be in the hand of the bestower, but the harder battle is surely the one against the greater odds.

Pressing on from the Kumusi, Vasey's 25th and 16th Brigades prepared themselves for the conquest of the Gona–Sanananda–Buna beach-heads. Allied intelligence estimated that the enemy were few in number and poor in physical condition. The beach-head appeared to lie ripe for the military plucking; the Japanese tiger was cornered in three positions on the coast. By an ironic twist of fate the relief of the 25th Brigade and the reduction of one of those three bastions were to fall to the 21st Brigade, with the 39th Battalion coming under command once more.

In the high passes of the mountains those two Maroubra Force partners had forged a confident trust in each other's soldierly qualities—qualities to be sternly retested along the stark shores and the stagnant swamps that set the stage for the resumption of their battle-brotherhood. To this day, when intensity and savagery of fighting are recalled by their survivors, one name rings clear—Gona!

15

Not to reason why

Prior to the Japanese landings in July 1942, Gona had the reputation of being perhaps the most picturesque location on the north-eastern coast of New Guinea.

> Overlooking a sweep of black beach sand and the blue waters of the Solomon Sea was a handsome church of grey woven sago-leaf; behind it the well kept Mission House with a red tin roof that acted as a catchment for rainwater. A pretty schoolhouse with reedy walls of sago-stalk stood near a green cricket field. Yellow crotons and red hibiscus bordered the path; palms and tall trees shaded the grounds.[1]

When Major-General Horii received his order to stage a fighting withdrawal back to the Gona–Sanananda–Buna beach-head, the Japanese troops stationed at Gona had nearly two months in which to prepare their defences. The ground at Gona had some features of paramount importance.

Approximately 100 yards to the west of the mission lay Gona Creek; a belt of coconut palms interspersed with banyan trees ran from the creek approximately three-quarters of a mile eastwards to a small creek, (called Small Creek by the Australians) and thence towards Sanananda. The ground around the mission was dominated by two significant areas of jungle and scrub—significant because these could provide the necessary covered approaches to the inner defences which might enable a determined and skilful attacker to breach them. The smaller had on its west the defended Gona Creek bank, on its south a bare killing field that no sensible attacker would contemplate crossing and on its east the track running north into the mission; practically, it was accessible for an attacker only across that track. The larger lay to the east of the track; it was too extensive for the maintenance of defensive works to prevent access to it but the final exploitation of such access was barred by a network of defensive posts and some tidal swamps closer in to the south-east and south of the mission, linking with the defences of the smaller area west of the track.

During the weeks preceding the battle for Gona, the Japanese toiled long and hard on a fire plan that transformed the area into a highly detailed and cohesive deathtrap for the unsuspecting Australian troops. They sited their defensive positions in three very distinct areas. Using Gona Creek as a natural barrier, the first consisted of numerous machine-gun posts stretching from the mouth of the creek approximately 150 yards along its east bank and eastwards, dispersed through the coconut palm belt along the coast towards the easterly Small Creek. Among these posts were slit trenches and, to the north of the mission, a shallow trench system. The second position formed a semicircle around the south-eastern and eastern sides of the mission. A series of slit trenches often filled with water lay scattered in and around the mission. The last of the positions spanned an area from the creek running approximately 100 yards due east to the main track running into the mission.

All three defensive positions had a number of distinct attributes which bore great testimony to the Japanese skill and defensive foresight in the design and construction of their fire plan.

The first was a masterly use of the existing ground. The thick coconut belt along the coast provided almost perfect positions for numerous snipers. Strapped high up in these palms Japanese snipers caused many Australian casualties, often showing particular interest in Bren gunners. At the base of the very tall banyan trees, the Japanese dug shallow pits around the large protruding roots which offered natural cover and camouflage. Owing to the close proximity of the village area to the coast only very shallow slit trenches could be dug before water was encountered. As a consequence, the Japanese machine-gun posts were raised a few feet above the slit trenches by the use of coconut logs. These logs were concealed by dirt and vegetation and were nearly always roofed. Between the logs were firing openings—each post was manned by machine-gunners who were usually supported by riflemen. The heavy coconut-log and sandbag walls and roofs made these posts almost impervious to machine-gun fire, grenade burst and artillery bombardment. Only direct hits from aerial bombs or point–blank artillery shells were capable of their outright destruction.

As a means of providing mutual fire support and a substantial killing ground, the Japanese burnt any kunai grass patches in front of their three defensive positions to a depth of up to 50 yards. The really vital aspect of the defence of the three positions and of many individual posts within them was the maximum use of enfilading fire. Captain Bidstrup MC, 39th Battalion:

> Machine-guns have an arc of fire. They're usually set up on what we call a fixed line; they can be fired within an arc. A fire plan is made so that all of the machine-guns have an arc of fire which crosses other arcs of fire. That is known as enfilading fire. You fire across the front, not at it.[2]

Hence any force committed to a storming of the Japanese positions might have to cross 50 yards of open ground whilst being subjected to an enormous intensity of enfilading fire from meticulously concealed posts.

The Gona beach-head was under the command of Lieutenant-Colonel Tomita. To man his defences he had elements of the 41st and 144th Regiments as well as base personnel who had been in the area since July. There is no record of the exact number of his troops. However some 680 were buried after the concluding battle, many wounded may have been evacuated by barge in late November and a significant proportion of the garrison—probably most of the remaining able-bodied—achieved a break out on the night of 8–9 December. An estimate of the number of Japanese defenders of Gona as somewhere between 800–1000 might seem a conservative one.

In order to effect a successful reduction of an enemy stronghold during the Second World War, it was generally considered that the attacking force needed a troop superiority of approximately three to one in combination with strong and effective fire support. When this requirement is borne in mind in relation to the numerical strength of the Japanese, particularly with their extremely lethal fire plan, Gona was always going to be an extremely difficult military nut to crack.

Generals MacArthur and Blamey based their assessments of the enemy strength upon characteristically inept and inaccurate G-2 American intelligence.

Blamey to Shedden   ALF. SWPA. Adv. HQ
                                                     14th November 1942
Letter   Most Secret
I think the very stiff fighting is over unless the Japanese succeed
in landing forces in the next week. We expect to begin our
advance on Monday morning and in a few days to sweep
through to Buna and Gona. The Australian troops have defeated
the bulk of the enemy forces, I believe, in the area between

Kokoda and the Kumusi River. The fighting has been stiffer than any we have been called to carry out yet. In the jungle area near Gorari the enemy left no less than 500 dead. A pleasing feature is that in spite of the closeness of the fighting, our casualties are very much less than the enemy's and our men are definitely superior to them in jungle fighting.[3]

It is obvious that Blamey had not yet fully acquainted himself with the horrendous battles at Isurava and Brigade Hill.

The final reduction of the Gona–Sanananda–Buna beach-head was planned as a three-pronged assault. The Australians under the command of Major-General Vasey, were given the task of capturing Gona and Sanananda. To this end Vasey instructed Brigadier Eather and his 25th Brigade and 3rd Battalion to capture Gona, while Brigadier Lloyd and his 16th Brigade were ordered to capture Sanananda. The capture of Buna was entrusted to the Americans. Whilst Vasey's force had been engaged in pushing the Japanese back over the Kokoda Trail and then to the Kumusi River, the Americans had concentrated their 32nd Division outside of Buna. This had been accomplished by a combination of airlifting, barge transport and an overland crossing.

By employing his two-pronged tactic, Vasey greatly impaired his potential to concentrate his force against either of his two objectives. It must be conceded that he unwittingly acted upon very poor Allied intelligence estimates of his enemy's strengths at those two objectives. However, it is important to record that the wastage of his force due to casualties and sickness had caused grave concern. Immediately prior to his crossing the Kumusi, Vasey's force had lost 53 officers and 900 other ranks as battle casualties in addition to a very substantial evacuation of the sick. The 2/1st Battalion of the 16th Brigade is an example in point: after leaving Port Moresby with 608 men all ranks, it had crossed the Kumusi with 355.[4]

Thus, the very concentration of force that had brought such striking success at Oivi–Gorari was to be abandoned, with a greatly weakened force before a beach-head where the ground forbade easy manoeuvre and where an enemy well sited, dug in and concealed and, above all, with his back to the sea, was determined to stand and fight—fight if need be to the last man. Therefore, before the Australians had even reached Gona, they had fallen foul of one of the prime principles of war—concentration of force. In addition, their estimate of the enemy strength was 270–280 men on 27 November,[5] some 600–700 desperate Japanese defenders short in their calculations. The penalty for the failure of the Australians to concentrate their forces and for the shortcomings of American G-2 intelligence was to be a very tragic one indeed. And subsequent grave tactical errors were to compound the difficulties of this potentially disastrous predicament.

It is not the purpose of this work to examine in detail the role of the 25th Brigade at Gona. However a number of points are worthy of notice.

On 20 November, Brigadier Eather had two of his battalions on the outskirts of Gona. Both battalions were pinned down on the edge of the cleared ground in front of the Japanese positions. Any movement by the Australians from the scrub or kunai grass across this ground was met with extremely intense Japanese machine-gun and small-arms fire. Well-concealed snipers also took a heavy toll of any forward movement.

Between 21–26 November, 25th Brigade made a number of attacks from the south and south-east. In addition, Eather positioned Lieutenant Haddy's Chaforce Company to the west of Gona Creek with the role of harassing the enemy from that flank and also of providing a standing patrol to the west of Gona to block any attempt by the Japanese to bolster their strength from that direction. A disturbing feature of the attacks from both the south and the south-east is that apparently there was a lack of adequate preliminary reconnaissance—a rare military phenomenon especially when it is remembered that the brigade and its commander were experienced and thus well versed in standard military procedure. This curious lack of reconnaissance and planning was to recur with the arrival and subsequent deployment of the 21st Brigade. In addition, the direction of these attacks was to be under almost constant change, without there having been any real concentration of force at a perceived point of vulnerability. The resulting casualties were extremely alarming, particularly when it is recalled that 25th Brigade had arrived at Gona very seriously depleted in strength. In fact the term 'brigade' is misleading when applied to 25th Brigade and the soon to arrive 21st Brigade. At no time during the attacks at Gona was either of these formations at any more than one-third brigade strength.

On 24 November Eather found that his brigade numbered approximately 900 men, including 180 men of the 3rd Battalion attached to his force. However the Japanese were not the Australians' only enemy; there were two others. The numerous swamps and intense heat along the coastal lowland region provided a near-perfect breeding ground for the dreaded anopheles mosquito, the malaria carrier. Compounding the weakened state of the troops, malaria became rampant amongst them and the resulting casualty rate was high. Scrub typhus, whilst not as prevalent as malaria, had an extremely high mortality rate. The predominant symptom of scrub typhus was a raging fever which, unlike the cold sweats and high fever of malaria, did not subside until the patient was either dead or cured. Captain Ken Murdoch, Staff Captain, 21st Brigade at Gona:

> Now, everybody was tired at Gona; everybody was sick at Gona! It was a point of honour there that your temperature had to be over 102 before you went back. If it was 102 and under you just stayed in and pushed yourself.[6]

By 26 November, Eather could do no more than contain his enemy within an area of approximately 300 yards square, in addition to employing a mortar and patrol program. That apparent stalemate at Gona was the cause of grave higher command concern, not merely about the lack of success but about the unexpected loss of time with scant achievement and the mounting of casualties without victory. As a result, it was decided to emplane the 21st Brigade to Popondetta and, in a revision of the tactical situation, determine whether to move it westwards from Soputa for the capture of Gona, or to commit it northwards to assist in attacks on Sanananda whilst using the 25th Brigade to contain Gona. Major-General Sir Ivan Dougherty CBE, DSO, ED:

On the morning of 25th Nov. I moved to Popondetta by plane, and thence by jeep to Div. HQ at Soputa where I met General Vasey there late in the morning . . .

He told me what the situation was at that time. 25th Aust. Inf. Bde, depleted and suffering from malaria and fatigue was in contact with Jap. forces holding Gona Mission area . . .

16th Aust. Inf. Bde, with some Americans of 126th Regt. U.S. 32nd Div, were astride the Sanananda Road about 3.5 miles north of Soputa. 16th Aust. Inf. Bde, also depleted in strength and suffering from malaria and fatigue, was unable to make further progress. Two companies of the Americans were then attempting to do an encircling move, but their whereabouts in the jungle were not known, beyond the fact that someone had an idea they were out on the left flank and getting in behind the Japs . . .

On the Buna side 32 U.S. Div. less detachments on Sanananda Road were unable to make progress. General Vasey told me that he was considering using 21st Aust. Inf. Bde to capture Sanananda by means of a wide encircling move— moving first via Jumbora to rear of 25th Aust. Inf. Bde, thence diagonally towards the coast about Basabua or Garara, and thence to Sanananda . . .

As an alternative means of using us, the General was considering our capturing Gona Mission Area, supported by 25th Aust. Inf. Bde.

As it would be some time before my Brigade had finished its move, he suggested that I remain at his HQ until the following morning, and then that I move to Gona to meet Brigadier Eather. He wished me to discuss the two alternatives with Brigadier Eather, and then advise him of what I thought best, when he would give me his decision.[7]

After an extremely taxing march from Soputa to Jumbora and then on to Gona, Dougherty arrived at Eather's headquarters on the afternoon of 26 November 1942. During this journey Dougherty contemplated the existing tactical situation.

. . . Gona was held up and 25th Brigade was exhausted. Vasey at one stage thought of going across to get Sanananda. I felt 'Well if we do that, we're likely to start a fourth situation if we run into enemy positions which are too strong for us to knock over.' . . . So I did say to him that I thought it was a better thing to finalise one of them straight away.[8]

Eather concurred. After Dougherty informed Vasey of his and Eather's assessment it was decided that the 21st Brigade would be used to eliminate the Japanese at Gona before moving on to Sanananda. This was an astute decision and one which would have facilitated Gona's much earlier fall had normal military procedure been followed. The events of 27–28 November are well worth examining in detail.

The 2/14th Battalion was the first of Dougherty's battalions to arrive at Gona. It emplaned at Port Moresby on 25 November and arrived at Gona on the 28th. Grievously under-manned after its losses in the Owen Stanley Campaign and the supplying of its Chaforce contingent, Lieutenant-Colonel Challen's command consisted of nineteen officers and 322 other ranks organised into three understrength rifle companies. Lieutenant-Colonel Cooper's 2/27th Battalion was the second to arrive. For the same reasons as applied to the 2/14th, it too was grossly understrength. Its 22 officers and 301 other ranks likewise supplied three scratch companies. The 2/27th emplaned for Popondetta on 26–27 November and did not arrive at Gona until late on the 28th. The 2/16th mustered only two companies from its 22 officers and 256 other ranks. The three battalions of 21st Brigade thus numbered 63 officers and 874 other ranks—approximately the strength of one battalion.

The 21st Brigade's first Gona attack was tentatively ordered by Vasey for 29 November. Dougherty concluded that as, at the most, only two of his battalions could arrive, march weary, inadequately prepared and barely in time for an attack on the 29th, it should be postponed until the 30th. Major-General Sir Ivan Dougherty DSO, CBE, ED:

> I told General Vasey that I thought the attack should be postponed till 30th, and he agreed with me. He left me intending to discuss the matter with higher authority and make strong representations for the postponement. He was to ring me when a decision had been made. At 0700 hrs on the 28th of November he rang me to tell me that in view of certain information that higher command possessed, the attack on Gona must take place on the 29th. I had an idea that this information had something to do with the Japanese attempts to reinforce their Gona–Buna troops.[9]

The obvious implication was that higher command, namely New Guinea Force Headquarters and more particularly General Headquarters, South-West Pacific Area, feared that the Japanese were going to reinforce Gona or make a landing to the west of it. But this intelligence was not actually cited.

There are a number of key points worthy of consideration regarding the potential reinforcement by the Japanese of their

Gona–Sanananda–Buna beach-head. Firstly, in late November, the battle at Guadalcanal was still raging with neither side having a really decisive edge. However Henderson Field still lay securely in American hands allowing the Americans to receive supplies and conduct land-based air force operations. As long as the airfield was held by the Americans their troops could fight on. In addition, the Japanese were losing significant numbers of ships, aircraft and reinforcement troops in their efforts to capture Guadalcanal. Strategically, the Japanese were bound to eliminate the Guadalcanal threat to their prime base at Rabaul before being in any condition to renew a major New Guinea thrust. Secondly, the Allies were able to bring to bear very concentrated air force harassment of any Japanese attempts at reinforcement of Gona–Sanananda–Buna. Thirdly, on the three occasions that the Japanese did send reinforcements of approximately two battalions towards the beach-head by destroyer,[10] they had limited success.

The four destroyers that left Rabaul on 27 November were turned back by Allied aircraft on that same day, with two of their number damaged. The force that departed on 28 November was attacked by Allied aircraft on or around the 30th and managed to land only 500 reinforcements at the mouth of the Kumusi River on 2 December. The third attempt was not to be undertaken until the 7th. In summary, while the Japanese desperately wanted to hold the beach-head pending a Guadalcanal victory, they could not reinforce Gona in any real offensive strength and, importantly, on 29 November, (the date fixed for the 21st Brigade attack) they were quite some days away from hoping to accomplish this. Captain S.Y. Bisset MC, 2/14th Battalion:

> Although it is said that the Jap was attempting to reinforce the Gona and Buna garrison with fresh troops from Rabaul and in fact did land 500 N/W of Gona, our aircraft and sea supremacy had made this virtually impossible. If the frontal attacks had

been delayed one or two weeks, the Japs would have been
starved and beaten out with minimum casualties.[11]

Major J. M. Hearman, 2/16th Battalion:

> The question of reinforcements for the Japs was not a factor in
> my mind at Gona. Obviously had the Japs been capable of
> reinforcing from the sea, Buna would have been his objective.
> The Japs in Gona had to be dealt with. They could have been
> starved out. However from the viewpoint of Allied morale and
> the need for the Australian Government to be able to claim a
> clear cut success, the operation at Gona provided the vehicle so
> badly needed.[12]

It is extremely difficult to contemplate an enemy's attempting
to land a force on or near an area held by only approximately
1000 of its number and confined to some 300 by 300 yards
of ground, when it did not have air and sea supremacy. The
far larger Buna beach-head was always the likely point of
reinforcement. Further, if Major-General Vasey had been
genuinely concerned at the prospect of an impending Japanese
reinforcement of Gona, he would not have contemplated
leaving Eather's debilitated force to contain it while despatch-
ing his fresh 21st Brigade force to Sanananda on 27 November, nor would he have considered it again on 1 December.

But the really astonishing feature of the hurried Gona
attacks by the 21st Brigade was that, irrespective of the limited
likelihood of Japanese reinforcement of the beach-head,
normal, prudent military procedure was abandoned by the
higher command. Indeed, an apprehended build-up of the
defence against an undermanned Australian attack was all the
more reason for a studied, deliberate appraisal of the ground
and the enemy strength and dispositions, in order to adhere to
a vital principle of war—economy of force. Captain H. J.
Katekar, Adjutant, 2/27th Battalion:

All those involved at command and staff level in a normal properly conducted operation, first of all have an appreciation of the situation; from the enemy's point of view and our own troops' point of view. That wasn't done at Gona. We were thrown in with scant information about the enemy; no aerial photographs, nothing to go on. I don't recall ever seeing a proper plan of the area showing where 25th Brigade was at that time when we were supposed to go in, or in fact, what the 2/14th were doing on our right. The whole of the thing was rushed and therefore one can expect there to be what actually transpired—a slaughter of good men! The correct way to get the information was to send in recce patrols. That's always the way you do it, because you get the enemy to disclose where he is. You don't go in with a full company rushing in against something that you know nothing about.[13]

Lieutenant-Colonel Ralph Honner DSO, MC:

And after the campaign was over of course, we were shown the aerial photographs which had been taken months before, and presumably put up on someone's wall as decorations when they would have been of invaluable assistance to us.[14]

Having been denied his request for time for the complete 21st Brigade to fully arrive and reconnoitre the ground, Dougherty prepared to push his initial Gona attack in on 29 November along the coast, using Small Creek approximately 1250 yards to the east as his starting point. By securing the ground on either side of Small Creek to a depth of approximately 150 yards, he expected that he would be able to establish a suitable start-line for his first attack to the west and also fend off any possible Japanese attempts to reinforce Gona from Sanananda.

By the morning of 28 November, when Dougherty was told that he must attack on the following day, the only one of his battalions to have arrived in the Gona area was the 2/14th.

He ordered Challen to move it slightly north of 25th Brigade Headquarters and then, leaving the track, proceed north-east towards Small Creek. The 2/14th was to concentrate or 'lie up' at a position (Point Y) approximately 400 yards south-east of Small Creek and then secure a start-line (Point X) for the attack on Gona just west of Small Creek. This movement was ordered for 28 November, to facilitate the attack on the following day. Lieutenant Kolb[15] was sent early on the morning of the 28th to reconnoitre the ground approximately a half mile to the east of Small Creek. The ordering of this patrol would have been a reaction by Dougherty to a suspicion of an intent by the Japanese to reinforce their Gona troops from Sanananda.

> During the 28th of November 25th Aust. Inf. Bde. reported that both sides of this small creek to a distance of 150 yards had been found by their patrols to be free of enemy. At 0930 I ordered the 2/14th Aust. Inf. Bn. to move past their previously arranged assembly position using the cover of the jungle along the edge of the kunai and to occupy the area on both sides of small creek.[16]

However, instead of using the scrub as cover for his movement to Point Y, Challen journeyed through the kunai patch.[17] It will always remain a matter of debate as to whether or not the Japanese were alerted to the 2/14th movement towards the Small Creek area by this mistake.

After arriving in the timber just south of Point Y, Challen sent a patrol under Lieutenant Dougherty[18] to occupy Point X and send back a guide for the remainder of the battalion. Owing to the paucity of information offered by the maps and to the featureless monotony of the terrain, Dougherty's patrol moved much too far to the east—and by late afternoon Challen had heard no word from it. Nevertheless, as he had received the news that a 25th Brigade patrol had reported the

Small Creek area free of the enemy, he proceeded to resume the move of the battalion towards it. The journey was a trying one, winding through jungle for the first 300 yards and, for the last 200–300, wading across a waist-deep sago swamp of the type common along that steamy coast. The sago palms, with large prickly prongs protruding from their trunks, reared up fifteen to twenty feet above slimy foul-smelling waters rising with the tide sometimes to shoulder height—delaying and perilous military obstacles.

After moving in single file through the swamp, Captain McGavin's B Company, acting as advance guard, reached the beach just to the east of Small Creek, approaching dusk. Its forward scouts encountered a small number of Japanese on the beach and B Company attacked. Captain Bisset remembers the action well:

> I was acting as adjutant to Challen, and it was on the late afternoon and night that the disastrous attack was made by our troops on orders from Brigade. No proper recce of the Jap positions had been made and at dusk moving at times through waist deep swamp, the attack was made through light scrub and tree cover into the well sited enemy positions, no-one knowing their exact whereabouts. Our troops were caught in enfilade fire from several bunkers and in the dark it was impossible to locate them. We lost six of our best officers and forty other ranks in this abortive and ill-conceived attack. It became necessary to withdraw and try to extricate our wounded.[19]

In efforts to locate and move round the Japanese flanks, the battalion lost more valuable men; a striking feature of the whole action was the high proportion of officers and NCOs who were either killed or wounded. Fierce and gallant frontal attacks were of little or no avail against the well-concealed and well-sited Japanese positions and their enfilade fire. Late on the night of 28 November, the 2/14th thus found itself in a very confused and worrying predicament. Its dead and wounded littered the ground in front of the Japanese positions and any movement in the darkness towards the recovery of the wounded was met with a hail of Japanese fire.

Sergeant Coy, who had been with Captain McGavin at the time of his death, had shot the sniper responsible and silenced two machine-gun posts with grenades. He then struggled to get two of his wounded to safety. Whilst taking orders for withdrawal from Captain Bisset to Lieutenant Evans, he was severely wounded, but would not allow his wounds to be dressed until he had reported back to Bisset the success of his mission.

Bisset, with the determined help of Lieutenant Clarke,[20] who had been wounded, rallied the men, collected the wounded under fire and, aided by Private Boys,[21] a signaller, guided the wounded to a signal cable which provided a lifeline back through the bog-ridden ground to the Regimental Aid Post.

By the early hours of the 29th the surviving attackers had withdrawn to Point Y after passing through a blocking position commanded by Captain Russell.

The events of the preceding day are noteworthy for a number of reasons. Dudley McCarthy writes:

Whether the 25th Brigade patrol, and one from the 2/14th itself which had broken out on the beach in the morning about half a mile east of 'Point X', had missed picking up occupied positions in which the Japanese were lying doggo by day, or whether the Japanese had been alarmed by the presence of the patrols and reacted by occupying the 'Point X' area, is uncertain. The former was probably the case. (Lieutenant Dougherty might have supplied additional information but he and his men had swung much too far to the east and emerged towards Basabua where they surprised and killed approximately twenty Japanese. Runners with this news had missed the battalion and reached brigade headquarters about 7.15 p.m., but the patrol itself did not arrive back until the 30th).[22]

The maps in the official report of operations by the 21st Brigade portray a radically different story.[23] The fact is that the 25th Brigade patrols did not venture to Small Creek at all, but instead patrolled to within approximately 300 yards of it. At that range it is little wonder that those patrols, faced with the screening vegetation of the coastal belt and the superb concealment within it of the Japanese positions, discovered no enemy in occupation of the area. Further, the 2/14th patrol mentioned (commanded by Lieutenant Kolb) had orders not to reconnoitre the Point X area directly but to swing round it wide to the east and examine the ground around Banumi. His patrol therefore came no closer to Point X than half a mile away. Thus, he also was much too far away to provide worthwhile information relevant to the 2/14th occupation of its Point X start-line for the proposed attack on 29 November. Thus any really worthwhile reconnaissance of the Point X position was always going to be derived from Lieutenant Dougherty's 2/14th patrol on the afternoon of the 28th. But due to an error in navigation, Dougherty emerged at far-off Basabua. The end result was that the 2/14th attacked over totally unreconnoitred ground and was cruelly decimated (particularly its officers) on the day before its scheduled attack. It is also worth remembering that the very same maps mentioned in the Dougherty Report bore an estimate of the Japanese strength at Gona, as 270–280. The estimate was identified as a 7th Division estimate.

The events of 28 November provided a prime example of tragic disaster resulting from the abandonment of established prudent military procedure because of the kind of higher command interference that was to characterise the battle of Gona. Both Dougherty and Vasey had urgently requested a delay of one day before attacking. Because of the refusal by New Guinea Force Headquarters of their requests, no adequate reconnaissance of the ground or of enemy positions was undertaken; no check was made on grossly inaccurate intelligence as to enemy strength; no proper appreciation of the situation was possible and, thus, there was no basis for planning an attack with much prospect of success. It was to have been an attack of the blind but it was crippled before ever reaching its unseen start-line. In a night of courage and carnage the 2/14th lost about 10 per cent of its strength in battle casualties—including 32 per cent of its officers. The Gona slaughter was in full spate.

The failure of the 2/14th to secure its Point X start-line on the evening of the 28th forced Brigadier Dougherty to revise his plan of attack for the morning of the 29th, the timely arrival of the 2/27th giving him wider scope:

> 2/14th Aust. Inf. Battalion to destroy enemy east of small creek while bombing of Gona Mission area was progressing the following morning. All mortar fire available was allotted to 2/14th Aust. Inf. Bn. 2/27th Aust. Inf. Bn to capture Gona Mission area, their action to have two phases.[24]

The first phase of the 2/27th Battalion attack was to be the securing of a start-line near Point X, slightly to the west of Small Creek. Lieutenant-Colonel Cooper's men were ordered to pass through a 2/31st Battalion, 25th Brigade, standing patrol, just south of the creek, on an approach route to their start-line. The gaining of the start-line was timed for 11 am to coincide with a bombing program and simultaneous artillery support.

With the start-line secured, phase two of the 2/27th attack was to commence with the release of two parachute flares from the last bombing plane. Major Hanson,[25] the forward observation officer (FOO) for the artillery, was ordered to meet Cooper at the start-line. Hanson was to arrive at the start-line with the help of a guide. His subsequent role was to direct the artillery fire to assist the 2/27th Battalion's advance to Gona Mission. The bombing program was more specific.

The target area was to be a rectangle, bordered by the sea in the north, Gona Creek on the west, and extending east from Gona Creek 400 yards and inland 250 yards. 0930–0950—12 fighters each dropping a 300lb bomb. 0930–1015—3 A20s drop parachute bombs and give machine gun fire. 1000–1100—6 B17s each eight (8) 500lb bombs. 1055–1111—3 A20s bomb and machine gun fire.[26]

Thus, while Dougherty's coordination of air support with his advancing ground force was well enough devised, the quality and, more importantly, the quantity of his divisional artillery support was almost unbelievably threadbare. Approximately 70 bombs in an area 250 yards by 400 yards against roofed weapon-pits and natural overhead vegetation cover can best be described as only thin. Lieutenant-Colonel Cooper's reaction is understandable:

But you might as well throw twenty large bricks into a football crowd. 'Big air attack laid on in preparation', Well it doesn't mean a damn thing down there on the ground, where it's not killing anything . . . and you just can't win the battle that way![27]

The 2/27th began its move at 10 am and at 11 am it reached its start-line as planned. But much else went wrong. Dudley McCarthy writes:

But delay followed a guide's error which caused Major Hanson, the artillery officer, to miss his rendezvous with Colonel Cooper. Instead of pushing ahead in spite of this, Cooper delayed, looking for Hanson. Thus the original timings were thrown out and it was not until about midday that the battalion, having made the beach without opposition, swung west against the waiting Japanese who had had time to recover in large measure from the effects of the perfectly executed air strike which had taken place on schedule.[28]

Lieutenant-Colonel Cooper:

> That's a pure invention! We kept on moving forward as fast as
> we could. That can happen in that country; it's not unlikely.
> Guides and people can get lost often.[29]

The real issue is quite clear. Forced to pursue an attack that he
did not want to initiate without the proper reconnaissance,
Dougherty had planned his westward thrust against Gona
from Small Creek. Inadequate knowledge of the ground and
of the enemy's positions and strength combined with insufficient patrol information on 28 November had cost the 2/14th
Battalion heavy casualties. The whole tragic process was to
recur. Despite the 'perfectly executed' bombing of the enemy
area, the 29th was to be a day of duplication of the slaughter
of the preceding evening.

For his advance westwards, Cooper gave the task of
pushing to the coast and then to the west along the beach to
Captain Cuming's[30] company of three officers and 77 other
ranks; Captain Sims and his three subalterns and 77 men were
to move through the coconut belt. They quickly met opposition and the more exposed right company swung around to
the left for better cover through which to press the attack.
Soon after midday both Sims's company, still pushing along
the coconut belt, and Cuming's company, moving through the
fringe of the kunai, were pinned down by intensive fire. A
gruelling three hours' shifting fire-fight ensued until Cuming's
company, 75 yards in advance, stormed north across Sims's
front to a stronghold near the water's edge where the Japanese
were dug in amongst the spreading and protruding roots of
banyan trees.

A withering fire mowed the attackers down as they charged
over open ground to their objective. Cuming, seizing a Bren
and followed by his second in command, Captain Skipper,[31]
plunged ahead into a tunnelled post where their bodies were

later to be discovered ringed by enemy dead. Their other two officers, Lieutenants Caddy and Bennie, were both wounded, Bennie mortally; and, badly cut about, the company had to withdraw to cover to avoid further losses.

Sims's company had also been heavily engaged and he had lost his three lieutenants, Flight killed and Johns and Sherwin wounded. During their fruitless actions the two companies had lost seven of their eight officers (four killed) and 48 men (fifteen killed).[32]

Great difficulty and danger were involved in evacuating the wounded. Japanese snipers took constant toll of any movement by the wounded or stretcher-bearers where there was no concealing cover. Corporal Gordon Smallacombe, a stretcher-bearer, was awarded a Military Medal for his many unselfish, heroic acts. Sergeant Paul Robertson, who had performed courageously in the Owen Stanley Campaign, sacrificed his life when he tried to rescue Corporal Henderson, who later died.

While the 2/27th had been engaged in its attack westwards from Small Creek on the 29th, the 2/14th had been clearing the Japanese from the area to its east. Supported by brigade mortar fire, the 2/14th moved around wide to the east and cut through to the beach just east of Banumi. A standing patrol from C Company was deployed there to resist any future Japanese movement towards the Australians' Gona right flank. Over the succeeding few days that patrol repulsed a number of Japanese incursions from the east without sustaining any casualties. After establishment of the standing patrol, the remainder of the 2/14th began its move west towards Small Creek. Finding Banumi unoccupied, the men of B Company, under the command of Lieutenant Evans, pushed forward until upon coming out of the scrub near the creek, they were met with heavy fire from concealed posts.

At that point Challen brought his mortar fire to bear upon the enemy locations and thrust his A Company, under command of Captain Treacy, through his B Company. This attack was no half-hearted affair. Captain Treacy himself, that stalwart officer who had shown all of his abundant, grim determination after being cut off near Alola during the Owen Stanley Campaign in August, gamely directed his men forward to within 30 yards of the enemy. His splendid physique, which he continually exposed to the enemy, provided an all too easy target and an enemy sniper claimed the life of one of the 2/14th's most revered sons. Responding to Treacy's leadership, Privates Valli[33] and Thompson[34] stormed the Japanese positions with Bren guns blazing and obliterated two of them before being killed by snipers.

A second attack was put in later in the afternoon with similar results. Lieutenant Kolb was killed leading a bayonet charge and, despite the desperate aggression of the troops, many brave veterans of Syria and the Owen Stanleys were tragically mown down. By the close of the day, the 2/14th had withdrawn east of Banumi. On 29 November, the 2/14th losses amounted to two officers, two NCOs and nine privates killed or died of wounds, and one officer, six NCOs and sixteen privates wounded.

> For the 30th November I decided that I would concentrate the supporting fire available on 2/27th Aust. Inf. Bn. front, and so for the first part of the day gave the artillery and mortars to Colonel Cooper to support an attack by him. Owing to his low numbers I gave him one company of the 2/16th Aust. Inf. Bn. He was to liaise with, and cooperate with, Colonel Cameron of 3rd Aust. Inf. Bn who was on his left.[35]

Lieutenant-Colonel Caro and his 2/16th Battalion had arrived at Gona on the 29th. Besides requiring him to bolster Cooper's men, Dougherty gave Caro the roles of protecting Brigade Headquarters and of providing a patrol block between the 2/14th on the east and the 2/27th on the west, to stop any movement from east towards the rear of the 2/27th.

In Cooper's dawn attack on 30 November, Captain Gill's fresh D Company pushed ahead of the positions secured by the depleted A and C Companies at the end of the previous day. But heavy fire began to mow down the leading company and the other two, moving to support it, were also checked, still 80–100 yards short of the enemy. Sergeant Roy Thredgold was involved in D Company's attack:

> We got within about a half a mile of Gona. And the crack, crack, cracks are coming out of the coconut palms. So we'd spread. We could see the beach away at about a hundred yards. If you didn't keep your head down a sniper would just pick you off. Now after we'd got to the edge of the kunai grass, we've got no alternative but to go over this stubble paddock . . . and the snipers are banging like hell, and the pillboxes are banging shit out of us; bullets going round our heads. We made about fifty yards, and jokers were going down like bloody rabbits, getting killed! So we ended up going back to where we bloody well started.[36]

Private Bert Ward was a Bren gunner in Gill's company. Attacking across open ground, Bren gunners were high priority Japanese targets. Ward has vivid memories of that day:

> It's one of those factors! Do you call it a premonition or what? But for the first and only time from the time I joined the army, I thought that morning that this was going to be it; that I was finished. Now that's the first and only time that I knew I was going to be hit. I didn't know when, I didn't know where. But I was convinced; I was a Bren-gunner and afterwards I found out that every original Bren-gunner in the Battalion was eventually hit![37]

Private Ward was destined to be no exception. After being hit in the head he was evacuated on the 2/27th Battalion's second day of the Gona battle. Officers also were still at special risk; Captain Gill and Lieutenant McDonald of D Company were both wounded, and Captain Best, A Company, was killed leading bayonet charges against enemy strong-posts, whilst farther to the rear Assistant-Adjutant, Lieutenant Pickering, was killed and the wireless operator, Corporal Burns, MM, was wounded by a sniper.

30 November had cost the battalion a further four officers and 42 other ranks for meagre gains. The problem was the same one that had dominated events on the two preceding days: frontal attacks over open ground against well-concealed and enfilading fire positions.

While the 2/27th Battalion had been thus unprofitably occupied to the west of Small Creek, the same day brought the first good news for the 21st Brigade's efforts at Gona.

> Later in the day I made the artillery available to 2/14 Aust. Inf. Bn, and told Colonel Challen that I hoped he could use it to assist him to destroy the enemy facing him. There was some enemy movement east of 2/14th Aust. Inf. Bn, and as the situation between Gona and Sanananda was not clear at that time I was mindful of a possible enemy reinforcing move from the east. For this reason I was anxious to destroy the pocket of enemy facing 2/14th Aust. Inf. Bn, and enable this unit to be free to watch the east. I discussed with Colonel Challen the possibility of him doing a sharp attack on the enemy pocket, assisted by 40 rounds of 25 pr. ammunition (this was all I could spare, plus what was required for ranging). I felt that this would successfully overcome the enemy provided the artillery fire was followed in smartly by the bayonet. 2/14th Aust. Inf. Bn. organised such an attack. It was completely successful, and resulted in only three casualties (wounded) for 2/14th Aust. Inf. Bn. Thus the coast was ours from 2/27th Aust. Inf. Bn's position to some distance east of Small Creek.[38]

The really striking feature of the successful 2/14th Battalion attack at Small Creek is the ample evidence of its being given time to harass the enemy with fighting patrols and, more importantly, to determine his positions prior to the successful attack. When the artillery, however fleetingly, was used in conjunction with a mortar barrage and grenade concentration at specific, reconnoitred Japanese positions, the enemy was decisively beaten with only three 2/14th wounded.

'But the victory was won at great cost' as W. B. Russell wrote in the 2/14th History. He had listed the battalion's battle casualties in its assaults at East Gona from the evening of the 28th to the late afternoon of the 30th—27 killed or dying of wounds and 51 others wounded; and he has left us a moving reminder of that tragic loss.

> It was a staggering blow to the Battalion still low in numbers and stricken from the Owen Stanleys . . . In the saddest and most solemn ceremony in the annals of the Battalion, nineteen of its best soldiers were laid to rest in the small cemetery prepared on that northern shore. Native carriers brought bright leaved shrubs to ornament the graves. The burial ceremony was performed by Padre Keith Dowding of the 2/14th, and Father Cunningham of the 2/16th . . .
>
> The sense of loss and seeming waste of so much that was good affected the sensitive mind and spirit of Padre Dowding to such an extent that he resigned his chaplaincy. He re-enlisted as a private, but was posted to another battalion.[39]

Having cleared the area immediately to the east of Small Creek, Brigadier Dougherty concentrated his attention on his western thrust towards Gona. To bolster Cooper's much weakened 2/27th Battalion he transferred Caro's second and last 2/16th Company under the command of Major Robinson[40] to Cooper by dawn the following day, 1 December. The plan for that day's attack involved two movements. The first was to be a continuation of the push along the coconut belt that had been planned and attempted during the two previous days. The second was to have Captain O'Neill's[41] 2/16th company and the left part of Lieutenant Egerton-Warburton's[42] (previously Captain Gill's) 2/27th company sweeping along the edge of the scrub area to the south-east of Gona and, in the process, linking up with Lieutenant-Colonel Cameron's 3rd Battalion which was to be positioned in the scrub. The two forces were then to push northwards into Gona and through to the beach. Major Robinson's 2/16th company was to act as the reserve.

At approximately 5.45 am artillery and mortar fire were brought to bear on the Japanese positions. The attack began at 6 am when Cooper's men fixed bayonets and moved forward. The right flank companies advanced along the coconut belt into the intense machine-gun fire forcing them to ground, but they managed to eliminate the first Japanese post. However they were again checked by further very heavy fire.

During that attack Lieutenant-Colonel Cooper, who had been quite close to the front directing the action, was wounded. Major Hearman from the 2/16th Battalion, was subsequently ordered to assume command of the 2/27th–2/16th composite battalion.

Meanwhile on the left flank a part of D Company made some small gains along the kunai grass before it too was halted under withering fire. Sergeant Roy Thredgold participated in that attack:

We came out of the kunai and were tearing through this bare patch of ground. And the next thing whack! One in the leg; ten past six in the morning. I just lay there from ten past six in the morning till lunch time. And Derek Parsons said 'Try and make it over to me Threddy!' The blood had congealed around the wound and so I tried to crawl over to him. The bastards must have been having a little sleep because Derek got right out of a shell hole he was in and pulled me back into it with him. This shell hole was full of muddy water and he kept pouring water out of my dixie over my head all day. Then at half past eight that night he said 'We'll come back for you Threddy!' Late that night I thought I'd had it. And the next thing I hear was 'Are you there Threddy!' 'Where are you Threddy?' It was black as pitch, and stinking bloody hot. Derek saved my life. They took me back on a stretcher. And through three attacks at Gona I didn't even see a bloody Jap![43]

However, that morning Captain O'Neill's 2/16th Company and a part of Lieutenant Warburton's 2/27th Company had made exceptional progress; their audacious dash and individual heroism might well have led to a crucial triumph instead of crushing tragedy but for the failure of the 3rd Battalion to join in the battle. Dudley McCarthy writes: 'It transpired, however, that the 3rd Battalion had seen nothing of the left flank of the attack passing in front of them and had made no movement forward.'[44]

Cameron's battalion was located, out of contact with the enemy, in the scrub on the east of the track leading north to Gona. It was to have moved north, skirting the east flank of the enemy positions between it and the mission area, to join in the 2/27th–2/16th attack. Apparently it was not as close to the battle area as the 21st Brigade had been led to believe it was; and a suggested reason for its non-participation was that it was unaware that the attack had proceeded as ordered. It simply made no move to support (as ordered) or even, it seems, to contact or observe the attack.

But the 2/27th–2/16th component did not falter. Here was a proud union of brave and determined men brought to a culmination—and the squandering—of all their combat experience and military commitment. Regardless of daunting odds O'Neill's Western Australians launched a ferocious assault upon the Japanese machine-gunners—and the South Australians stormed forward with them. Private Jack Breakey, 2/27th Battalion was amongst them:

> We started to walk, and then the Western Australians started to run and they were doing this yelling out, so I began doing it with them! When we got through the kunai grass there was the area of burnt off grass and two rows of native huts. And there were two Jap machine-guns that we had to go through. You could feel the bullets around you; you could actually feel them! And after we came through this enfilading fire there seemed to be considerably less of us around somehow or another.[45]

In their wild surge forward the attackers, though delivering savage Bren gun and Owen gun fire, were enveloped in a curtain of death. The bare ground in front of the intact Japanese positions that the 3rd Battalion might have assailed was strewn with the unstirring slain and the frantic wounded seeking the refuge of shell holes under the merciless fusillade that had cut them down. By the time Lieutenant Mayberry's[46] eighteen-man platoon in the centre of the attack had blasted its way into the mission he had only five of his Western Australians left with him.

No sooner had O'Neill's remnants occupied the mission than their own artillery opened up on it. The mission became untenable and they decided to move into the jungle to the left. As they approached the jungle the ten-minute barrage ended and a Japanese force emerged from the cover. There was a swift engagement, two more of the Western Australians lost their lives and a dash westwards to the creek saved the unwounded survivors who swam across to the watching sentries of Haddy's Chaforce company. Private Jack Breakey, 2/27th Battalion:

> There were three 2/27th and four 2/16th Battalion blokes left I think; we got to the other side and found that we'd left a

Western Australian sergeant behind. So I went back and got him and off we went back.[47]

Captain O'Neill, seriously wounded, had also been left behind. When night fell Corporal McMahon and Private Yeing of Haddy's force swam Gona Creek, found a punt and on it brought back the dying O'Neill through the darkness from the eastern bank of the creek where he had been lying all day.

The storming of the mission that had claimed so many lives had not ended the day's fighting. Though the 3rd Battalion was missing from the left flank, the 2/16th reserve company carried on the planned attack on the right flank. At 10.30 am Major Robinson and fourteen of his men assaulted a troublesome stronghold on the beach consisting of posts about five yards apart, well dug in, strongly barricaded and reinforced and protected by enfilade fire from the direction of the mission. The attack was preceded by 90 rounds of three-inch mortar fire on the mission and two-inch mortar fire on the beach posts. The final charge was pushed home with determination and courage despite several casualties, including Robinson. There were 50 enemy dead counted in the captured posts on 75 yards of beach gained. A fierce counter-attack forced the survivors out soon afterwards and Robinson, still fighting, was wounded again.

The Australians spent the rest of the day rescuing and evacuating their wounded and preparing to hold their reduced gains. During that night the thundering sound of bombing out to sea could be heard, as Allied aircraft turned some Japanese shipping away to the west of the beach-head. Despite that reverse the enemy managed to land 500 troops at the mouth of the Kumusi River on 2 December.

By that time Gona had become little more than a shambles. Eather's 25th Brigade was hardly fit for anything more than a holding of its positions. Its campaign in the Owen Stanley Range, its fighting on the way to and at Gona, and its debilitation by malaria had quite simply worn it out.

21st Brigade had arrived at Gona on 28–29 November at about the strength of only one full battalion. It was to be pushed into attacks where detailed reconnaissance of the ground and the enemy's strength and, as a consequence, sensible, measured planning and adequate fire support for offensive operations had been denied its brigadier and his battalion commanders. The result was an unforgivable loss of fine and experienced young officers and men who had endured greatly in Syria and on the Kokoda Trail and who, had they outlived Gona, might have offered the nation so much in the future.

During the morning of 2 December Lieutenant Hicks of the 2/16th Battalion, with a platoon of twenty men made a successful attack on a major beach post, at a cost of nine wounded, including himself. Lieutenant Warburton and a platoon of D Company 2/27th Battalion, helped to consolidate the captured position.

At around midday Vasey held a conference at Eather's head-quarters. In attendance were Vasey himself and Brigadiers Eather, Dougherty and Porter. Porter had only just arrived, and his 30th Brigade, consisting of the 39th, 49th and 55th/53rd Battalions, was only then arriving in the area. Vasey had originally intended to relieve the 25th Brigade with the 30th Brigade; however, the unexpectedly heavy Gona casual-ties brought about a change in plans. He decided to send Dougherty and his 2/14th Battalion, and the 39th Battalion under command to Sanananda to assist in its capture; and he decided to amalgamate the depleted 2/27th and 2/16th Bat-talions, under the command of Lieutenant-Colonel Caro, to assist Eather's 25th Brigade in a blocking or holding role at Gona. Vasey's decision is a clear pointer to higher command confidence that the Japanese were in no position to reinforce Gona effectively by sea. Had he not been backed by such assurance he would not have contemplated leaving such an under-strength and debilitated force to contain the beleaguered beach-head. Vasey's plans were to last only a day, as the 2/14th Battalion soon discovered that the mapped 'track' along the coast was interrupted by very thick scrub and large areas of swamp and was, therefore, not a suitable infantry route to Sanananda. Consequently, during the evening of 3 December Vasey changed his plans yet again, deciding to bring Dougherty and the 2/14th and 39th Battalions back to Gona and to relieve the 25th Brigade completely. Future attacks upon Gona were to be undertaken by the depleted 2/14th and composite 2/27th–2/16th Battalions and the fresh 39th Battalion. The 49th and 55th/53rd Battalions were ordered to move to the Sanananda Track.

Between the 2nd and the 5th, fighting patrols led by Lieutenant Haddy, Chaforce, and Lieutenant Warburton, 2/27th Battalion, attacked strong-posts in the mission area. Sergeant Roach of the 2/27th Battalion, performed several acts of exceptional bravery for which he was awarded a Distinguished Conduct Medal. Eather's 25th Brigade left Gona on 4 December.

Herring to Blamey   HQ, N.G.F.,
Letter   6th December 1942
Eather is spending tonight with me. From what he tells me the enemy garrison or what is left of it at Gona must be having a rotten time. Our fellows on the west of the creek pick off about 6 Japs a day and his fellows used to account for some too. As one of his Bns was moving out, one of his fellows hit a Jap and the Bn went out cheering. They look on the successful hitting of a Jap in much the same way as one might regard the bowling over of a rabbit.[48]

It is tragic indeed that those in the higher levels of command, who decided the fate of armies, did not pay more attention to the unnecessary 'bowling over' of so many of their own troops. The role of the Allied High Command during the battles at the Gona–Sanananda–Buna beach-head merits examination here.

General MacArthur's influence upon the destiny of Australian troops during 1942–43 in New Guinea was paramount.

If the liberation of the South West Pacific Region and the Philippines is portrayed as General MacArthur's crowning achievement, then the campaigns on the Kokoda Trail and at Gona–Sanananda–Buna constitute his darkest hour as a general, for there his mistakes were many and extremely costly.

American G-2 intelligence was consistently inaccurate during those campaigns; it had failed dismally in the first Owen Stanley Campaign in terms of the enemy intent and his strength.[49] Further, MacArthur's intelligence prior to the battles at Gona–Sanananda–Buna predicted a speedy end to the fighting there because of the enemy's debilitated physical condition and his greatly reduced numbers. The Japanese, in fact, probably marshalled some 10 000 defenders along those beach-heads, with about half of them stationed at Buna.

However MacArthur's most tragic and costly mistake during those campaigns was his failure to appreciate the ground and combat conditions encountered by troops under his command. William Manchester, his most recent biographer, provides a truly fascinating insight into that failure:

> . . . MacArthur, in short, never saw the battlefield. Six days later the field commander wrote bluntly that the commander-in-chief hadn't visited the front once 'to see at first hand the difficulties our troops were up against', and later he wrote bitterly that 'the great hero went home without seeing Buna before, during or after the fight while permitting press articles from his G.H.Q. to say he was leading his troops in battle. MacArthur . . . just stayed over at Moresby 40 minutes away and walked the floor. I know this to be a fact.' After the war Douglas Southall Freeman, a biographer of Lee, asked Eichelberger, 'Just when did General MacArthur move his headquarters to Buna?' Eichelberger

dodged the question, and subsequently the General said to him, 'Bob, those were great days when you and I were fighting at Buna, weren't they?' and laughed. Eichelberger interpreted this as a 'warning not to disclose that he never went to Buna.'

The fact that he did not is baffling. In Brisbane he told Philip Lafollette that he would never follow the example of those World War I commanders who had clung to their chateaux in rear areas while flinging 'millions of men to their slaughter in the stupidity of trench warfare'. Yet in Papua he did something very close to that.[50]

It must be remembered that the nature of the terrain intrinsically governed the events at Gona, Sanananda and Buna, and the tactics employed by the two sides to implement their opposing intentions—the intent of the enemy to hold the total beach-head, to the death if necessary, and the equally determined commitment of the Allies to take all three strongholds as soon as possible.

As a logical consequence of his unfamiliarity with the ground, both in the Owen Stanley Range and at Gona–Sanananda–Buna, MacArthur had no grasp whatsoever of the tactics required for operations in either region. William Manchester:

'Indeed,' Eichelberger observed, 'the commander in chief's knowledge of details was so faulty that his directives to me, e.g. a letter of the 24th of December that spoke of attacking, "by regiments, not companies, by thousands, not hundreds" indicated that he knew nothing of the jungle and how one fights there— that he had no detailed knowledge of how our forces were divided into many corridors by swamps.'[51]

That attitude is most definitely one that the historian would associate with the frame of mind of the generals of the First World War; the concept of commitment of huge concentrations of one's force combined with an almost blasé acceptance of heavy casualties was perhaps the most deplorable aspect of command during the Great War. Yet General MacArthur was forever preoccupied with committing unrealistic numbers of men to the battlefield whilst being prepared to suffer horrific casualties in the process. His signals sent to Allen via General Blamey during October are vivid testimony to this frame of mind. Captain Katekar, 2/27th Battalion Adjutant:

> And who judges their performance by their casualties? Fancy that being the yardstick! Because you've got light casualties you're not doing your job—you should have heavy casualties, get your men slaughtered, you'll be a hero! What sort of general's that? In fact I'd be inclined to hold heavy casualties against a commander! If you go wasting manpower, I'd regard that as poor command, apart from the humane side of it. I'm very bitter about that to this day.[52]

General MacArthur was not an astute leader of his senior commanders, whether American or Australian. Logically, he had two alternatives for his control over them. Firstly, if a general chooses to remain ignorant of the ground of a battle and, as a consequence, of the tactics required for victory upon it, he must delegate total responsibility to, and have trust in, his subordinates. Alternatively, he must journey to the ground, familiarise himself with it and therefore with the required tactics, and then either conduct the battle himself or replace inept commanders with those who are competent. In short, a general, to be in total control of the military conduct of his battle and all of its many and varied components, must choose one of those two logical courses—MacArthur did neither.

Tragically, such military irresponsibility was not confined to MacArthur; Blamey and Herring also failed to adequately familiarise themselves with the battle at Gona, and instead reacted by ordering repeated attacks and applying pressure upon their subordinates—to the detriment of the proper conduct of operations.

From 30 November 1942, the Allied higher command reacted to the failure of their troops to capture the beach-heads by instituting still further attacks at all three besieged localities. When these failed, commanders were blamed. The Americans replaced Harding with Eichelberger and made sweeping changes of command at battalion and company level. A not dissimilar fate awaited some of the Australian officers at Gona. A final reckoning of the infamy of Koitaki would weigh heavily upon the 'running rabbits' in the final days before the capture of Gona.

The rushed and largely ill-conceived attacks upon Gona and indeed upon Sanananda and Buna starting during November 1942 were instigated by higher command for political reasons. General MacArthur's eyes were focussed not upon the potential of the Japanese to reinforce their beleaguered troops at the beach-heads, but upon the need for a speedy victory in order to secure a higher Roosevelt Administration recognition of his theatre of operations and a consequent increase in American manpower and resources for his front. In this, he was also in direct competition with the American Navy in its South Pacific Theatre of Operations. William Manchester:

George Marshall and Admiral King think that the English are underestimating the Japanese; they want the Anglo–American commitment in the Pacific doubled from 15 per cent of Allied resources to 30 per cent . . . Then the Americans disagree among themselves. King wants the emphasis on Nimitz's central Pacific; Marshall thinks it should be on MacArthur's South-West Pacific . . .

Preference goes to the central Pacific, a heavy blow to MacArthur. But even Nimitz is dissatisfied with his share. The war against Japan winds up near the bottom of the Combined Chiefs' list of concerns, below the second-front build-up in

Britain, the strategic bombing of Germany, aid to Russia, the fighting around the Mediterranean, and the struggle against Nazi-U-Boats.[53]

In the final analysis, the battle for Gona from 20 November until 3 December 1942, had been a military disaster. 25th Brigade had sustained in excess of 200 battle casualties whilst in five short days the 21st Brigade had lost 340 men out of a total strength of approximately 800—and although the enemy had suffered many casualties, comparatively little ground had been gained.

The Japanese defenders were cornered and surrounded with no hope of escape, yet, when attacked, they could produce a murderous wall of enfilading fire.

That the Australians did not falter might seem a triumph of spirit and courage and discipline but, in retrospect, a tragically empty triumph. As General Bosquet remarked of the charge of the Light Brigade at Balaklava: 'It is magnificent but it is not war.' It was not rational warfare; it was blundering waste. Except for the horses, Tennyson's familiar lines were still apt.

'Forward, the Light Brigade!'
Was there a man dismayed?
Not tho' the soldier knew
someone had blunder'd:
Theirs not to make reply,
Theirs not to reason why,
Theirs but to do and die,
Into the valley of Death
Rode the six hundred.

16

Embarrassed to be alive

After the 39th Battalion's arduous participation in the Owen Stanley Campaign from late July to early September, much had happened to it before its arrival at Gona on 1–2 December. As a consequence of its being placed on AIF establishment on 14 September, the battalion had lost its E (machine-gun) Company; most of its personnel going to other companies. On 15 September, 100 former members of the 53rd Battalion were absorbed into the battalion, whilst two days later a further 300 reinforcements from Australia bolstered its depleted ranks.

No great rest was accorded its commanding officer, adjutant and intelligence officer. On 11 September, Lieutenant-Colonel Honner and Lieutenants Lovett and McNamara left the battalion to participate in Honner Force, which comprised some 500 men including the 2/6th Independent Company and a company each from the 36th, 49th and 55th Battalions. Its orders were to journey adjacent to the Goldie River and then, by travelling north-east, to cut the Japanese line of communication on the Kokoda Trail between Nauro and Menari. Honner

Force had the additional role of blocking any Japanese attempt to attack Port Moresby by an outflanking movement along its route. However, both tasks disappeared as the Japanese made a rapid withdrawal to Templeton's Crossing in late September. Honner returned to his battalion on 1 October.

Having been denied a coastal passage to Sanananda, Brigadier Dougherty and his 2/14th and 39th Battalions were, on the evening of 3 December, ordered by Vasey to return to Gona and relieve the 25th Brigade. On completion of that relief Dougherty assumed command of the Gona area. By nightfall on the 4th he had his 2/14th Battalion deployed just to the east of Small Creek and in contact with Lieutenant-Colonel Caro's composite 2/27th–2/16th Battalion which occupied the ground from Small Creek westwards to the Japanese positions, but astride the main track south from Gona Mission. Lieutenant-Colonel Honner's battalion was quite out of touch with the others.

From a tactical standpoint the tragedy of the battle for Gona between 19 November and 9 December is that not one senior officer was adequately acquainted with the ground over which he was required to attack, or with the ground in total. In all the prior frantic haste, none of the three 21st Brigade Battalion commanders had been given sufficient time for thorough reconnaissance. Challen had skirted the area to the east and had fought his battle at Small Creek; Cooper had approached Gona from the south-east and had been plunged straight into battle on the coast; Caro had remained at Brigade Headquarters whilst his battalion had been broken up into separate groups and sent to bolster the rapidly diminishing numbers of the 2/27th Battalion on 30 November and 1 December.

By chance, Lieutenant-Colonel Honner became the first of Dougherty's battalion commanders to examine the ground. His reactions both shortly after the war and in an interview with the author are striking. In *The 39th at Gona* (1955) he commented:

. . . We had seen the unpromising ground in front of the 2/16th and 2/27th Battalions, stretching flat and featureless to the northern Japanese positions near the beach. There was no adequate cover for daylight attack in that sector, though some most gallant and equally futile attempts had been made there with heavy losses.

On the opposite side the enemy were protected by a creek; our western company occupied its left bank but could not attack across it. The rest of the battalion was on the southern front which was divided into two sectors by a track running north to the mission and parallel to the creek. In the sector between the road and the creek was a broad belt of low kunai grass; and a long stretch of this grass in front of the timber line that marked the enemy's position had been cut off at ground level. To the right of the road there were covered approaches right into the enemy lines; this was obviously the best area from which to launch an attack.

Strangely enough its possibilities seem to have been overlooked while bloody losses were sustained in reckless attacks elsewhere. Brigadier Eather had told me that in this area the 3rd Battalion posts were so close to those of the Japanese that the favourite pastime of both forces was throwing grenades at one another. I relayed this information to Captain Joe Gilmore but when his A Company took over from the 3rd Battalion he immediately obtained my permission to move his company forward to make contact with the enemy and dig in there, which he did, not yet within grenade range but in what had been no-man's land.[1]

Honner's conversation with Eather is verified by Major-General Dougherty who was also present at that meeting.[2]

The most suitable and indeed, the only sensible position from which Gona should have been attacked and captured was that south-eastern scrub area occupied by the 3rd Battalion. Had suitable aerial photographs and maps been available and,

315

above all, had proper reconnaissance been undertaken, Gona might well have fallen days earlier and with significantly fewer Australian casualties. Lieutenant-Colonel Cameron had the covered approach route into the defences right before him. Whether, after a week at Gona, he was unaware of his true position or whether his communications with his company commanders were deficient would seem to be irrelevant to the point at issue. Whatever the cause, his battalion did not move as planned with the 21st Brigade companies in a concerted attack, with the unfortunate result that those companies were exposed to intense cross-fire which should have been suppressed by the 3rd Battalion.

The continued failure of the Australians to exploit the potential of this approach to Gona proved to be a costly one indeed. During an interview with the author in September 1986, Lieutenant-Colonel Honner was quite adamant about the prospects of an earlier success at Gona:

Yes easily! From where it was eventually taken; through Cameron's sector which became Gilmore's A Company sector. It took a day to do it, but the point was that there was cover all the way. It doesn't matter what cover you have getting close to the enemy if in the last stretch he's got an unbroken field of fire where he can mow you down. But if you've got a covered approach right into the heart of his defences he's gone! This was the cover that was available at Gona and yet they persisted in ordering attacks along the two open stretches; the one in front of Bidstrup and the one along the beach, and that meant huge casualties.

In spite of all the instruction on military tactics there is still some unconscious adherence to the idea that the shortest distance between two points is a straight line and they go for the frontal attack knowing that the enemy are ready for a frontal attack, and have got fields of fire to prevent a successful frontal attack. They will not go to the trouble to go round the flanks or the rear and attack from the unexpected quarter because it might be more difficult or take longer. You shouldn't have troops mown down in frontal attacks.[3]

During 5 December, the Australians were engaged in limited patrolling and an alteration of some of their positions. Dougherty recalled Challen's 2/14th Battalion from the Small Creek area to relieve Captains Lee and Thurgood and their Chaforce protection of the 21st Brigade Headquarters. Late on that day, Lieutenant-General Herring informed Dougherty that the enemy were most likely to land reinforcements at the mouth of the Kumusi River during the next few days. It is important to note that Vasey would still, as late as 7 December, consider a containment of Gona rather than any further fruitless attacks. His attitude reinforces the view that at no time did higher command consider that there was a serious threat of substantial Japanese reinforcement of the Gona beach-head.

The 39th Battalion's baptism of fire at Gona was planned for a dawn attack on the 6th—one of two thrusts aimed by 21st Brigade at Gona's fall. The composite 2/27th–2/16th Battalion under Lieutenant-Colonel Caro was to resume its penetration along the coconut belt adjoining the beach, whilst Captain Bidstrup's D Company, 39th Battalion, was to strike north between the main track and Gona Creek. Bidstrup's assault was to be mounted through the kunai grass and then over approximately 50 daunting yards of bare ground facing the enemy positions.

To support Bidstrup's attack, a three-inch mortar barrage was brought down on the Japanese positions shortly before daylight. Then, as dawn was breaking, a smoke screen was laid to cover the rush of 16 and 17 Platoons over the open ground towards the enemy strong-posts.

Against those well dug-in and stoutly roofed strong-posts the mortar barrage proved ineffectual, and, at close quarters, the smoke tended to assist the fixed defence rather than the rampaging attack. The shrouding smoke made the concealed Japanese posts even harder to locate while the Australians loomed large as they swirled out of the haze into the sights of enfilading machine-guns. But the ensuing carnage failed to quench the courage of the attackers, exemplified by the conduct of two determined men.

Private Skilbeck[4] single-handedly performed three tasks during the intense battle that had erupted in front of the Japanese positions. On four occasions he crossed that open stretch of ground through very heavy fire to bring information back to Captain Bidstrup's headquarters on the edge of the kunai. This was no place to pause! But Skilbeck, on each occasion added the task of rescuing a wounded comrade to his role as runner. Later given the job of leading a reserve section forward during the very height of the battle, he made yet another desperate journey forward into the enemy's fire to retrieve another casualty whose wounds prevented his crawling or walking to safety. Skilbeck's cool efficiency and gallantry won him a Military Medal.

While Skilbeck was running the gauntlet with 17 Platoon on the left, Sergeant Morrison[5] on the right led 16 Platoon resolutely forward showing scant regard for the intense fire which wounded him first in a hand and then in a leg, bringing him to ground. From there he continued to give much needed direction to his men's assault. His inspiring leadership was the more noteworthy since he had taken over his command only three days earlier when the platoon's former commander was wounded by a Beaufighter on the unfinished trek towards Sanananda.

Bidstrup's dawn attack, on orders that came from higher command, was perhaps more surely doomed to failure than most of those at Gona had been during the preceding days. Without any appreciation of the fatal ground, those orders called for a futile repeat attack where stronger forces had already failed against the invulnerable sector of the Gona perimeter. In the final analysis, the ground occupied was a modest 50 yards of kunai grass of no value to either side; the price paid by the two platoons flung forward from it was twelve men killed and 46 wounded.

Lieutenant-Colonel Caro's attack through the coconut belt fared no better. The leading platoon commanded by Lieutenant White[6] made a spirited dash towards the first Japanese post. White was wounded in a leg, and whilst being carried out was shot again, this time mortally. A smoke barrage was laid down in order to evacuate the wounded. A patrol later recovered White's body having found it amongst numerous enemy dead. This action cost the 2/16th Battalion four men killed and six wounded.

However there was some small, encouraging success early on that costly dawn of 6 December. Lieutenant-Colonel R Honner DSO, MC in *This Is The 39th*:

The left of 'D' Company's attacking platoons had been protected by the creek; a section from 'B' Company, led by Corporal R. G. Edgell[7] had been detailed to give them protection on the other flank by quietening any posts on the right of the area through which the attack would pass. When the attack broke against the enemy line his section burst through. He carried on in the semi-darkness through a network of enemy posts and much wild shooting until he reached his objective—the far line of the timber on the outskirts of the mission village. When he realised that 'D' Company would not be joining him there, he decided to cross the track and make his way back through 'A' Company's lines.

Meanwhile, Lieutenant Nelson[8] of 'A Company had led his platoon forward in the dark on a fighting patrol towards the mission school. But the platoon came under enemy fire when shoulder deep in the water and slime of a sago swamp. Nelson was wounded and his platoon unable to cross the swamp under fire, retired. Then Lieutenant Tuckey[9] took a patrol out to attack a post which had fired on Nelson's platoon, and was engaging it in a fire fight in the first grey light when Edgell's section burst in on its flank. With his Owen gun, and the assistance of his Bren gunner, Edgell killed a dozen of the enemy in that post, before leaving Tuckey who went on still looking for trouble until he found it—he was wounded in both legs.

As night fell on the 6th, the Australians could draw little satisfaction from their labours. Casualties were high, and the ground gained was negligible. That night was like so many others at Gona—pitch-black darkness and constant rain which soaked the men and filled their weapon-pits with water. Almost constant vigilance was interspersed with spasmodic sleep.

Another attack was planned for the following day. A and C Companies, 39th Battalion, were to mount an assault upon the southern Japanese posts, whilst the composite 2/27th–2/16th Battalion was to once again press forward through the coconut belt. The plan miscarried because of faulty airforce bombing. Captain Bidstrup vividly remembers not only the bombing of the area, but the resulting dry sense of humour of his commanding officer:

> And they were going to bomb using dive-bombers. When the raid was over, one of the planes was to waggle its wings and we'd go in. The dive-bombers proceeded to let their bombs go behind us; we could see them coming over. They fell closer to us than the Japs! And Ralph [Honner] said 'We're not going in!' And I can remember Ralph standing up and saying, 'Give me a squadron of Stukas!'[10]

Honner rang Brigade Headquarters and informed Dougherty that he had cancelled his attack because the aerial activity had merely alerted the enemy to the likelihood of attack without having subjected him to any bombardment. He also requested that Allied aircraft be excluded from interference in future attacks.

While the Australians had been thus engaged at Gona during 6–7 December, a small but determined Japanese attempt at reinforcement of the beleaguered troops at Gona was in progress from the west. The relieving force had two components. The first consisted of approximately 100 troops who had survived the slaughter at Oivi–Gorari during November. These troops were in poor condition, barefooted and debilitated, as witnessed by the Australians during spasmodic skirmishing between 20 November and early December. But when a Japanese destroyer managed to land a further 500 fresh and well-equipped troops near the mouth of the Kumusi River on 2 December, the total Japanese force moving towards Gona numbered some 600 troops.

It will be remembered that at the beginning of the Gona campaign, Brigadier Eather had deployed his 2/16th Battalion Chaforce company under the command of Lieutenant Haddy, on the western bank of Gona Creek. The physical condition of Haddy's troops had deteriorated quite markedly. They had been almost constantly involved in the Papuan campaign since arriving at Alola in the Owen Stanley Range in late August—in the desperate withdrawal and then in the avenging pursuit. They had been strafed by Japanese and Allied planes alike during November, and had been engaged in varied action ranging from offensive patrolling to providing mortar fire against approaching enemy barges. By 6 December they were down to barely platoon strength and racked with malaria and dysentery.

On 30 November, Haddy had relieved Lieutenant Greenwood's standing 2/14th Battalion patrol at a small village—to become known as Haddy's Village—near the Amboga River and about two miles west of his own Chaforce base. During the heavy rain on the night of 6 December, the Japanese moved into and around Haddy's positions. Haddy sent Private Bloomfield[11] back to his Chaforce base on the western side of

Gona Creek for all available reinforcements. These 'available reinforcements' numbered a paltry fifteen weak but tenacious 2/16th men who, led by Sergeant Jones,[12] set out forthwith to Haddy's rescue. In a skirmish with a Japanese patrol, Jones was wounded and Corporal Murphy[13] assumed command and forestalled any further Japanese advance until reinforcements could be sent from Gona.

Brigadier Dougherty was quick to sum up the situation. Believing that the capture of Gona was now close to fruition, he ordered a 2/14th Battalion reinforcement of Haddy's and Murphy's men, with orders to deny the enemy the ground to within 1200 yards of Gona. Challen dispatched Lieutenant Dougherty and a party of 50 men who surprised the enemy who were in considerable strength approximately half a mile south-east of Haddy's Village. The fact that the enemy outnumbered him by at least four to one did not deter the ever aggressive Dougherty.

After having concentrated his force in a coconut grove, he drove into the centre of the enemy, shocking them in fierce hand-to-hand fighting in which he alone accounted for fourteen of the enemy dead. The Japanese responded with an attempted encirclement which was countered by the courage—and the automatic weapons—of Corporal Weeks and Private Crilly so that the patrol could withdraw to form a new defensive line. For the loss of six of his men wounded, Dougherty's aggression inflicted the enemy with over 90 casualties and prevented him from any further forward movement. Dougherty was recommended for the Victoria Cross but failed even to be mentioned in Dispatches. Corporal Weeks and Les Crilly were each awarded the Military Medal. Lieutenant Dougherty was involved in further aggressive patrols in the next few days—these being responsible for many casualties. In one of these patrols whilst emptying his submachine gun into the enemy at close quarters he was killed by a sniper—his loss was felt keenly by his battalion. Captured enemy documents later indicated that the Japanese believed that they had beaten back an Australian two-company force with great success. In the evening Lieutenant-Colonel Challen arrived in the area with the remainder of his battalion to consolidate the prevention of Japanese infiltration towards Gona from the west.

At about the same time, two of Haddy's men returned to Brigade Headquarters to report that more of their number were on their way and that Haddy had ordered the evacuation of the village as the Japanese had closed in. That was the last direct report of one of the 2/16th Battalion's favourite and most respected sons.

It was established that when in the desperate fighting on 7 December Haddy had seen the area as being untenable, he had ordered his men to retire whilst he and Private Stephens[14] covered their withdrawal. For some days the men of the 21st Brigade could only ponder their fate. Haddy had surrendered his life during the last of so many selfless and gallant actions which had won him such high regard in his battalion, both in the Owen Stanleys and at Gona.

When Haddy's Village was eventually recaptured, the body of Stephens was found at its sentry post in the command hut; and beneath the hut's raised platform Haddy lay, still at bay, ringed by dead Japanese. Another 'running rabbit' had fought tigerishly to the very last.

A regimental medical officer is in an excellent position to become familiar with the men of his battalion. Major Steward has provided a moving tribute to the character of Lieutenant Alan Haddy:

Haddy for me had been the very embodiment of all the virtues of the Australian infantryman—great-hearted, laconic, loyal. I remembered him in one hotspot coolly hurling a grenade at the enemy. 'Mix that with your rice you bastards!' he called as the bomb left his large and powerful hand. This calm and inspiring company sar-major so lately promoted to commissioned rank

brought to soldiering the philosophy of the ancient Spartans;
'come home with your shield or come home on it' . . .

Some people pass swiftly from memory like a name glimpsed
on a visiting card. Not Alan Haddy. I will remember him all my
life, and whenever I think of him I will remember the lines of
Longfellow, 'so when a great man dies, for years beyond our
ken, the light he leaves behind shines upon the path of men.'[15]

With the Japanese thus forestalled on the left flank, Brigadier
Dougherty determined that he would mount an all-out assault
upon Gona on 8 December with all available artillery support.
Much hinged on this attack as he was warned by Vasey's chief
staff officer that his numerically strongest unit, the 39th Battalion, might be required to move to assist the 30th Brigade
operation at Sanananda. Dougherty's strength now stood at
37 officers and 755 other ranks—barely battalion strength. The
2/14th Battalion numbered six officers and 133 men; the
2/16th Battalion five and 99; the 2/27th Battalion four and
142, and the 39th Battalion 22 and 381. Much would now
depend upon the attack to be mounted by his strongest unit—
the 39th Battalion.

The plan for the assault upon Gona on the 8th had three
distinct parts. The first was an attack to be staged by Captain
Seward's C Company, 39th Battalion, on the left of the track,
pushing towards the southern Japanese defences. Captain
Gilmore's A Company, 39th Battalion, were to stage the
second attack. This was to be through the scrub south and
south-east of the mission. The third component of the attack
was to be undertaken by the composite 2/27th–2/16th Battalion along the coast. The artillery fire plan for this attack was to
be radically different from those in preceding attacks in two
key respects.

The first was the far greater degree of fire support. The air
support for the attack upon Gona on 29 November consisted of
dropping 75 bombs; Challen's attack near Small Creek had been

given the paltry support of 40 rounds of 25-pounder shellfire; and Cooper's attack on 1 December, 150 rounds of 25-pounder shellfire. In this all-important attack on the 8th, the artillery support was to consist of 250 rounds of 25-pounder shellfire. The second point was the nature of the shells used. In prior attacks the high explosive (HE) shells used had proven largely ineffectual. Exploding on impact, they often burst among the tops of the tall coconut palms instead of on the targeted ground; or, if they did hit the ground or the bunker roofs, they exploded there with little damage to the sheltered enemy.

In conference with his forward observation officer (FOO) from the artillery and Brigadier Dougherty, Lieutenant-Colonel Honner requested delayed-fuse shells for his barrage on 8 December, his idea being that such shells would penetrate the cover of enemy posts, or some two feet into the soft ground beside them, and then explode with deadly or stunning effect so that the survivors could be overcome by attackers storming against them while they were still in a state of shock.

With the disastrous attack staged by Captain Bidstrup's D Company on the 6th uppermost in his mind, Honner decided to order a subtle change to his attack. He instructed Captain Seward not to pursue his attack with too much vigour on the left flank. He did so for two compelling reasons.

Firstly, C Company would surely sustain heavy and unnecessary casualties as had D Company on the 6th. Secondly, Honner felt very confident that success would come through Captain Gilmore's attack through the scrub. He deemed it important to be in a position where he could use Bidstrup and Seward's D and C Companies to exploit his anticipated gains in Gilmore's sector.

Predictably, the thrust on the coast, despite the unfailing aggression and bravery of the composite battalion, came to a grinding halt because of the very same factors that had brought about the failure of previous attacks in the same sector—the assault was yet again mounted over relatively open ground and with poor fire support.

On the left Captain Atkinson's[16] 2/16th company pushed north-west into a storm of machine-gun fire. Dudley McCarthy:

> Once again Lieutenant Mayberry shone out even in that brave company. With a scratch crew of six men he stormed headlong against a key position. Badly wounded in the head and right arm he still fought on and urged his men forward. His shattered right arm refusing its function, he dragged the pin out of a grenade and essayed a throw with his left hand. But the arm was too weak. He forced the pin back with his teeth and then lay for some hours in his exposed position before he was rescued. The other two platoon commanders also went down, Lieutenant Inkpen[17] mortally wounded.[18]

Meanwhile about 50 men from a 2/27th company bravely led by Captain Johnson,[19] also charged across open ground towards the enemy strong-posts along the beach, hoping that the previous attacks on, and harassment of, the enemy would have caused a reduction of his fire. But this was not to be the case—many casualties resulted including Captain Johnson and Lieutenant Hewitt[20], both wounded. This was the third time Captain Johnson had been wounded in action. He later rejoined the 2/27th Battalion and was belatedly awarded a DSO for his courageous leadership.

Away on the left of the track Captain Seward sustained relatively light casualties and, in accordance with Lieutenant-Colonel Honner's orders, did not pursue his attack beyond a brisk fire-fight to deter the enemy in front of him from crossing the track to strengthen the opposition to the main assault.

In the all important scrub attack in Captain Gilmore's sector, astute planning of surprise over the most suitable approach, the desired fire support and the 'fickle military finger of fate', all combined to bring about the long-sought-after capture of Gona. Lieutenant-Colonel Honner DSO, MC:

> My plan was for the infantry to advance at a quarter to one at
> the end of the fifteen minutes' mortar bombardment while the
> artillery barrage still had two minutes to go. I expected they
> would take most of a minute to reach the enemy and have a
> minute amongst them with our artillery still firing.[21]

In this decision, Honner took the calculated risk that his A
Company troops would sustain few, if any, casualties from their
own guns for the priceless advantage of rampaging amongst
the enemy whilst they were still reeling from the artillery
barrage. Great minds think alike! Lieutenants Dalby and
Kelly[22] decided that they and their men would crawl forward
on all fours as close as possible to the enemy positions during
the preliminary bombardment so as to give the enemy as little
time to recover as possible, to respond to their attack. They had
no idea that their CO had 'extended' the barrage into the first
crucial minute of their planned close contact, and, similarly,
Honner knew nothing of the snake-like anticipatory advance
of A Company's two forward platoons. One telling minute of
surprise thus became two. Lieutenant Dalby well remembers
the attack and his initial reaction, in the heat of battle, to the
exploding shells of his own artillery:

> The first two Japs I shot didn't know what had hit them! They
> had their heads bowed because of the artillery still bursting in
> front and around us, and they had expected us to be twenty to
> thirty yards away when the artillery lifted. But Colonel Honner
> had fiddled the timing! In retrospect if he'd have told me I
> would have said 'bloody good idea', but how the hell could he
> have told us, being honest about it? He couldn't have.
>
> The first post had a medium machine-gun surrounded by
> light machine-gunners, so I suppose you'd say the post was an
> area of about twenty by ten feet; counting supporting riflemen

there were about twenty or twenty-five blokes in the post. I
think you were just shit-frightened and you knew what you had
to do. Anything that moved got shot.[23]

Following in Dalby's aggressive footsteps came Corporal
Ellis[24] who maintained the platoon's momentum by single-
handedly accounting for the next four enemy posts. Dalby's
platoon carried the left flank of the A Company assault
through the defended scrub area east of the track. Lieutenant-
Colonel R Honner DSO, MC in *This is the 39th:*

> Farther to the right Lieutenant Kelly's platoon fought through
> to the northern edge of the timber overlooking the beach and
> swung left along it. There it suffered some casualties, including
> three or four killed by fire from enemy pits round the mission
> school. Private R. E. G. Wilkinson,[25] the Bren-gunner of the
> reserve section whose task was right flank protection of the
> platoon, moved out into the open, in spite of the sweeping fire,
> to obtain observation of the enemy positions. He could not see
> them from the ground so mounted his gun on a post about four
> feet high and, standing in full view of the enemy, raked them
> with fire until he had silenced all opposition around the school.

The impetus of initial success was not to be lost. Through the
wide breach opened up by the three platoons of A Company
poured the reinforced survivors of D Company to avenge their
bloody repulse of two days earlier; and hot on their heels
hurried C Company eager for positive action after their brief
diversionary demonstration in the face of the impenetrable
cross-fire west of the track. All through the afternoon and into
the evening the three companies fought on; when night closed
in, the central defended area and half the enemy perimeter had
fallen to the 39th Battalion. The Japanese still clung to their
posts on the beach and in the south-west stronghold but they
must have realised that Gona was no longer tenable.

That night of 8–9 December is blazoned most strongly upon the minds of the veterans of Gona. The Japanese survivors, knowing that they had inflicted as many deaths upon their enemy as had been possible, determined that they would stage a break-out in the hope of joining their comrades at Sanananda. They chose two primary avenues of escape; the first was through the kunai grass corridor between the Australian-occupied scrub and the coastal fringe; the second was by sea, wading out to by-pass the Australian positions on the coast. Major-General Sir Ivan Dougherty CBE, DSO, ED:

> And at the end of the day I had to report that the attack was unsuccessful whereas in fact it had been successful, because the Japanese at midnight on the night of the 8–9 of December staged a breakout. Frank Sublet rang me and told me that they were being infiltrated. And I said 'Frank, just order your men to stay in their holes and just shoot anything that moves on top of the ground, it doesn't matter what it is, shoot it!' These men were the Japanese remnants of Gona, they were finished![26]

Major Frank Sublet MC, CO Composite 2/27th–2/16th Battalion:

> We had a Bren-gunner sited on the beach for support. This machine-gunner became invaluable during that night because quite a few Japanese came out of their bunkers and tried to move along the beach to Sanananda. The machine-gunner got quite a few of them. Others went out into the kunai. Our chaps had positions all through the kunai and so did the 39th and they walked straight into our fire! And there was a lot of hand-to-hand fighting in the dark.[27]

Major Sublet had arranged for Captain Katekar to lead several 2/27th Battalion men occupying a captured beach post in a midnight attack against the next of a series of enemy-occupied posts. However, this proved unnecessary as at about 11 pm the Japanese had commenced their break-out. Captain Katekar has a vivid recollection of this unexpected event:

> There were Japs going everywhere, wading out to sea, and going through the kunai. We were shooting them down like animals. But before that I remember the deathly silence being broken by one of our chaps yelling out, 'He's stabbing me, he's stabbing me!' And I said 'For Christ's sake, shut up you stupid bastard'. Someone else said, 'He's having a nightmare'. We soon learned that he wasn't having a nightmare; it was a Jap with a sword having a go at him![28]

During the night the besiegers accounted for some 100 or more Japanese soldiers trying to escape. However, it would seem that at least a similar number of fugitives did pass through the ill-connected cordon and headed off towards Sanananda.

By early morning the 39th held all the jungle edge looking across the open ground to the beach where a few enemy posts still held out. Lieutenant Sword, commanding an A Company platoon that had cleared the huts in the mission area and the pits around them, saw parties from the 2/27th–2/16th moving westwards along the beach. He immediately led his platoon towards the sea, clearing out pockets of the enemy until he reached the beach where he was killed in the capture of the last post to fall.

As soon as A Company's telephone line came up to the mission area, Lieutenant-Colonel Honner sent back to Brigade Headquarters a message consisting of two simple words— 'Gona's gone!' Those two words were splashed across the major newspapers of the Australian nation. Gona was indeed gone, but at a tragic and almost totally unnecessary cost.

The scenes that were witnessed in Gona on 9 December were totally repugnant to the most hard-nosed veterans of the two Australian battalions. A range of surviving veterans' memories most vividly portrays the carnage and also some characteristics of the Japanese martial code of behaviour.

Sergeant John Manol, Intelligence Section, 39th Battalion:

I'll never forget the feeling of revulsion I had when Gona fell. Gona was a terrible sight to behold; most of the trees, coconut palms, etc. were blown apart by bombs and artillery and mortar fire. Rotting corpses were everywhere, scores of bodies. The huts and water tanks were riddled with bullet holes and the stench was terrible. Gona had been taken at a terrible cost of lives. Walking past Jap positions I saw so many corpses; their mouths, eyes and nostrils full of maggots in that heat; every dead body was putrified in such a short time.

Walking along the beach the next day I was amazed to find a white painted cross, outside a chapel, the only thing in Gona that had not one single scar or bullet hole in it. And at the time it gave me an eerie feeling.[29]

Lieutenant Doug McClean MC, D Company, 39th Battalion:

They seemed to want to die and we were delighted to oblige them. They didn't give in, they didn't surrender and therefore there is no point in saying we showed them mercy. I found troops with grenades unexploded in their hands who'd been trying to push them through these narrow apertures in the logs that the Japs had dug in so well. If ever anyone had earnt a VC those blokes had![30]

Major Frank Sublet MC, CO 2/27th–2/16th Composite Battalion:

Their hygiene was shocking! You see, they were pinned down so closely in their posts that they couldn't move around or out of them during daylight, so they were using them for latrines, for feeding and of course they couldn't bury their dead, because they'd get shot in the attempt. I don't know whether it was by choice or not but they stacked their dead on top of, and underneath bags of rice, to fire over them! Some of them had fought in respirators because of the stench.[31]

Lieutenant-Colonel Ralph Honner DSO, MC:

We reverently buried our gallant dead and moved out as burial parties went in to dispose of the Japanese—they had buried 638 of them by the end of the next day, but many days later we still stumbled over the ones they didn't find, or momentarily stopped brushing our teeth in the lagoons as decayed bodies nudged past us. We did not envy the burial parties their task. We had seen the Japanese put on their respirators when our bombardments churned up the stench of their comrades' rotting corpses. And many of our battle-hardened veterans, fighting their way forward over that polluted ground, were unable to face their food. It was sickening to breathe, let alone eat.[32]

Brigadier Ivan Dougherty DSO, CBE, ED, 21st Brigade:

Gona was a dreadful sight! All the dead hadn't been buried. There were Japanese and Australians, and I remember sitting down on a log while this unpleasant procedure was going on. It was something that one can never forget. I remember my feelings were, that I never again wanted to see a picture of a palm tree with a romantic scene underneath it. There was a strong repulsion of the whole thing.[33]

The 21st Brigade had been bled almost white by its furious Gona fighting. From 28 November until 9 December it had lost 34 officers and 375 other ranks, which constituted a staggering 41 per cent of its strength. Its sickness casualties were also horrific though no accurate count of their total could be kept. However, the history of the 2/27th Battalion records its sickness casualties at Gona as 87. This statistic is interesting from two perspectives. Firstly, those 87 men were evacuated sickness casualties. This is a tragic statistic when it is remembered that nearly every man at Gona was sick during this period. A soldier fought on, carried on, regardless of a temperature of up to 102 and/or suppressed malaria or dysentery or tropical ulcers. Secondly, the 2/27th Battalion's sickness casualties should be considered as being fairly representative of the 21st Brigade's sickness casualties as each of its three battalions had endured the Owen Stanley Campaign, had experienced the same length of time and conditions of rest from the end of the Owen Stanley Campaign to its arrival at Gona, and had fought under the same conditions and for the same length of time at Gona. The 21st Brigade's 34 officers and 375 other ranks were not the only Australian casualties in the battle for Gona. The 39th Battalion lost six officers and 115 other ranks; the three battalions of the 25th Brigade lost seventeen officers and 187 other ranks between 19 November and the early morning of 23 November with more to follow in the next couple of weeks along with those of the 3rd Battalion and the Chaforce companies. The quoted incomplete battle casualties total 57 officers and 677 other ranks.

It is all too easy to dismiss such figures as routine battle statistics—the expected end result of warfare. Should they be expected? Not only the historian should be concerned to weigh the cost they count. When it is remembered that 638 Japanese were buried at Gona from 10 December onwards and perhaps another 200 were either evacuated or buried during the early stages of the campaign, the respective losses of the two sides were similar. When the hopeless position of the Japanese garrison at Gona is borne in mind, these Australian losses are totally unacceptable from any intelligent perspective. In fact, from a tactical standpoint, the Allied high command played right into the Japanese hands. Captain Katekar, 2/27th Battalion:

We had to put men straight into the muzzles of guns there to be chewed to pieces without any sense of what was going to be achieved, except that they were going to be killed and wounded. We had to do that; we couldn't sit down and wait for the bastards to be starved out, which would have obviously happened if the commanders had known the situation. Those Japs were completely bottled up. They couldn't raise a squeak really in the way of an offensive. They were a spent force, bottled up and prepared to die. But they were going to die and take as many of our men as they possibly could—and we gave them every opportunity to do that![34]

Captain J. K. Murdoch, Staff Captain 21st Brigade, at Gona:

The lack of appreciation by higher authority of what it cost. They just did not know what was going on! Nobody knew and nobody would take advice as to what was going on. And therefore Gona was a continuation of the shortcomings of the Kokoda Trail. By the time Gona was fought the rear headquarters should have known what was going on; they just didn't appreciate it until the following year when the Nadzab and Ramu Valley operations happened.[35]

Lieutenant-Colonel Cooper has left the historian with a tremendously succinct summation of the Gona campaign:

If you want a tiger to fight terribly fiercely, just put it in a corner with no way to escape! And it's the same with military forces. There's an old principle here, especially when you've got somebody cornered with no way of escape; you can rarely take the whole thing off at once. You try to eat it away and bite off pieces. Therefore attacks are organised with all your forces to concentrate on one area, which makes for your breakthrough.

Gona was a bloody massacre, unnecessarily brought about by fighting soldiers not being allowed to practise their art; being pushed into action with bad support and insufficient time to conduct the operation—a panicky rush.[36]

Lieutenant-Colonel Cooper's criticism is all the more damning when one considers the quality of the commanders on the spot.

Dougherty, Caro, Cooper, Challen and Honner had all been promoted several times since their enlistment in the AIF. Their experience had been gained under the most demanding test of all—action during the Middle East campaigns. The same can be said of their junior officers and, excluding the 39th Battalion, most of their other ranks. Thus these officers and men were greatly experienced troops who had been tried and tested in battle. In addition, the 21st Brigade and the 39th Battalion had fought in the Owen Stanley Campaign, and fought magnificently. The four battalions and their officers were thus well versed and trained, prior to Gona, in this type of fighting. Warfare is an art, however repugnant and it is also a science. There are age-old principles and procedures. Had Dougherty and his battalion commanders been given their rightful chance to see the available aerial photographs of Gona, to reconnoitre the ground, to assess the enemy's positions and strengths, to receive adequate fire support and, as a consequence, to concentrate their decisive force at the only really promising point of attack, which was through the southeastern scrub, then Gona must surely have fallen earlier and at a drastically reduced cost.

Not only did higher command deny the senior commanders on the spot the sensible right to conduct their battle, but it removed three of the 21st Brigade's senior officers from the battlefield and the Brigade. This was a direct result of its own inept and ignorant interpretation of events. This higher command perspective can be traced back to the titanic battle at Brigade Hill during the Owen Stanley Campaign and to the infamous Koitaki parade.

The Blamey diatribe at Koitaki had its genesis in the perceived Owen Stanley failure of Maroubra Force. The misconception of the battle at Brigade Hill crystallised this higher command perspective and, more importantly, cast a cloud of doubt over the competence of the battalion commanders in that battle.[37]

When the bloodied and costly battle at Gona began to drag on, commanders on the spot were blamed. This state of affairs had its parallel at Buna. General MacArthur's solution to the delay there was to order General Eichelberger to assume command, to replace officers who 'would not fight', and to push in 'regiments, not companies, by thousands not hundreds'.[38] Whilst it is true that some American commanders and their troops were very inexperienced and had not fought well, this preoccupation with a speedy victory regardless of losses, along the Gona–Sanananda–Buna beach-head, led to a similar degree of pressure by the Australian high command at Gona. After being wounded at Gona on 1 December and evacuated, Lieutenant-Colonel Cooper did not regain a battalion command—a great injustice to a soldier who had led his battalion with such zeal and competence both at Mission Ridge and Gona. His replacement was Major Hearman from the 2/16th Battalion. He lasted a matter of a few days, because he had protested at the unjustifiable slaughter of his men and the poor fire support afforded them during repeated futile attacks along the beach.[39] Hearman was replaced by Lieutenant-Colonel Caro, by wide repute, after the Syrian and Owen Stanley campaigns, one of the most experienced, competent, resolute and trusted commanders in the AIF. Caro's command of the 2/27th–2/16th Composite Battalion lasted but three days. He too, became very bitter about the blind slaughter of his troops and protested at the futility of frontal attacks over open ground into Japanese enfilading fire without adequate fire support.

In all this, Brigadier Dougherty was merely the instrument of execution. These decisions in essence emanated from higher command—Generals MacArthur and Blamey. The innuendo and the trial by ignorance at Koitaki became the removal from command at Gona.

Dougherty had been unhappy at the rejection of his own advice, his own urgent requests, at the outset of his campaign; he could not have been happy at the consequent massacre of his own men and the abrupt rejection of his own commanders. Captain Murdoch, Staff Captain 21st Brigade at Gona: 'I would say that it was a directive to Brigadier Dougherty that Caro be removed, because it happened quite suddenly. I walked back with Alby, back to the ADS'.[40]

Major Hearman 2/16th Battalion:

Even at this stage, (shortly after Koitaki) there were suggestions that there could be a witch-hunt for officers who were known to show an unconcealed respect for Brigadier Potts. I recall a conversation initiated by the 2/16th Bn, Adjt., Capt. John O'Neill who was killed at Gona, along these lines . . .

Both Lt-Col Caro and I were relieved of command of the 2/16th Bn. without, so far as I am aware any very convincing reason being given to either of us . . .

I can say that when I did eventually rejoin the 2/16th Bn in the beginning of April 1945, I was shown great consideration and kindness by Brig. Dougherty. I am sure that any differences we may have had at Gona stemmed from honest differences of opinion *and army politics.*[41]

Some days after the fall of Gona, Padre Begbie of the 2/27th Battalion held a most solemn and moving burial service for those who had fallen from the ranks of 21st Brigade. Pondering the horrific loss of so many brave and magnificent men, an unidentified 2/27th Battalion soldier informed a comrade that he felt 'embarrassed to be alive'.

17

Silent

The fall of Gona on 9 December did not mark the end of fighting in the area for the battle-scarred and worn remnants of the 21st Brigade and the 39th Battalion.

The enemy force that had crossed the Amboga River on the night of the 6th was still pressing against the 2/14th Battalion deployed to hold it west of Gona. Captain Stan Bisset MC, 2/14th Battalion:

> This Japanese force was initially badly mauled by Lieutenant Dougherty's patrol south-east of Haddy's Village. The combined remnants of the 2/14th established a position near where this attack had been made. During the next few days aggressive patrolling caused many enemy casualties. Sergeant Wally Fyfe and his men beat off attacks and in retaliatory raids destroyed two enemy machine-gun posts.
>
> Fighting patrols harassed the enemy and on the 8th of December, patrols led by Dougherty and Evans killed sixteen and wounded many more, capturing light machine-guns, mortars and rifles. The enemy continued its abortive attacks on

the battalion position and sustained casualties. Standing patrols were able to prevent infiltration and encirclement. On the 9th of December further enemy casualties were inflicted by the 2/14th mortars and patrols led by Lieutenants Rainey, Young and Corporal Stringer. Lieutenant Dougherty was involved in further aggressive patrols in the next days.[1]

Although only too well aware that the Japanese Amboga Force was some considerable distance from its new goal, possibly Sanananda, and was further handicapped by a most tenuous line of communication due to Allied air superiority, Brigadier Dougherty decided that it must be eliminated at the earliest opportunity. To this end, he summoned Lieutenant-Colonel Honner to his Headquarters late on 9 December to order the 39th Battalion to capture Haddy's Village. At 8 am on 10 December, the 39th left Brigade Headquarters south of Gona laden with six days' rations, ten miles of signal wire and all the ammunition they could carry. Lieutenant-Colonel Ralph Honner DSO, MC:

> The going was slow as creeks had to be crossed and in places a fresh track cut through the jungle, and evening found us in a native garden where we spent our first comfortable night for a week—and our last for more than a week. In the morning we crossed a tributary of the Amboga and struck a new track along which the guides started leading us upstream. I turned the battalion round and led it downstream, re-crossed the river leaving D Company to guard the last crossing, and soon received the guides' assurance that we were approaching the right village. I then ordered B Company, which had missed the heavier fighting at the mission, to go ahead with the guides.[2]

The guides, from the 2/14th Battalion, were Lieutenant Schwind[3] and Sergeant Iskov[4], both of whom had been to the Amboga area. Honner and his battalion had made their wide outflanking move from east to west, well to the south of the confrontation between the 2/14th and forward elements of the Amboga Force, to mount a surprise attack from the south on Haddy's Village.

As two of B Company's forward scouts and Sergeant Iskov came to within approximately 200 yards of the village defences, providence decreed the 39th Battalion a most frustrating miscarriage of the planned surprise of its attack. Oblivious to the Australians' presence, a Japanese lieutenant-colonel, a major and a third officer approached along the track in carefree fashion with towels for bathing. Honner, just passed by the leading section, was quickly informed. He decided it was impossible to knock out the enemy without some firing and gave orders for the two scouts and Iskov to shoot the luckless three should they come close enough for a certain kill. B Company would then charge on the enemy. The execution was sure and the exploitation was swift. Lieutenant-Colonel Ralph Honner DSO, MC:

> . . . the front section rushed straight on down the track to secure a foothold across the line of swamp protecting the enemy's southern defences. An enemy machine-gun opened up on them and the section-leader, Edgell, who had already distinguished himself five days earlier, received two bullet wounds in his right arm. They did not slow him down; he changed his Owen gun to his left hand in full career and, blazing away with it, charged the enemy gun, killing the three men manning it. This enabled the section to establish itself far enough ahead to allow the company to move up and launch its attack from forward of the swamp which the enemy post had covered. Two of Edgell's men had also been wounded by the machine-gun fire, and he assisted in their evacuation and reported on the forward situation before going to the RAP for attention to his own wounds.

The leading platoon, Plater's[5], carried on the attack along the main track. It struck strong resistance but pressed on, leaving a trail of enemy dead to mark its progress until it was held up by a strong post on its right. Plater stalked this post single-handed, killed the two officers and four others manning it, and captured their machine-gun and five bomb-throwers. For the next four hours he led the platoon in one attack after another on enemy posts, forcing a passage himself with grenades and Owen gun, and personally placing his sections in position when he was able to move them forward. Shortly before nightfall he was manouevring a section into position to strike at a machine-gun post when the section-commander was wounded beside him. He was dressing the corporal's wound when he was himself shot through the shoulder-blade. However Plater took the section in hand, led it forward, and destroyed the enemy post. After consolidating his position he staggered back to report to company headquarters and had to be carried out on a litter.

As soon as Plater's platoon had struck opposition, Lieutenant Harry Mortimore's platoon, carrying out the standard drill, had swung round to its right and Lieutenant Phil Gartner's[6] to its left. Gartner, who had been our most diligent tree-top sniper at the mission, pressed home his attack against strong opposition and, after four hours of hard fighting, gained a glimpse of huts in the village. By this time his platoon was reduced by casualties to section strength and was replaced by C Company. Gartner's ten men were sent out to the right of Mortimore's platoon to give it flank protection, and Gartner took command of Plater's now leaderless platoon in the centre.

C Company, only twenty-five strong after its gallant fighting at the mission, tried to advance on the left but was held up by heavy fire from two medium machine-guns. The company dug in for the night, and about midnight the enemy counter-attacked, over-running one platoon position, from which a few wounded survivors came in next morning.[7]

The rest of the forward troops, equally battle-worn and malaria-weakened and desperately wearied by a long day's fighting, had also dug in for an utterly miserable night. Lieutenant-Colonel Ralph Honner DSO, MC:

> . . . The village was on high ground between the beach and a swamp, and was flanked by the Amboga River on the west and a creek on the east, both fordable by sand bars at their mouths. When it rained, as it did throughout this night, not only the swamp line but all the low ground we occupied to invest the village was covered by water from a few inches to a couple of feet deep. Our only men not in the water were the wounded. For them we built table-high platforms to keep them above that unpleasant tide in which floated all the refuse of the living and the dead. All through that deluged night I sat, tree-backed, upon a log to lift my face above the spreading sewer. When the flood receded, latrines and new-dug graves and weapon-pits looked all alike.

On the 12th, with insufficient numbers to surround the village, Honner decided to push around his left flank to the sea to cut the enemy off from reinforcement or escape over the Amboga sandbar; and by the 14th with his last reserve platoons of D Company accelerating the advance on the left, he had committed his entire force to his extended front line methodically breaching the tangling jungle and its concealed network of enemy posts. The next day more guns, holding up the progress of all four companies, were located and knocked out; and Lieutenant Moore's platoon, overlooking the beach near the river, was able during the night to cut the enemy's telephone line to the west. Lieutenant-Colonel Ralph Honner DSO, MC:

> Only along Gartner's track was the ground open enough to permit the bombardment of enemy posts. Each day he pounded them with 2-inch mortar bombs and rifle grenades from some shallow hole beside the open track. The enemy along the track

turned all their weapons on him during these sessions but he coolly sat and fired bomb after bomb to help the other companies forward.

At nine o'clock in the morning of the 16th he was sniping at the enemy when he was hit by a burst of machine-gun fire . . .

Forty yards his platoon pushed on through the jungle in the next six hours, and thirty-five dead enemy on the ground they captured showed how bitterly the Japanese had fought to hold every yard of it. At three o'clock in the afternoon even the lion-hearted Gartner could do no more. His left leg was useless even for crawling, and he had to be carried from his post.

On the right Mortimore's platoon pushed on against similar opposition over similar dead bodies and, after dark, seized positions under huts in the south-east corner, giving daylight observation of most of the village. On the left, later in the night, thirty enemy, carrying shovels, grenade dischargers and other equipment besides their rifles, came from the west and crossed the sand bar to enter the village. But they were ambushed by D Company's left platoon, and at daylight fifteen new corpses, including that of an officer, lay out on the bloodied beach.

The next morning an enemy group crossed the river up-stream from our forward positions, waded, near-naked, through a knee-deep swamp and attacked D Company headquarters from the rear. They were all killed and their machine-gun was captured.

Through the day the steady advance continued, and at night we were not idle. When darkness fell on the 17th Lieutenant McClean of D Company led a platoon round our left flank, destroyed an enemy post and consolidated a position on the beach. The enemy were now almost surrounded, only fifty yards of open beach separating McClean's outposts from the aggressive 2/14th Battalion, led by Captain Bill Russell, which, since its arrival, had fought its way across the eastern creek and assiduously done its share of destruction. Shortly after midnight

an enemy barge was heard off shore by our beach posts,
and later two Japanese came out of the sea to be killed by
the 2/14th.[8]

The 2/14th had been blocking the Amboga Force's eastward
push midway between the village and Gona Mission. On
14 December its remaining opponents had been withdrawn
towards the village and the 2/14th had harried them with pug-
nacious patrolling rewarded by the elimination of elements of
the retiring screen, by the 2/14th's arrival in the afternoon of
the 15th at the creek on the eastern outskirts of the village and
by its linking up with Mortimore's right-flank platoon of the
39th. The trap was closed, but not without cost; Sergeant
Truscott, a tower of strength throughout the Gona Campaign,
was killed while making a forward reconnaissance.

The still formidable Haddy's Village contingent of the
2/14th—about 100 strong—came under Honner's command
with two of its most competent leaders, Captains Russell and
Bisset, but only two other officers—Captain Cortis, the
medical officer, and Lieutenant Schwind, one of the 39th Battalion's Amboga guides. It needed no instruction from Honner
as it carried its independent war across the hazardous barrier
of the eastern creek into enemy territory.

From 15–18 December, the 2/14th, without taking
unnecessary risks, was able to pinpoint and destroy a number
of Japanese light and heavy machine-gun posts with a
minimum of casualties. On the 16th, Acting Sergeant Ted
Shelden's platoon moved across the creek into the village.
When held up by enemy fire, Shelden crawled forward
alone under covering fire from his platoon and, approaching
within a few feet of each of three posts in turn, killed the
occupants with grenades and Tommy gun. By dusk two
sections were established in positions captured from the
enemy, Corporal Russell being killed while manouevring
his section during the action.

Next morning, Sergeant Fitzpatrick's platoon also moved across the creek, capturing two posts and killing eight of the enemy. The same day saw the dramatic employment of a newly available weapon. Captain Stan Bisset MC, 2/14th Battalion:

A strong enemy post with heavy and some light machine-guns was causing trouble to both battalions and several brave 39th men had been lost in trying to silence it. The 2/14th Battalion had just been issued with the new and deadly 68 grenades, fired from a discharger cup—Pte. 'Digger' Walters of A Coy. with complete disregard for his own safety moved to a position in the village within seventy yards of this post and with the heroic Shelden spotting for him, fired the grenades from his E.Y. rifle with great effect and was able to destroy all guns and cause indescribable slaughter.[9]

As 18 December loomed the fall of the last Japanese defences drew near. Lieutenant-Colonel Ralph Honner DSO, MC:

During all this time, Corporal Andy Heraud of C Company had been busy. Twice in the night he had led a patrol of four men amongst the enemy positions looking for a medium machine-gun which was holding up his section. He spent four hours searching for the gun without finding it—four hours of stalking and grenading enemy posts, but never the one with the gun he wanted.

And at two o'clock in the morning, Corporal Stan Ellis of A Company, who had already shown his mettle at the mission, went out alone, wormed his way to within ten yards of another medium machine-gun, and with a shower of grenades killed its crew. He had spent the three previous days in no-man's land trying to locate and silence that gun. He went out before daylight each morning, dug himself a hole near where he thought the hated post had to be and, throughout the day, threw grenades at it and carried on a sniping war with the enemy round about. In the three days he killed between twelve and twenty of them with his Owen gun. Each night he returned to his section to plan the next day's operations. Now, on this last morning, he came back to lead his section in the final assault.

On the morning of the 18th Heraud located the machine-gun he had been looking for during the night. It was in a strongpost in the jungle a few yards in front of his section but invisible through that impenetrable dark-green wall. The section outflanked the enemy post, killed its defenders and captured the gun. Then A and C companies both moved forward in the face of still heavy fire to the edge of the jungle.

From there the final assault was made. Dalby, who had taken the first post in the capture of Gona Mission led the attack. Again his dash carried him amongst the enemy ahead of his men. And again he made a machine-gun his objective . . .[10]

That gun was firing from the post demolished by Private Walters of the 2/14th the previous day. Dalby killed its crew of three and as the whole Australian line surged forward all remaining resistance was quickly overwhelmed. Lieutenant-Colonel Ralph Honner DSO, MC:

The enemy wounded had been evacuated across the sand bar or by barges calling in the night, and perhaps a considerable number of the unwounded went with them. As it was there were twenty fresh Japanese graves beside the mouth of the Amboga, and we buried a hundred and seventy more of their dead. We had done well to defeat an enemy of superior numbers holding a strong defensive position on his own chosen ground.

As soon as the village fell, malaria-ridden troops, who had hung on fighting till the fight was over, staggered to the R.A.P. for special treatment. And to my Intelligence Officer came one of our last-minute reinforcements, asking shyly, 'Please sir, would you show me how this gun works? I never had one of these before'. I glanced up to identify the strange weapon; it was the ordinary .303 rifle that every recruit cuts his teeth on. And I looked at the lad in wonderment; he was probably the best of that batch of newcomers[11]—the first to respond to the invitation to join the A.I.F. He had played his part with a fixed bayonet and a stout heart in all his section's battles through the jungle filth, the swamp miasma and the fetid stench, too proud to proclaim his ignorance of the functioning of a rifle bolt to these friends who had accepted him as one of themselves.[12]

The fall of Haddy's Village on 18 December signified the end of the major fighting in the vicinity of Gona. Lieutenant-Colonel Challen assumed command of the Gona area whilst Brigadier Dougherty and the 39th Battalion were ordered to march to yet another fight—along the Sanananda track. Dudley McCarthy:

... the composite 2/16th—2/27th took over in the Haddy's Village area on the 19th, at the end of a phase of operations which (west of Gona) had cost the Australians a further 129 casualties, of whom the 39th battalion lost 2 officers and 105 men.

These figures focus sharp attention on that battalion as they brought its total battle losses in the Gona area to 8 officers and 220 men for the sixteen-day period from the 3rd to the 18th. Their special significance lies in the fact that the 39th was a militia battalion. It is true that its commander, Honner, was not only a veteran A.I.F. officer but an outstanding leader, even in that tried force. Many of its other officers were also proved A.I.F. veterans. On the other hand, French's and Gartner's service had been entirely with militia battalions, as had Plater's (although he was a Duntroon graduate). And almost all of the men in the ranks were militia men without previous experience of action before they arrived in New Guinea. A number of them steadfastly refused to join the A.I.F. under any circumstances, at least two of these being N.C.O.s who were decorated for bravery and skill.

Although, therefore, undoubtedly much of the dash and devotion (perhaps the major part) of the men of this battalion could be attributed directly or indirectly to their A.I.F. leaders, just as obviously this could not have been the whole explanation. Perhaps the key lies finally in the fact that the 39th had already acquitted itself well in battle with the Japanese before its arrival at Gona. Had enough battle wisdom come from that experience to make the battalion the fighting force it proved itself to be? Again a positive answer must surely be sharply qualified for the reinforcements who had built the battalion's shattered strength could, at best, have been only vicariously battle-wise. Most significant, too, in this connection, is the fact that about 100 of those had come from the 53rd Battalion whose record had not been good. And high praise was given these men after Gona by the original members of the 39th! Surely the final element in the complex answer must be found in the pride with which the battalion remembered its earlier experiences and that it had been the first Australian unit to meet the invaders. From that recollection moral strength must have flooded in like a tide bearing with it a high purpose, a will to endure greatly, and a contagious inspiration for newcomers. So it was that this militia battalion became the pivot on which the capture of Gona finally swung, pressed to a successful conclusion a difficult and costly action after the fall of the main Gona bastion, and accepted losses which were remarkably heavy even for the type of warfare that developed in Papua.[13]

On 16 August 1942, Brigadier Potts had led a proud, battle-tested, victorious and utterly confident force of two battalions into the Owen Stanley Range. His 2/14th Battalion numbered 24 officers and 577 other ranks; his 2/16th Battalion set forth with approximately 600 men all told, and on 5 September at Mission Ridge, his 2/27th Battalion deployed some 28 officers and 560 other ranks—roughly 1800 fit young men—amongst the elite soldiers of the Australian Army. The 2/14th Battalion left Gona with its forward troops numbering 21, and when it gathered up its walking wounded and holding camp personnel its numbers grew to 57. The 2/16th, when relieved at Gona, had eight officers and 48 other ranks and the 2/27th left the area with three officers and 67.

The startling casualties on the Kokoda Trail and at Gona in deadly combination with the debilitating campaign conditions had transformed those magnificent battalions of August 1942 into meagre, ragged groups of malaria-shaken skeletons.

This history began with an examination of the events that led to the formation and deployment of the 49th Battalion in March 1941, and the arrival of the 39th and 53rd Battalions in January of the following year to constitute the 30th Brigade garrison at Port Moresby.

Whilst the 39th Battalion was desperately embroiled in the critical fighting along the Kokoda Trail, its sister battalions, apart from a brief and tragic action by the 53rd Battalion along the Abuari–Missima–Kaile track while the Battle of Isurava raged, had been involved in the ever changing plans to defend Port Moresby from seaborne invasion. By December 1942, the 49th Battalion had given continuous service at Port Moresby for some twenty months.

By the beginning of December, the failure of two desperate attempts to capture Sanananda, and the very heavy battle and sickness casualties incurred, were the cause of grave concern to the Allied high command.

The first assaults had been undertaken by Brigadier Lloyd's 16th Brigade over a period of approximately two weeks. These brave and resolute troops had failed for three key reasons. Firstly, the physical deterioration and wastage of Lloyd's battalions, because of their long involvement in the pursuit of the enemy over the Owen Stanley Range and through to the beach-head, had been dramatic. Secondly, the extremely threadbare American intelligence appreciation of the size, deployment and psychological strength of the Japanese defence at Sanananda and

Gona had caused extravagant wastage of Australian manpower, throwing too little at too much. Thirdly, the same inadequacy of fire support and aerial bombing, as was evident at Gona, greatly impaired forward movement against an enemy so well dug-in and operating with such a skilled fire plan.

The second attempt to reduce the Sanananda beach-head had been concentrated around the American force. It too, had failed.

Blamey to Curtin ALF, SWPA, Adv. HQ. N.G.,
4 December 1942

Letter   Most Secret and Personal.
. . . I had hoped that our strategical plans would have been crowned with complete and rapid success in the tactical field. It was completely successful strategically in as much as we brought an American Division on to Buna and an Australian Division on to Gona simultaneously. But in the tactical field after the magnificent advance through the most difficult area, the Owen Stanley Range, it is a very sorry story.

It has revealed the fact that the American troops cannot be classified as attack troops. They are definitely not equal to the Australian militia, and from the moment they met opposition sat down and have hardly gone forward a yard. The action, too, has revealed a very alarming state of weakness in their staff system and in their war psychology. General MacArthur has relieved the Divisional Commander and has called up General Eichelberger the Corps Commander, and sent him over to take charge. He informs me that he proposes to relieve both the regimental commanders, the equivalent of our brigade commanders, and five out of six of the battalion commanders; and this in the face of the enemy. I am afraid now that the bulk of the fighting will fall on our troops in spite of the greatly larger numbers of the 32nd U.S. Division.

The brigades that went over the mountain track are now so depleted that they are being withdrawn and I am utilising the only remaining AIF brigade in Port Moresby and a brigade of Militia, that has been intensively trained here, and I think we will pull it off all right . . .[14]

'The only remaining AIF brigade in Port Moresby' had been the 21st Brigade. By 4 December it was embroiled in its desperate Gona attacks. The 'intensively trained' militia brigade was none other than the 30th Brigade. There can be no doubt that its 49th and 55th/53rd Battalions were intensively trained—but for other purposes; there were no wharves for unloading at Sanananda and no defences against seaborne attack to be dug there.

Lieutenant-Colonel Lovell had been commanding the 55th Battalion for only a few weeks before it had been amalgamated with the 53rd Battalion. In an interview with the author in June 1989, he was under no illusion as to the priorities in 'intensive training':

I had no opportunity to really carry out any intensive training for two reasons; firstly, they were being employed as wharf-labourers unloading ships, and secondly, in October and November, we were employed on the construction of the defence of Tuaguba Hill.[15]

When the 36th Battalion joined the 49th and 55th/53rd Battalions at Sanananda, its commanding officer, Lieutenant-Colonel Isaachsen[16] also observed the results of this 'intensive training':

When we got over to Sanananda, when Brigadier Porter found that quite a few of the fellows had never fired a Bren-gun or Tommy-gun—never thrown a grenade—he ordered that these fellows come back not far from his Brigade Headquarters and be given actual experience in firing a Bren, a Tommy-gun and throwing a few grenades. This was within a few days of us arriving at Soputa.[17]

Lovell and Isaachsen had both served with the AIF in the Middle East; had been promoted and given command of the 55th/53rd and 36th Battalions respectively, and had both been denied the time to instigate the standards of training that they had taken for granted in AIF formations. And the 49th Battalion had fared no better; Fred Cranston in *Always Faithful:*

> . . . the battalion had experienced about 100 air raids, and while casualties from these had been extremely light, the raids were far from pleasant. The unit had also dug defences in all areas of Port Moresby and surrounding districts. In relation to this, Bill Noyes recalls that his company dug defences from Bootless Inlet to Port Moresby and was then given the task of erecting a rest camp at Koitaki (after winning the brigade competition for the best prepared defensive area). From there, they were soon ordered back to join the battalion to commence jungle training.
>
> Though jungle training would have been a great morale booster for the troops after months spent in digging, they had no sooner arrived in the training area and dug the battalion latrines, when they were ordered to move again. This was the end of the jungle training for them even though almost all of Bill Noyes' company (and no doubt others) never fired an Owen or Bren-gun on a range . . .[18]

Kevin Barry participated in the 55th/53rd attack along the Sanananda track on 7 December. In an interview with the author in Sydney in November 1988, he described his early training and subsequent action at Sanananda:

> When we arrived at Moresby I was in the signals and I was only there a couple of weeks and I got malaria and I was crook for weeks. I ended up at Koitaki convalescent camp. Then I was seconded away to join a group to put up a telegraph line from ten miles out of Moresby into Moresby.

. . . Then when that was over we were walking up and down Mount Tuaguba digging defensive positions outside of Moresby. Walk up in the morning, dig and walk back down again at night.

Bearing in mind at this time I'd never ever held a rifle in my hand, never ever fired one—didn't know anything about it . . .

Then when the Japs started to come over the Range, out we go to a rifle range somewhere . . .

Next minute we're over there [Sanananda] and we're lining up at 3.15 p.m. on the 7th of December, fixed bayonets, and I'm a forward scout with Johnny Achbold; we both got wounded the same day—so out we go and they say charge—into the jungle we go . . . And all of a sudden the shit hit the fan. Machine-guns; and I'm going along and I can hear this and I'm hanging on to the rifle and I'm shit scared—Then in the next minute I'm up in the air—lost the rifle, lost my tin hat— hit in the shoulder . . . That was the sum total of my war-time experience . . .[19]

During their first fruitless attacks in the Sanananda area on 7 December, the 55th/53rd Battalion suffered 130 battle casu- alties, eight of them officers, while the 49th Battalion lost a staggering total of fourteen officers and 215 other ranks— nearly 48 per cent of the battalion strength. Within the follow- ing fortnight the 55th/53rd sustained 75 further casualties, including six officers, and the 49th increased its total of killed, wounded and missing by 55. The introduction of the 36th Bat- talion into the Sanananda stalemate did not change the pattern within Brigadier Porter's command of confused repulsed attacks and heavy pointless losses. High casualties may not necessarily be the measure of high success or even of high endeavour; they can be merely savage statistics of the futile squandering of unvalued lives. Dudley McCarthy:

By this time Brigadier Porter had become bitterly critical of both the 36th and 55th/53rd Battalions. He said that any success which was theirs was 'due to a percentage of personnel who are brave in the extreme' and 'the result of unskilful aggression'. He was caustic in referring to their deficiencies of training and spirit.[20]

For the displaced ditch-diggers and wharf-labourers of seaside Port Moresby, there was little job satisfaction from on-the-site training in their unaccustomed employment in Sanananda's hinterland. But their deficiencies and decimation were not disasters of their own contrivance. These were the ultimate tragic harvest of their country's 22 years of culpable unpreparedness; of Australia's unthinking reliance on Britain and its bastion of Singapore; of two generations' irresponsible neglect of their army and of the calamitous mismanagement of the two-army system. Australia retained a large long-trained army idle at home until there was no longer a need for it elsewhere. She then proposed to expend it against isolated but still lethal enemy remnants stranded by the receding tide of the Pacific War. When there had been a dire need for more trained troops in Papua, it was not policy to disturb the uncommitted cohorts in Australia while there was a pool of unskilled labour at Port Moresby to be disposed of.

Despite the apathy and the blundering, Australia was stirring once more to the beat of a distant drum. If history looks beyond the blunder to see heroic Gallipoli as symbolic of the birth of a nation, it may well perceive the triumph over disaster of the Kokoda Trail and Gona campaigns as marking the onset of Australia's sturdy adolescence. The fall of Singapore had signalled the end of British power in Asia; the sun was setting on the dying Empire; the embattled heir, aspiring to a loftier station under a later sun, was ascending the Golden Stairs, the pathway of the paladins of the Papuan War. Those paragons have carried us up on eagles' wings. How high and constant is their fame?

To the generation of Australians who fought and suffered overseas and those who lived and worked in Australia during the Second World War, the 7th Division became known as the

'Silent Seventh'; silent because its campaigns received little recognition and less publicity. It had fought in the bloody Syrian Campaign, a silent campaign because its enemy were French, Vichy French, and the French were Australia's allies. Its 18th Brigade had battled alongside the 9th Division in Tobruk with great distinction, yet publicity projects Tobruk as a purely 9th Division operation. But the very pinnacle of the Silent Seventh's semi-secret service in the war was reached in the Papuan campaigns. The dogged 25th Brigade fought its way almost from sea to sea, over the Kokoda Trail, at Oivi-Gorari and at Gona; but it was not an acceptable time to publicise its progress when Americans at Buna were making none. The superb 18th Brigade, after its decisive victory alongside the 7th (militia) Brigade at Milne Bay, swept to stunning success at Buna and Sanananda where the American 32nd and 41st Divisions had been bogged down in failure; but they could not expect over-exuberant applause when the wrong (and smaller) team had clinched those long-sought victories. The tremendous achievement along the Kokoda Trail of the truly magnificent 21st Brigade and the gallant young 39th Battalion was something that even the Australian higher command did not seem to want to know about—or to let anyone else know about. And the desperate triumph of those former Maroubra Force partners at Gona was perhaps too ill-timed—while Buna and Sanananda had not fallen—to win appropriate notice from the supreme publicity machine. The cloud of ignorance and silence remains to this day; yet the significance of those campaigns to Australian history is monumental.

The young veterans of the 39th Battalion left the littered northern beaches bloodied but unbowed, the human spirit braced by bonds of mateship and fortified by a fierce unyielding pride. Lieutenant-Colonel Ralph Honner DSO, MC:

> . . . when the last beach-head had fallen, and we trudged back along the track from Sanananda on January 23rd, 1943, we

mustered only seven officers and twenty-five other ranks—weak from long-suppressed malaria and somewhat tired of the 'mud and blood' symbolised by our battalion colours.

Our R.M.O. said some of us were not fit to undertake the next day's march to Dobadura airfield. Higher authority refused us vehicles for the less fit, ruling that no one could ride unless he fell out on the march—there would be vehicles behind us to pick up all the stragglers. In the 39th's book, marchers didn't straggle, so we all marched, all the way, to Dobadura—for some, a long torture on the verge of unconsciousness that only pride and the solicitous support of their comrades made endurable. Then, in the wake and the dust of truck-loads of cheering, fresh-looking troops who had seen little campaigning and less fighting, but had learnt that it paid to straggle, we marched with parade-ground precision on to the Dobadura airfield—haggard, silent, sweating scarecrows under the tropic sun. And when an amazed bystander enquired, 'What mob's this?' we kept out eyes straight ahead—all except my second-in-command at the end of the line, who barked, 'This is not a mob!' and added, relenting, 'This is the 39th!'[21]

Little did the 39th Battalion dream that it was destined not for greater deeds but for the guillotine. The 30th Brigade was reconstituted in early 1943 with a wealth of battle experience in its 3rd, 39th and 49th Battalions, unequalled in any other militia brigade. Yet, in a formation reduction move, it was the one sentenced, by a final stroke of military genius, to summary extinction. Its corporate strength was destroyed and its severed individuals were scattered, in random packets large and small, throughout a score of AIF and militia units.

It is ironic that the 53rd Battalion, the most neglected of the brigade's original battalions and the one embroiled in the most controversy in its unfortunate campaigning, should have been the only one—through its earlier incorporation in the 55th/53rd Battalion—to survive the disbandment.

The devoted 39th Battalion with its brilliant battle record, its shining testimony to the true fighting prowess of the Australian soldier and its hard-won esprit de corps, was mindlessly destroyed.

The battalions of the 21st Brigade had emerged from the slaughter of Gona with their ranks shattered and their heroes dead, but with an unbroken spirit—a spirit, indeed, tempered in the forge of suffering to a tougher steel on which to build again a proud elite to win fresh laurels on farther fields. They bore with honour their badge of silence—the silence of unboasted challenge and achievement. For the executed 39th Battalion there could be no more laurels, no more life; its silence was of the grave.

However, even that silence might have its eloquence for those attuned to it. To mark Kokoda Day a greying column marches through Melbourne's broad Domain to its memorial Shrine and a simple ceremonial that wakes old pain and pride. The haunting piping of 'The Flowers of the Forest' throbs on the pensive air. Boys who became men in battles shrouded in the mists of time file in to be moved by the recital of the Roll of Honour, to be stilled by the 'Last Post', sounding the passing of a day that has gone, and to be stirred by the thrilling 'Reveille' with its assurance that there is another day. They lay their sprigs of lantana before the Rock of Remembrance, remembering how lantana lined Kokoda's winding track and leaned over those who fell beneath its fronds to journey forever far beyond Kokoda. Then they come out into the brightness of their promised day, seeing afresh the free Australia those ragged bloody heroes helped to pay for with their lives—their last and lasting gift.

Afterword

Re-reading *Those Ragged Bloody Heroes* after nearly fourteen years, Peter Brune's groundbreaking narrative of the 1942 New Guinea battles seems even darker and more pessimistic than it did when it first appeared. Certainly there is the celebration of the courage and endurance of ordinary soldiers from a generation Brune has increasingly come to admire. It also celebrates the heroes: Ralph Honner arriving at just the right moment to retrieve the situation at Isurava, then returning with the—by then—legendary 39th Battalion to capture Gona; ordinary soldiers like Staff-Sergeant Cowey, waiting in the darkness outside Kokoda for any of his men who had lost their way; 'Tubby' Jacob dying in a futile accident while trying to help an exhausted soldier.

These men, Brune believes, are special. They were, in the words of Padre Fred Burt, 'the men who saved Australia'— undoubtedly from extensive attacks on the mainland, possibly from invasion. But, Brune insists, these men were betrayed by a government that surrendered its sovereignty to the vain and pompous MacArthur; by commanders who threw away the lives of their men to maintain their own positions and to impress the Americans; and above all, by a Commander-in-Chief whose loyalty to his subordinates was forgotten when pressure from above became too great.

While Brune carefully spells out the strategy and tactics of the key battles, sometimes, as with Brigade Hill and Cameron's idiotic first assault on Kokoda, his emphasis is on the experience of the men themselves. Each soldier is identified by rank and battalion, then allowed to speak for himself. Whole narratives are related in the raw, unvarnished prose of the participants. At its best, as with the account of the 2/27th Battalion's epic march to bring all their wounded back to live and fight another day, this is profoundly moving.

The danger for any historian working this way is that they can become, in their imagination, one of the people they're portraying, losing their objectivity and relating legends. Not Peter Brune. As I discovered when I collaborated with him on *200 Shots*, Peter checks and cross-checks the narratives with the participants, inviting them to become his collaborators in a search for the truth. He then compares his accounts with the documents.

The result has been a whole range of important discoveries. Brune quotes from the unexpurgated *Report of 21st Brigade: Owen Stanley Campaign* before it was condensed and rewritten by order of Land Forces Headquarters. He found that battalion reports cited in good faith by the Official Historian were written up months later back in Australia; inevitably, the men made diaries and personal accounts written at the time available to him, thus adding to the documentary record. Peter Brune was not afraid to be critical of participants who had been of immense help to him if he believed it was justified—read closely his account of Brigadier Dougherty's conduct of operations at Gona: he is tactful, but remains objective.

One of the book's most significant passages is Brune's analysis of the infamous Koitaki Parade, which led him to believe that Blamey's unjustified abuse of the men who'd 'given so much' affected operations at Gona. Naturally Brune had to first establish what happened. For years the official line had been that Blamey hadn't accused 21st Brigade of cowardice when he used the phrase 'The rabbit that runs is the rabbit that gets shot'; that he was really talking about the Japanese. Brune exposes this as drivel—no sane commander could possibly describe Japanese tactics this way. Then he marshals testimony from a formidable array of participants, men who actually heard what Blamey said. Most devastating of all, he cites the previously ignored account by the Commander-in-Chief's ADC Norman Carlyon.

Brune was not the first to describe Blamey's conduct in this way—that honour went to Padre Fred Burt of the 2/16th Battalion, who denounced the future field marshal in a series of talks at RSL clubs in the 1940s. He was quickly silenced. Then there came Raymond Paull in *Retreat from Kokoda* (1958). As Brune describes in *A Bastard of a Place*, Paull was attacked in columns of the *Age* by cronies of Blamey, headed by Sir Edmund Herring. He was subsequently bullied into a half-hearted retraction by John Hetherington when the latter was working on *Blamey: Controversial Soldier* for the Australian War Memorial, and Paull was dying. In the 1980s H. D. 'Blue' Steward in *Recollections of a Regimental Medical Officer* insisted Blamey *had* accused 21st Brigade of cowardice, and repeated this account convincingly and at greater length when I interviewed him shortly after his book was published. But until *Those Ragged Bloody Heroes* appeared, the standard line from official and semi-official sources was that it had all been an unfortunate misunderstanding; 'After all', said one senior officer to me of Steward's book, 'I was there too'.

After Brune's account, the official line was completely discredited. He also argues that Blamey's attitude caused Brigadier Dougherty to doubt the competence of his battalion commanders and to interfere with the conduct of operations at the beach-head. The result was disastrous and is the only lapse in a career that deservedly earned Dougherty his reputation as one of Australia's finest soldiers.

But why read *Those Ragged Bloody Heroes* so many years later, especially when Brune himself has, with *A Bastard of a Place*, described a war in New Guinea in much greater detail? It is, of course, always fascinating to look at the beginning. I believe without *Those Ragged Bloody Heroes* we would not have Peter FitzSimons' *Kokoda,* with its marvellous evocation of the experience of battle and masterly narratives of Isurava and Gona. Nor would there be Stewart Braga's superb biography of 'Tubby' Allen, *Kokoda Commander*, that finally does justice to an extraordinary Australian soldier and includes a devastating exposé of the intrigues by the loathsome Edmund Herring. And then there are Peter's own books: *The Spell Broken*; *We Band of Brothers*; and *Gona's Gone!* (Brune always believed the Kokoda battles should be seen as a part of the one campaign, an argument he presents most forcefully in *A Bastard of a Place*.) As well, we have Chris Masters' *4 Corners* documentary, *The Men who Saved Australia*. During an interview with Jack Sim, Chris discovered exactly what Ralph Honner had said to the 39th Battalion when they were relieved at Menari. This led Brune to investigate the way Honner compared the Kokoda experience with the mud, blood and heroism of Shakespeare's *Henry V* (it was clear that Honner had the St Crispin's Day speech in mind when he was addressing the men). This was no specious glorification of the Kokoda experience; war correspondent Chester Wilmot found the hedgerow fighting in Normandy not far from the field of Agincourt similar to his experiences on the Kokoda Track.

Still, this is historiography: fascinating and valuable in tracing how our understanding of the 1942 conflict has evolved. But what does *Those Ragged Bloody Heroes* tell us now? Even after fourteen years the book is the most reliable history of the Kokoda battles to date. Above all, it comes from the men themselves. Often Peter reached key figures just in time, so while many fine writers and historians write *about* Kokoda and Gona, in the pages of *Those Ragged Bloody Heroes* you actually *meet* 'the men who saved Australia'.

Neil McDonald
February 2005

Notes

Foreword

1 Scott, Geoffrey *The Knights of Kokoda*
2 Major-General Sir Frank Kingsley Norris, KBE, CB, DSO, ED, quoted by the author at the close of chapter 13
3 Bomana War Cemetery, Papua New Guinea
4 Private J.W. Burton, B Company, 39 Battalion, quoted on p. 161, *We Were There*—by John Barrett

1 Peace in our time

1 Rowell *Full Circle* p. 43
2 The term 'chocolate soldier' is thought to have come from a comic operetta called *The Chocolate Soldier* by Franz Lehar

2 The threshold of fear

1 Cranston *Always Faithful* p. 129
2 Major-General B.M. Morris, CBE, DSO, (1 AIF 55 Siege Bty; 5 Div. Arty 1917–18.) Comd Aust. overseas base ME, 1940; Aust. Military Liaison Officer India 1940–41; Comd 8 MD. 1941–42; Comd. NG. Force 1942; ANGAU 1942–46. Regular Soldier; of

Upper Beaconsfield, Vic., Born East Melbourne, 19 December 1898

3 This parade and Lieutenant-General Sturdee's statement are well documented. See Long *The Six Years' War* p. 205; Cranston *Always Faithful*, The History of the 49th Battalion p. 137; letters from 49th Battalion veterans

4 Sergeant K.J. Irwin, letter 20 March 1989

5 Lieutenant-Colonel K.H. Ward, CO, 53rd Battalion. Killed in action 27 August 1942

6 *Report of the Barry Commission on Cessation of Papuan Civil Administration in 1942*, paragraph 18

7 Colonel H.M. Conran, ED, CO 39th Battalion 1941–May 1942

8 Major-General G.A. Vasey, CB, CBE, DSO, (1 AIF.; 2 Div. Arty and Brigade Major 11 Inf. Bde) AA. & QMG. 6 Div. 1939–41; GSO, 1 6 Div. 1941; Comd 19 Inf. Bde 1941; GOC, 6 Div. 1942, 7 Div. 1942–44. Regular soldier, of Melbourne Victoria. Born 29 March 1895. Killed in an aeroplane crash 5 March 1945

9 Major-General S.H.W.C. Porter, CBE, DSO, 2/5th Battalion 1939–41; CO, 2/6th Battalion 1941, 2/31st Battalion 1941–42; Comd 30th Bde 1942–43, 24th Bde 1943-45. Born 23 February 1905

10 Major M.L. Bidstrup, interview 7 October 1986

11 Lieutenant H.E. Mortimore, interview 7 June 1986

12 Captain S.V. Templeton, 39th Battalion. Born Belfast, N. Ireland. Killed in action 26 July 1942. Exact age unknown

13 Lieutenant H.E. Mortimore, interview 7 June 1986 Lieutenant A.H. Seekamp, interview 24 April 1986 Lieutenant A.G. Garland, interview 7th June 1986

14 Fought from 5–8 May 1942, the battle marked the first occasion that opposing navies had confronted each other without actually coming within close range. This battle heralded the beginning of carrier-based naval engagements and confirmed the belief that the battleship was no longer to be the prime naval weapon

15 Raymond Paull *Retreat From Kokoda*

16 ibid. p. 22

17 ibid. pp. 21–22
18 Major N.M. Symington, interview 15 July 1987
19 Major M.L. Bidstrup, interview 14 July 1987
20 Major W.G.T. Merritt, 39th, 7th MG. Battalion LO 3rd Div. 1944–45. Born 8 December 1911
21 Lieutenant-Colonel Owen, 2/22nd, 39th Battalions. Killed in action 29 July 1942
22 Captain H. Dalby, interview 6 March 1986
23 Private L. Armitage, interview 8 June 1986
24 Lieutenant A.G. Garland, interview 7 June 1986
25 Major M.L. Bidstrup, interview 7 January 1986

3 The devil's design

1 Major H.J. Katekar, document entitled 'My Personal Experiences and Impressions during Operations in Papua (August 1942–January 1943) written in 2/4th AGH, Redbank, Qld, commencing 10 May 1943'; original lent to author January 1989
2 Captain H. Dalby, interview 6 March 1986
3 Private A.N. Ward, interview 8 December 1986
4 ibid.

4 No do-or-die stunts

1 Dudley McCarthy *South-West Pacific Area First Year* p. 115
2 Captain H.T. Kienzle, CBE, ANGAU. Miner and planter of Yodda Valley. Born Levuka, Ovalau Island, Fiji, 19 May 1905. Died January 1987
3 Captain G.H. Vernon, Medical practitioner and planter of Daru, Papua. Born England 16 December 1882. Died 16 May 1946
4 ANGAU—Australian New Guinea Administrative Unit
5 Major N.M. Symington, interview 15 July 1987
6 ibid.
7 Captain H.T. Kienzle, letter entitled 'A brief account of myself from birth to early November 1942 after recapture of Kokoda' December 1986

8 ibid.

9 Documents received December 1986

10 Lieutenant A.H. Seekamp, interview 24 April 1986

11 Captain F.P. Brewer, ANGAU. Patrol Officer of Port Moresby; killed in aircraft accident 20 October 1944

12 Captain H.T. Kienzle, letter December 1986

13 ibid.

14 Brigadier J. Field, CO, 2/12th Battalion 1939–42; Commander 7th Brigade, 1942–45

15 Lieutenant A.G. Garland, interview 7 June 1986

16 Lieutenant A.H. Seekamp, interview 24 April 1986

17 Major D.I.H. McClean, 39th Battalion, 1st Para Battalion. Born 9 July 1915

18 Sergeant E.J. Morrison, 39th Battalion. Born 5 March 1919

19 Major D. McClean, interview 7 June 1986

20 Dudley McCarthy *South-West Pacific Area First Year* p. 126

21 Lieutenant H. Mortimore, interview 7 June 1986

22 Captain C.M. Stevenson 2/14th and 2/2nd Battalions. Born 13 January 1918

23 Lieutenant H. Mortimore, interview 7 June 1986

24 Warrant Officer 2 J.D. Wilkinson, 1st Corps. Troops Supply Column; ANGAU. Born 3 November 1907

25 Copy of Wilkinson's Diary, p. 3—kindly lent to author by Captain H.T. Kienzle, December 1986

26 Major M.L. Bidstrup, interview 11 June 1986

27 ibid.

28 Lieutenant A.G. Garland, interview 7 June 1986

29 Dudley McCarthy *South-West Pacific Area First Year* p. 129

30 ibid.

31 Wilkinson's Diary, p. 3

5 A desperate baptism

1 Captain H.T. Kienzle—diary

2 July, August and September

3 *Medical Report on Native Carriers Lines of Communication Kokoda*

Front 2 July–12 October 1942 Captain G.H.Vernon—kindly lent by Captain H.T. Kienzle December 1986

4 24 July 1942 – C Company Captain Dean leaves Ilolo. Arrives Deniki 30 July 1942

25 July 1942 – A Company Captain Symington leaves Ilolo. Arrives Deniki 1 August 1942

Approximately 29, 30, 31 July 1942 – D Company Captain Bidstrup and E Company Captain Merritt leave Ilolo. D Company arrives Deniki 6 August 1942. E Company arrives Isurava as Battalion reserve to force at Deniki 5 August 1942

5 Major N.M. Symington, interview 15 July 1987

6 Captain H. Dalby, interview 6 March 1986

7 Major M.L. Bidstrup, interview 7 January 1986

8 Lieutenant-Colonel A.G. Cameron, 2/22nd Battalion; CO, Maroubra Force August 1942; CO 53rd Battalion August 1942; CO 3rd Battalion 1942; CO 2/2nd Battalion 1943

9 Wilkinson's Diary, p. 3

10 Raymond Paull *Retreat From Kokoda*

11 ibid. p. 71

12 Verified by Lieutenant W.K. Gillespie, interview March 1986; L.W. Wood, letter April 1987; R.A. Kemp, letter April 1987; N.W. Greenwood, letter March 1987

13 Major N. Symington, interview 15 July 1987

14 Captain D.K. Goldsmith, interview 25 May 1987. Captain Goldsmith was seconded after 21st Brigade's release from the campaign to service with DC 3s guiding planes to their drop zones

15 Captain H.T. Kienzle, letter December 1986

16 *39 Battalion Unit Diary—the August Diary 1942*

17 Captain H.J. Jesser, PIB. Born 11 April 1917

18 Captain H.N. Sorenson, 39th Battalion. Born 2 September 1917

19 Captain M.G. Evensen, PIB. Killed in action 25 October 1944

20 Major N. Symington, interview 15 July 1987

21 Major M.L. Bidstrup, interview 13 March 1986

22 Lieutenant-Colonel R. Honner, 2/11th Battalion; CO, 39th Battalion 1942–43; CO 2/14th Battalion 1943

23 Lieutenant-Colonel R. Honner, interview 1 September 1986

24 Captain K.R. Jacob, 2/10th and 39th Battalions. Killed in action Isurava, August 1942

25 RMO – Regimental Medical Officer

26 Captain J.A. McK. Shera, RMO, 39th Battalion. Born 9 August 1913

27 Lieutenant R.L. McNamara, 2/10th and 39th Battalions. Born 28 November 1908

28 Reverend Father N.J. Earl, Chaplain 39th Battalion and 109 CCS. Born 2 March 1911. Died 1979

29 Major M.L. Bidstrup, interview 14 January 1986

30 *39 Battalion Unit Diary—the August Diary 1942*.

31 Raymond Paull *Retreat From Kokoda* p. 75

32 Confirmed in interview; Major Symington, 15 July 1987 Major Bidstrup, 11 June 1986

33 Raymond Paull *Retreat From Kokoda* p. 75

34 Lieutenant H.W. Crawford, 2/10th, 39th Battalions.
Born 4 June 1908. Missing, presumed dead, 8 August 1942

35 Sergeant H.W. Marsh, 39th Battalion. Born 10 February 1919

36 *39 Battalion Unit Diary—the August Diary 1942*. Confirmed by Captain Bidstrup, interview 15 January 1988

37 Major M.L. Bidstrup, interview 7 January 1986

38 Warrant Officer J.D. Wilkinson, Diary p. 5

39 Lieutenant F.R. Neal, 39th Battalion. Born 26 April 1920

40 Victor Austin *To Kokoda and Beyond* p. 114

41 ibid. p. 118

42 Sergeant J.p. Cowey, 39th Battalion. Born 23 February 1890

43 Victor Austin *To Kokoda and Beyond* p. 113

44 ibid. pp. 113–115

45 ibid. pp. 114–115

46 ibid. pp. 120–121

47 Warrant Officer J.D. Wilkinson, Diary p. 6

48 Major N. Symington, interview 15 July 1987

6 On our last bloody legs

1 The 39th Battalion Association (1941–43) were entertained by a group of Japanese veterans in Sydney in 1985. The Japanese expressed the view that at the time, they believed that there were a large number of Australians fighting against them at Kokoda. They were amazed when told of the actual strength of the 39th Battalion

2 Captain H. Dalby, interview 6 March 1986

3 Sergeant J. Manol, interview 8 June 1986

4 *39 Battalion Unit Diary—the August Diary 1942*

5 Captain D.J. Simonson, 39th, 25th Battalions. Born 21 May 1920

6 Captain H. Dalby, interview 6 March 1986

7 Captain W.C. Pentland, 39th, 2/1st Gd. Regt. Born 5 December 1914

8 Dudley McCarthy, *South-West Pacific Area First Year* p. 138

9 Major M.L. Bidstrup, letter 16 May 1988

10 Corporal J.W. Boland, 39th Battalion. Born 23 June 1919

11 Captain H. Dalby, interview 8 March 1986

12 Lieutenant-Colonel R. Honner, letter June 1988

13 Lieutenant-Colonel R. Honner *The 39th at Isurava*

14 Lieutenant-Colonel R. Honner, interview 1 September 1986

15 Major B.J. French, 39th, 2/6th Battalions. Born 17 November 1918

16 Lieutenant-Colonel R. Honner, interview 1 September 1986

17 Lieutenant R.H. Sword, 39th Battalion. Born 20 February 1914. Killed in action 9 December 1942

18 Lieutenant-Colonel R. Honner *The 39th at Isurava*

19 Lieutenant D.R. Clarke, 2/14th, 39th and 2/2nd Battalions. Born 16 November 1916

20 Major M.L. Bidstrup, interview 13 March 1986

7 Confident even cocksure

1 Lieutenant-Colonel R. Honner, interview 1 September 1986

2 Major-General Sir J. Stevens, 1st AIF., Spr. 2 Div. Sig. Coy; Lt. Aust Corps Sig. Coy; Commander 6 Div. Sigs 1939–40; Commander

21 Brigade 1940–42; GOC 4 Div. 1942, NT. Force and 12 Div. 1942–43; 6 Div. 1943–45. Born 7 September 1896

3 Brigadier A.W. Potts, 1st AIF. Captain 16th Bn; CO 2/16th Battalion 1941–42; Commander 21st Brigade 1942, 23rd Brigade 1942–45. Born 16 September 1896. Died 1967

4 Lieutenant-Colonel F.H. Sublet, 2/16th Battalion. Born 13 May 1910; letter 20 July 1987

5 Captain S.Y. Bisset, 2/14th Battalion. Born 27 August 1912; letter 28 June 1987

6 Captain R.N. Thompson, 2/14th Battalion. Born 7 April 1918; letter June 1987

7 Lieutenant-Colonel R. Honner, letter June 1988

8 Major J. Gerke, 2/16th Battalion. Born 7 June 1915; letter 10 July 1987

9 Lieutenant F.H. Sublet, letter 20 July 1987

10 Major J.E. Gwillim, 2/14th Battalion. Born 7 January 1920; letter July 1987

11 Lieutenant-General S.F. Rowell, 1st AIF. 3 Light Horse Regt. 1914–15; BGS. 1st Aust. Corps 1940–41; Deputy Chief General Staff, Aust. Military Forces 1941–42; Officer Commanding 1st Aust. Corps 1942; Director Tactical Investigation, War Office, 1943–46; Chief General Staff 1950–54. Born 15 December 1894

12 Major-General A.S. Allen, 1st AIF., 13th Bn and CO 33rd Bn 1916–19; Commander 16th Infantry Brigade 1939–41; General Officer Commanding 7th Div. 1941–42, 6th Div. 1942-43, NT. Force 1943–44. Born 10 March 1894

13 W.B. Russell *The History of the Second Fourteenth Battalion* p. 122

14 The 2/27th Battalion, the 3rd Battalion of the 21st Brigade arrived in Port Moresby on 14 August 1942 and were kept at Itiki pending the outcome of both the Milne Bay operations and the supply situation at Myola

15 Major-General Gordon Bennett had commanded the 8th Division during the Malayan Campaign. When the Malayan Peninsula succumbed to the Japanese, the 8th Division fell back to the fortress of Singapore. Upon the fall of Singapore, Gordon

Bennett escaped to Australia with a small contingent of officers. Controversy has since reigned over his decision to do so. He wrote a report concerning the Japanese and the tactics they employed. Captain Sublet obviously saw its contents. However the impact of the report is open to some question, as other officers have little or no recollection of having examined it or of having been lectured as to its contents, eg Captain D.K. Goldsmith, 2/16th Battalion, Captain S.Y. Bisset, 2/14th Battalion

16 Lieutenant-Colonel F.H. Sublet, letter 20 July 1987

17 Chester Wilmot was a reporter with the Australian Broadcasting Commission and actually journeyed along the Kokoda Trail in that capacity.

18 Notes on the New Guinea Campaign, Major-General A.S. Allen Papers, Aust. War Memorial File 5; *Observations on the New Guinea Campaign* by Chester Wilmot, 26 August–26 September

19 Lieutenant-Colonel A.S. Key, 2/8th, 2/14th Battalions. Born 1 July 1906. Presumed dead in 1943 whilst a prisoner of war

20 Major J.E. Gwillim, letter July 1987

21 Sergeant R.O. Clemens, 2/14th Battalion. Born 14 November 1916, letter 3 July 1987

22 Corporal R. Watson, 2/14th Battalion. Born 14 September 1920, letter 13 July 1987

23 Sergeant R.N. Thompson, letter July 1987

24 Corporal R. Watson, letter 13 July 1987

25 A notable exception was the most capable facilities and supply found at Menari under the supervision of Warrant Officer B. Johnston

26 Dudley McCarthy *South-West Pacific Area First Year* p. 198

27 S.F. Rowell *Full Circle* p. 115

28 *Report Into Operations 21 Brigade—Owen Stanley Campaign* This comprehensive report was written after the conclusion of the Owen Stanley Campaign. A copy was most kindly lent to the author by Mr Ken Murdoch, President 2/16th Battalion Association 1987

29 Lieutenant-Colonel J.K. Murdoch, interview 25 February 1989

30 Captain S.Y. Bisset, letter 28 June 1987

31 Lieutenant-Colonel F.H. Sublet, letter 20 July 1987

8 Unawed in the gates of death

1 An observation made by Osmar White, a journalist with the *Sydney Telegraph*, after having journeyed over the Kokoda Trail

2 Signal from Potts to Allen, 26 August 1942. 7 Div. Signals Owen Stanley Campaign, Australian War Memorial

3 Captain N.A.W. MacDonald, 53rd and 55/53rd Battalions. Born 11 July 1906

4 Private D.J. MacGraw, 53rd Battalion. Born 27 September 1918. Killed in action 24 August 1942

5 Sergeant F.W. Meani, 53rd, 39th, 2/4th Battalions. Born 8 October 1921

6 Lieutenant A. Isaachsen, 2/27th, 53rd Battalions. Born 4 February 1918. Killed in action 25 August 1942

7 Major F.J. Ahern, 53rd, 36th Battalions. Born 10 June 1920

8 Captain H.E. Dickenson, 2/14th Battalion. Born 20 February 1913

9 H.D. Steward *Recollections of a Regimental Medical Officer* p. 108

10 Sergeant J. Manol, interview 8 June 1986

11 Lieutenant R.H. Sword, 39th Battalion. Killed in action 9 December 1942

12 Lieutenant A.J. Davis, 2/14th Battalion. Born 7 January 1907. Killed in action 28 August 1942

13 Sergeant A.V. Buchecker, 39th Battalion. Born 22 January 1920

14 Captain C.CPp. Nye, 2/14th Battalion. Born 1 November 1916. Killed in action 8 September 1942

15 Major R.W.C. Cameron, 2/14th Battalion

16 Lieutenant R.L. Logan, 53rd Battalion. Born 17 September 1918. Killed in action 27 August 1942

17 *Report into Operations 21 Brigade—Owen Stanley Campaign* p. 7

18 Captain G.M. McGee, 2/16th Battalion. Born 20 November 1913. Died 7 September 1943

19 Lieutenant G.E. Pearce, 2/14th Battalion. Born 17 October 1909

20 Lieutenant-Colonel A.E. Caro, 2/16th Battalion. Born 29 June 1905

21 Lieutenant-Colonel F.H. Sublet, letter 10 July 1987

22 ibid.

23 ibid.

24 Lieutenant T.H. Bisset, 2/14th Battalion. Born 30 June 1910. Killed in action 29 August 1942

25 The bracket inclusion is that of the author

26 Captain S.Y. Bisset, letter 28 June 1987

27 W.B. Russell *The History of the Second Fourteenth Battalion* p. 135

28 Captain M.A. Treacy, 2/14th Battalion. Born 24 November 1915. Killed in action 29 November 1942

29 Corporal C.R. McCallum, 2/14th Battalion. Born 24 July 1907. Died of wounds 8 September 1942

30 Lieutenant W.P. Cox, 2/14th Battalion. Born 24 December 1913. Killed in action 29 August 1942

31 Lieutenant L.A. Bear, 2/14th Battalion. Born 26 November 1921

32 Captain R.N. Thompson, 2/14th Battalion. Born 7 April 1918

33 Lieutenant J.G. Clements, 2/14th Battalion. Born 13 May 1920

34 Lieutenant A.R. Avery, 2/14th Battalion. Born 7 April 1917

35 Private B.S. Kingsbury, 2/14th Battalion. Born 8 January 1918. Killed in action 29 August 1942

36 From the citation notifying Kingsbury's posthumous award of the Victoria Cross.

37 Corporal J. Craig, Privates J. Wallshaw and L. Gibson, 2/14th Battalion

38 Lieutenant-Colonel R. Honner *The 39th at Isurava*

39 *39 Battalion Unit Diary—the August Diary 1942* p. 33

40 John Barrett *We Were There* p. 13

41 Lieutenant-Colonel R. Honner *The 39th at Isurava*

42 *Report into Operations 21 Brigade—Owen Stanley Campaign* p. 8

43 Lieutenant G.E. Pearce, 2/14th Battalion. Died of wounds 6 December 1942

44 Sergeant W.H. Irwin, 2/14th Battalion. Born 5 March 1913

45 Lieutenant-Colonel F.H. Sublet, letter 20 July 1987

46 Major J. Gerke, letter 10 July 1987

47 Lieutenant-Colonel F.H. Sublet, letter 20 July 1987

48 Corporal H.W. Fielding, 2/14th Battalion. Born 5 November 1915, letter 20 July 1987

49 Sergeant W.R.D. Smith, 2/14th Battalion. Born 6 July 1911

50 Corporal J.A. Metson, 2/14th Battalion. Born 1 August 1918

51 Major J.E. Gwillim, letter July 1987

52 Lieutenant-Colonel F.H. Sublet, letter 20 July 1987

53 Captain S.Y. Bisset, letter 28 June 1987

54 Lieutenant-Colonel F.H. Sublet, letter 20 July 1987

9 Rupert's clinic

1 Major Sir J.R. Magarey, 2/6th Field Ambulance AGH., 105 CCS. Born 21 February 1914. Died 1990

2 Major J.M. Oldham, 2/6th Field Ambulance, 102 AGH. Born 14 October 1912

3 *Report into Operations 21 Brigade—Owen Stanley Campaign* p. 27

4 Captain D.R. Wallman, 14th Field Ambulance. Born March 1896

5 Captain W.W. McLaren, 14th Field Ambulance and ANGAU. Born 24 May 1914

6 Captain A.B. Hogan, RMO, 53rd Battalion. Born 5 October 1920

7 *Report Into Operations 21 Brigade—Owen Stanley Campaign* p. 29

8 ibid. p. 39

9 ABC Field Unit No. 1 *And Our Troops Were Forced to Withdraw* by Chester Wilmot

10 *Report into Operations 21 Brigade—Owen Stanley Campaign* p. 40

11 H.D. Steward *Recollections of a Regimental Medical Officer* p. 120

12 *Report into Operations 21 Brigade—Owen Stanley Campaign* p. 40

13 ABC Field Unit No. 1 *And Our Troops Were Forced to Withdraw* by Chester Wilmot

14 Major Sir J.R. Magarey, interview 10 June 1987

15 H.D. Steward *Recollections of a Regimental Medical Officer* p. 127

16 Moribund – at the point of death

17 Major Sir J. R. Magarey, interview 10 June 1987

18 *Report into Operations 21 Brigade—Owen Stanley Campaign* p. 42
19 ibid.
20 Lieutenant-Colonel F.H. Sublet, letter 20 July 1987

10 Full of fight but utterly weary

1 ABC Field Unit No. 1 *And Our Troops Were Forced to Withdraw* by Chester Wilmot ('Crofty' – Major Rhoden, 2/14th Battalion; 'Albert' – Lieutenant-Colonel Albert Caro, 2/16th Battalion)
2 Lieutenant-Colonel H.B. Challen, 2/8th, CO 2/14th Battalions 1942–43, GSO 1 (Liaison) I and II Corps New Guinea Force 1943–45. Born 26 November 1906
3 Sergeant R. Rosengren, interview 8 June 1986
4 Captain H. Dalby, interview 7 June 1986
5 Victor Austin *To Kokoda and Beyond* p. 171
6 Lieutenant-Colonel P.E. Rhoden, 2/14th Battalion (CO 1943–45)
7 Raymond Paull *Retreat From Kokoda* p. 82
8 Sergeant J. Manol, interview 7 June 1986
9 Lieutenant-Colonel F.H. Sublet, letter 20 July 1987
10 Captain D.K. Goldsmith, interview 25 May 1987
11 Malcolm Uren *A Thousand Men at War* pp. 136–137
12 Lieutenant G.T. Hicks, 2/16th Battalion. Born 15 January 1916. Died of wounds 5 December 1942
13 Warrant Officer G.E. Morris, 2/16th Battalion. Born 30 April 1911
14 Lieutenant-Colonel F.H. Sublet, letter January 1988
15 Major-General K.W. Eather, CO 2/1st Battalion 1939–41; Commander 25th Brigade 1941–45; GOC 11th Division 1945–46. Born 6 June 1901

11 A question of momentum

1 Lieutenant C.E. Edwards, 2/27th Battalion, 1940–44; various appointments 1944–45. Born 7 April 1917—extract from his personal diary
2 Lieutenant-Colonel G.D.T. Cooper, 2/10th Battalion; CO 2/27th

Battalion 1942 and training appointments. Born 2 April 1912

3   Major H.J. Katekar, interview 12 July 1988

4   Sergeant J.H. Burns, 2/27th Battalion. Born 14 October 1920. Author of *The Brown and Blue Diamond at War*; interview 14 December 1988

5   Lieutenant-Colonel Sir A. Lee, 2/27th Battalion, 1940–43; 2/16th Battalion 1943–44; CO 2/9th Battalion, 1944–45. Born 30 July 1912

6   Diary kept by Captain C.A.W. Sims, 2/27th Battalion. Original most kindly lent to author October 1988

7   Private A.A. Little, 2/27th Battalion. Born 14 August 1922. Interview 25 November 1986

8   Lieutenant-Colonel C.A.W. Sims, interview 24 August 1987

9   Lieutenant R.D. Johns, 2/27th Battalion. Born 8 October 1920

10 Minutes of the Advisory War Council Meetings, Vol. V. Minute Nos 870–1073; 1 April–17th September 1942. pp. 510–645. Australian Archives, Canberra, CRSA. 2682/1 Minute No. 1067

11 Private A.N. Ward, interview 8 December 1986

12 *Report into Operations 21 Brigade—Owen Stanley Campaign* p. 12

13 Lieutenant C.E. Edwards, Diary

14 Lieutenant H. Lambert 2/16th Battalion. Born 2 February 1913. Killed in action 8 September 1942

15 John Burns *The Brown and Blue Diamond at War* p. 119

16 Major H.J. Katekar, interview 12 July 1987

17 John Burns *The Brown and Blue Diamond at War* p. 120

18 Raymond Paull *Retreat From Kokoda* 1958

19 ibid. p. 202

20 ibid. pp. 202–203

21 ibid. p. 203

22 Lieutenant-Colonel G.D.T. Cooper, interview 13 August 1988

23 Major H.J. Katekar, interview 12 March 1988

24 W.B. Russell *The History of the Second Fourteenth Battalion*

25 ibid. p. 165

26 *Report into Operations 21 Brigade—Owen Stanley Campaign* p. 14

27 ibid.

28 Raymond Paull *Retreat From Kokoda* p. 211

29 ibid. p. 182

30 Major H.J. Katekar, interview 12 July 1987

31 Corporal E.N. George, 2/27th Battalion. Born 20 June 1918; interview 12 July 1987

32 Major H.J. Katekar, interview 12 July 1987

33 Raymond Paull *Retreat From Kokoda* p. 235

34 Sergeant J.H. Burns, interview 14 December 1988

35 Lieutenant-Colonel Sir A.J. Lee, interview 13 July 1988

36 Major H.J. Katekar, interview 12 July 1987

12 92 this way

1 Lieutenant-Colonel C.A.W. Sims, interview 24 August 1987

2 ibid.

3 ibid.

4 ibid.

5 Corporal E.N. George, interview 7 December 1986

6 Lieutenant-Colonel C.A.W. Sims, interview 24 August 1987

7 ibid.

8 Lieutenant C. Edwards, diary most kindly lent to author Major H.J. Katekar, document entitled 'My Personal Experiences and Impressions During Operations in Papua (August 1942–January 1943) written in 2/4 AGH, Redbank, Qld, commencing 10 May 1943'; original most kindly lent to the author January 1989

9 Doug Keane, 2/27th Battalion, interview 24 November 1986

10 Corporal G.R. Williss, 2/27th Battalion, interview 25 November 1986

11 Lieutenant-Colonel G.D.T. Cooper, interview 19 September 1986

12 The wounded were cared for by the selfless devotion of Sergeant John Burns, MM and Private Alf Zanker

13 The rabbit that runs

1 Warrant Officer A.H. Thomson, 2/27th Battalion, Signals 21st

Brigade, 2/42nd Australian Cypher Section. Born 26 March 1920; interview 8 December 1986

2 Captain T.H. Hodge, 2/16th Battalion

3 Major W.B. Russell, 2/14th Battalion. Born 3 March 1911

4 Captain S.Y. Bisset, letter 28 June 1987

5 *Report into Operations 21 Brigade—Owen Stanley Campaign* p. 15

6 ibid.

7 W.B. Russell *The History of the Second Fourteenth Battalion* p. 170

8 Raymond Paull *Retreat From Kokoda* p. 222

9 H.D. Steward *Recollections of a Regimental Medical Officer* p. 132

10 Dudley McCarthy *South-West Pacific Area First Year* p. 232

11 ibid. p. 271

12 Minutes of Advisory War Council Meetings, Vol. V. Minute Nos 870–1073; 1st April–17th September 1942. pp 510–645. Australian Archives, Canberra, CRSA. 2682/1 Minute No. 1067

13 ibid. p. 640

14 ibid. p. 641

15 Dudley McCarthy *South-West Pacific Area First Year* p. 236

16 S.F. Rowell *Full Circle* p. 127

17 A detailed analysis of the command crisis in New Guinea during this period is to be found in D.H. Horner *Crisis of Command* pp. 163-187

18 Raymond Paull *Retreat From Kokoda* p. 257

19 Lieutenant-Colonel J.K. Murdoch, 2/16th Battalion and Staff Captain, 21st Brigade 1942–43

20 This document was most kindly lent to the author by Lieutenant-Colonel J.K. Murdoch, August 1987

21 Lieutenant-Colonel Sir A. Lee, interview 13 July 1988

22 For example: Lieutenant-Colonel G.D.T. Cooper, interview 13 August 1988; Lieutenant-Colonel R. Honner, interview 1 September 1986; Captain S.Y. Bisset, letter 28 June 1987; Captain D.K. Goldsmith, interview 25 May 1987

23 From a photostat copy of Brigadier Potts' Farewell Address to 21st Brigade, kindly given to the author by Lieutenant-Colonel J.K. Murdoch, August 1987

24 H.D. Steward *Recollections of a Regimental Medical Officer* p. 147

25 Captain S.Y. Bissett, letter 28 June 1987

26 Captain R.N. Thompson, letter August 1987

27 Lance Corporal J.A. Hocking, letter August 1987

28 Lieutenant-Colonel G.D.T. Cooper, interview 19 September 1986

29 Sergeant J. Burns, interview 14 December 1988

30 Private L. Thredgold, interview 7 December 1986

31 Norman D. Carlyon *I Remember Blamey* p. 111

32 Lieutenant-Colonel G.D.T. Cooper, interview 19 September 1986

33 Major H.J. Katekar, interview 13 August 1988

34 Lieutenant-General Sir E. Herring, RFA. 1914–18, France and Macedonia; CRA. 6th Division 1939–41; GOC 6th Division 1941–42, NT. Force 1942, II Corps 1942, I Corps and New Guinea Force 1942–43. Born 2 September 1894

35 Gavin Long was the historian in charge of the War Memorial histories of the Second World War.

36 Sergeant J. Burns, interview 14 December 1988

37 G.H. Fearnside and Ken Clift *Dougherty—A Great Man Amongst Men* pp. 135–136

38 Major-General Sir I.N. Dougherty, CO 2/4th Battalion, 1940–42; Commander 23rd Brigade 1942, 21st Brigade 1942–45. Born 6 April 1907

39 Lieutenant-Colonel J.K. Murdoch, from the account of the relief of Brigadier A. Potts; copy sent to the author

40 Lieutenant C.E. Edwards, interview 24 November 1987

41 Lieutenant-Colonel F.H. Sublet, letter 20 July 1987

42 Major-General Sir I.N. Dougherty, interview 12 November 1988

43 The brackets are those of the author

44 Major-General Sir I.N. Dougherty, interview 12 November 1988

45 Major H.J. Katekar, interview 3 August 1988

46 Lieutenant-Colonel F.H. Sublet, interview 6 August 1988

47 ibid. (Lieutenant-Colonel J.K. Murdoch, who was Staff Captain 21st Brigade and Captain S.Y. Bisset 2/14th Battalion confirm this view; interview 25 February 1989, letter 28 June 1987 respectively)

48 Verified by Lieutenant-Colonel J.K. Murdoch
49 Lieutenant-Colonel F.H. Sublet, letter 20 July 1987
50 Major-General Sir F.K. Norris—quote

14 To the beach-head

1 Dudley McCarthy *South-West Area Pacific First Year* p. 255
2 Brigadier J.E. Lloyd, 1st AIF., Lieutenant 23rd and 24th Battalions. Indian Army 1918–22. CO 2/28th Battalion 1940–42. Commander 16th Brigade 1942–43. 2nd Australian P.W. reception GP 1945. Born 13 April 1894
3 Dudley McCarthy *South-West Pacific Area First Year* p. 334

15 Not to reason why

1 Lida Mayo *Bloody Buna* p. 14
2 Major M.L. Bidstrup, interview 1 March 1989
3 John Robertson and John McCarthy *Australian War Strategy 1939–45; A Documentary History* p. 372
4 Dudley McCarthy *South-West Pacific Area First Year* p. 335
5 *Report On Operations 25 November 1942–14 January 1943* by Brigadier I.N. Dougherty, Commander 21 Aust. Inf. Bde (with appendices). See Appendix 2. A copy of this document was most kindly lent to the author by Major-General Sir I. Dougherty in Sydney, 12 November 1988. The report will subsequently be referred to as 'The Dougherty Report'
6 Lieutenant-Colonel J.K. Murdoch, interview 25 February 1988
7 The Dougherty Report p. 1
8 Major-General Sir I. Dougherty, interview 12 November 1988
9 The Dougherty Report p. 3
10 Lida Mayo *Bloody Buna* pp. 140–141
11 Captain S.Y. Bisset, letter 28 June 1987
12 Major J.M. Hearman, 2/16th Battalion; letter 21 April 1989
13 Lieutenant-Colonel G.D.T. Cooper, Major H.J. Katekar, Lieutenant-Colonel C.A.W. Sims, 2/27th Battalion; interview 4 April 1989

14 Lieutenant-Colonel R. Honner, interview 1 September 1986

15 Lieutenant G.L. Kolb, 2/14th Battalion. Born 23 August 1917. Died of wounds 1 December 1942

16 The Dougherty Report p. 3

17 Confirmed by Major-General Sir I. Dougherty, interview 12 November 1988

18 Lieutenant R.H. Dougherty, 2/14th Battalion. Born 10 August 1919. Killed in action 11 December 1942 (no relation to Brigadier Dougherty)

19 Captain S.Y. Bissett, letter 28 June 1987

20 Captain E.R. Clarke, 2/14th Battalion. Born 22 August 1913

21 Sergeant F.R. Boys, 2/14th Battalion. Born 4 April 1918

22 Dudley McCarthy *South-West Pacific First Year* p. 427

23 The Dougherty Report Appendix 2

24 ibid. p. 4

25 Brigadier A.G. Hanson, CO, 2/1st Field Regiment, 1942–45; CRA, 3rd Division 1945. Born 17 September 1908

26 The Dougherty Report p. 3

27 Lieutenant-Colonel G.D.T. Cooper, interview 13 August 1988

28 Dudley McCarthy *South-West Pacific First Year* p. 428

29 Lieutenant-Colonel G.D.T. Cooper, Major H.J. Katekar, Lieutenant-Colonel C.A.W. Sims; 2/27th Battalion; interview 4 April 1989

30 Captain J.C. Cuming, 2/27th Battalion. Born 22 July 1913. Killed in action 29 November 1942

31 Captain J.W. Skipper, 2/27th Battalion. Born 3 May 1914. Killed in action 29 November 1942

32 Those killed were: Lieutenant J.S. Bennie, Lieutenant J.O. Flight; Those wounded were: Lieutenant E.M. Caddy, Lieutenant A.B. Sherwin

33 Private M.Valli, 2/14th Battalion. Born 15 August 1918. Killed in action 29 November 1942

34 Private G.F. Thompson, 2/14th Battalion. Born 27 May 1919. Killed in action 29 November 1942

35 The Dougherty Report p. 6

36 Sergeant R. Thredgold, 2/27th Battalion. Born 29 January 1917; interview 8 April 1989

37 Private A.N. Ward, interview 8 April 1989

38 The Dougherty Report p. 6

39 W.B. Russell *The History of the Second Fourteenth Battalion* pp. 193–194

40 Major A. Robinson, 2/16th Battalion. Born 13 April 1906

41 Captain J.H. O'Neill, 2/16th Battalion. Born 30 May 1920. Died of wounds 5 December 1942

42 Captain W.A. Egerton-Warburton, 2/27th Battalion. Born 4 January 1918

43 Sergeant R. Thredgold, interview 8 April 1989

44 Dudley McCarthy *South-West Pacific First Year* p. 432

45 ibid.

46 Lieutenant L.P. Mayberry, 2/16th Battalion. Born 18 June 1912

47 Private J. Breakey, 2/27th Battalion, interview 8 April 1989

48 John Robertson and John McCarthy *Australian War Strategy 1939–45; A Documentary History* p. 375

49 See Chapter 4

50 William Manchester *American Caesar, Douglas MacArthur, 1880–1964* pp. 326–327

51 ibid. p. 326

52 Major H.J. Katekar, interview 4 April 1989

53 William Manchester *American Caesar, Douglas MacArthur 1880–1964* p. 330

16 Embarrassed to be alive

1 Lieutenant-Colonel R. Honner *The 39th at Gona*

2 Major-General Sir I. Dougherty, interview 12 November 1988

3 Lieutenant-Colonel R. Honner, interview 1 September 1986

4 Corporal A.J. Skilbeck, 39th and 14/32nd Battalions. Born 1 April 1921

5 Sergeant E.J. Morrison, 39th Battalion. Born 5 March 1919

6 Lieutenant C.M. White, 2/16th Battalion. Born 3 August 1917. Killed in action 6 December 1942

7 Corporal R.G. Edgell, 39th Battalion. Born 17 September 1912

8 Captain J.W. Nelson, 39th, 2/4th Battalions. Born 23 October 1915

9 Captain P.A. Tuckey, NGVR, 39th and 2/14th Battalions. Born 28 February 1909. Killed in action 11 December 1944

10 Major M.L. Bidstrup, interview 1 March 1989

11 Corporal C.A. Bloomfield, 2/16th Battalion. Born 8 August 1915

12 Warrant Officer R.E.A. Jones, 2/16th Battalion. Born 11 May 1911

13 Sergeant G.B.J. Murphy, 2/16th Battalion. Born 18 February 1919

14 Private S.A. Stephens, 2/16th Battalion. Born 23 January 1910. Killed in action 7 December 1942

15 H.D. Steward *Recollections of a Regimental Medical Officer* pp. 152–153

16 Major W.M. Atkinson, 2/16th Battalion, 1st Aust. Parachute Battalion. Born 1 March 1911

17 Lieutenant L.G.J. Inkpen, 2/16th Battalion. Born 13 August 1919. Killed in action 8 December 1942

18 Dudley McCarthy *South-West Pacific First Year* p. 441

19 Captain R.L. Johnson, 2/27th Battalion

20 Lieutenant S.G. Hewitt, 2/27th Battalion

21 Lieutenant-Colonel R. Honner *This is the 39th*

22 Captain H.H. Kelly, 39th and 2/2nd Battalions. Born 24 July 1919

23 Captain H. Dalby, interview 3 June 1989

24 Sergeant S.J. Ellis, 39th and 2/5th Battalions. Born 30 March 1911

25 Corporal R.E.G. Wilkinson, 39th Battalion. Born 12 May 1919

26 Major-General Sir I. Dougherty, interview 12 November 1988

27 Lieutenant-Colonel F.H. Sublet, interview 6 August 1988

28 Major H.J. Katekar, interview 3 March 1988

29 Sergeant J. Manol, letter 5 June 1989

30 Major D.I.H. McLean, interview 6 June 1986

31 Lieutenant-Colonel F.H. Sublet, interview 6 August 1988

32 Lieutenant-Colonel R. Honner *This is the 39th*

33 Major-General Sir I. Dougherty, interview 12 November 1988

34 Major H.J. Katekar, interview 30 September 1988

35 Lieutenant-Colonel J.K. Murdoch, interview 25 February 1989

36 Lieutenant-Colonel G.D.T. Cooper, interview 4 April 1989

37 See Chapter 11

38 See the previous chapter

39 Confirmed by Hearman's Adjutant, Captain H.J. Katekar, interview 4 April 1989

40 Lieutenant-Colonel K. Murdoch, interview 25 February 1989

41 Major J. Hearman, letter 24 April 1989

17 Silent

1 Captain S.Y. Bisset, letter August 1990

2 Lieutenant-Colonel R. Honner *This is the 39th*

3 Captain L.C.J. Schwind, 2/14th Battalion. Born 15 October 1912

4 Lieutenant R.F. Iskov. 2/14th Battalion. Born 1 May 1920

5 Captain R.S. Plater, 53rd and 39th Battalions. Born 5 September 1921

6 Major P.E. Gartner, 39th, 2/2nd and 1st New Guinea Infantry Battalions. Indian Army 1945–47. Born 5 August 1920

7 Lieutenant-Colonel R. Honner *This is the 39th*

8 ibid.

9 Captain S.Y. Bisset, letter August 1990

10 Lieutenant-Colonel R. Honner *This is the 39th*

11 *39 Battalion Unit Diary—the August Diary 1942* On 20 November, about 30 young Western Australian reinforcements marched in. (Transferred from an Employment Company, they had no infantry training whatsoever.)

12 Lieutenant-Colonel R. Honner *This is the 39th*

13 Dudley McCarthy *South-West Pacific First Year* p. 447–448

14 Australian Archives; A 5954, Box 532

15 Lieutenant-Colonel D.J.H. Lovell, interview June 1989

16 Lieutenant-Colonel O.C. Isaachsen, 2/27th Battalion. CO 36th Battalion 1942–45. Born 5 June 1911

17 ibid. interview July 1989

18 Fred Cranston *Always Faithful* p. 171

19 Private K. Barry, 55/53rd Battalion. Born 21 April 1922; interview 13 November 1988

20 Dudley McCarthy *South-West Pacific First Year* p. 501

21 Lieutenant-Colonel R. Honner *This is the 39th*

Bibliography

Interviews

Armitage, Private L., 39th Battalion, Melbourne, 8 June 1986

Ashton, Private A.G., 2/27th Battalion, Adelaide, 26 November 1986

Barry, Private K., 55/53rd Battalion, Sydney, 13 November 1988

Bidstrup, Major M.L., 39th Battalion, Adelaide, 9 November 1985, 7 January, 14 January, 13 March, 11 June, 25 August, 13 November 1986, 1 March 1989

Breakey, The late Private J., 2/27th Battalion, Adelaide, 8 April 1989

Budden, The late Lieutenant F., 55/53rd Battalion, Sydney, 31 August 1986

Burns, Sergeant J.H., 2/27th Battalion, Adelaide, September 1988

Cameron, The Honourable C., former MHR., Adelaide, 9 August 1988

Cooper, Lieutenant-Colonel G.D.T., 2/27th Battalion, Adelaide, 19 September 1986, 13 August 1988, 4 April 1989

Crowley, Private K., 39th Battalion, Melbourne, 8 June 1986

Dalby, Captain H., 39th Battalion, Adelaide, 6 March, 24 April, 27 July, 6 October 1986

Dougherty, Major-General Sir I.N., Sydney, 12 November 1988

Bibliography

Edwards, Lieutenant C.E., 2/27th Battalion, Adelaide, 24 November 1986

Fotheringham, Major J.D., 49th Battalion, Adelaide, 17 July 1986

Garland, Lieutenant A.G., 39th Battalion, Melbourne, 7 June 1986

George, Corporal N., 2/27th Battalion, Adelaide, 7 December 1986

Gilbert, Private M.N., 2/27th Battalion, Adelaide, 26 November 1986

Gillespie, Lieutenant W.R., 49th Battalion, Adelaide, October 1986

Goldsmith, Captain D.K., 2/16th Battalion, Adelaide, 25 May 1987

Honner, Lieutenant-Colonel R., 39th Battalion, Sydney, 1 September 1986, 11 November 1988

Isaachsen, Lieutenant-Colonel O.C., 36th Battalion, Adelaide, June 1989

Katekar, Major H.J., 2/27th Battalion, Adelaide, 13 August, 30 September 1988, 4 April 1989

Keane, Private D., 2/27th Battalion, Adelaide, 24 November 1986

Lee, Lieutenant-Colonel Sir A.J., 2/27th Battalion, Adelaide, 13 July 1988

Little, Private E.A., 2/27th Battalion, Adelaide, 25 November 1986

Lovell, Lieutenant-Colonel D.J. H., 55/53rd Battalion, Adelaide, April 1988

Magarey, The late Major Sir J.R., 2/6th Field Ambulance, Adelaide, 10 June 1987

McClean, Major D.I.H., 39th Battalion, Melbourne, 7 June 1986

Manol, Sergeant J., 39th Battalion, Melbourne, 7 June 1986

Mortimore, Lieutenant H.E., 39th Battalion, Melbourne, 7 June 1986

Murdoch, Lieutenant-Colonel K., 2/16th Battalion, Adelaide, 25 February 1988

Rosengren, Sergeant R.S., 39th Battalion, Melbourne, 8 June 1986

Seekamp, Lieutenant A.H., 39th Battalion, Adelaide, 24 April 1986

Sherwin, Lieutenant A.B., 2/27th Battalion, Adelaide, 24 June 1986

Simonson, Captain D.J., 39th Battalion, Adelaide, 3 July 1988

Sims, Brigadier C.A.W., 2/27th Battalion, Adelaide, 24 August 1987, 26 September 1988, 4 April 1989

Stephens, Private J., 55/53rd Battalion, Sydney, 31 August 1986, 13 November 1988

Sublet, Lieutenant-Colonel F.H., 2/16th Battalion, Adelaide, 6 August 1988

Symington, Major N.M., 39th Battalion, Adelaide, 15 July 1987

Thomson, Warrant Officer 2 A., 2/27th Battalion, Adelaide, 8 December 1986, 8 April 1989

Thredgold, Sergeant L.J., 2/27th Battalion, Adelaide, 7 December 1986

Thredgold, Sergeant R.T., 2/27th Battalion, Adelaide, 8 April 1989

Ward, Private A.N., 2/27th Battalion, Adelaide, 8 December 1986, 8 April 1989

Wilkins, Private C., 55/53rd Battalion, Sydney, 13 November 1988

Williams, Private A., 2/14th Battalion, Adelaide, 3 July 1986

Williams, Private C.J., 2/27th Battalion, Adelaide, 26 November 1986

Williss, Corporal G., 2/27th Battalion, Adelaide, 25 November 1986

Correspondence: questionnaires, diaries, letters

Avery, Lieutenant A., 2/14th Battalion, 2 July 1987

Angus, Private D.E., 2/16th Battalion, August 1987

Andrews, Sergeant C., 49th Battalion, March 1986

Bisset, Captain S.Y., 2/14th Battalion, 28 June 1987

Brown, Captain S.Y., 55/53rd Battalion, 9 April 1987

Barry, Private K., 55/53rd Battalion, 10 June 1987

Clemens, Private R.O., 2/14th Battalion, 3 July 1987

Cranston, Warrant-Officer 2 F.H., 49th Battalion, March 1986

Deoberitz, Captain A.A., 49th Battalion, July 1986

Dunlop, Sergeant W.R., 53rd Battalion, March 1987

Edwards, Lieutenant C.E., 2/27th Battalion, July 1987

Evans, Private M.J., 53rd Battalion, March 1987

Fielding, Corporal H.W., 2/14th Battalion, 20 July 1987

Gwillim, The late Major J.E., 2/14th Battalion, July 1987

Glavin, Warrant Officer 1 J., 2/14th Battalion, 6 July 1987

Gerke, Lieutenant J., 2/16th Battalion, 10 July 1987

Bibliography

Greenwood, Private N.W., 49th Battalion, March 1987

Gresham, Lieutenant E.N., 55/53rd Battalion, April 1986

Harris, Private R.L., 53rd Battalion, 17 August 1989

Hearman, Major J., 2/16th Battalion, 23 April 1989

Hocking, Lance Corporal J.A., 2/16th Battalion, August 1987

Honner, Lieutenant-Colonel R., 39th Battalion, October 1988

Irwin, Sergeant, K.J., 53rd Battalion, 20 March 1989

Ison, Sergeant L., 55/53rd Battalion, April 1987

Jeffrey, Private J.N., 2/14th Battalion, 8 August 1987

Jeffrey, Private W., 2/14th Battalion, 31 July 1987

Jolley, Lance Corporal J.N., 2/14th Battalion, 21 July 1987

Katekar, Major H.J., 2/27th Battalion, August 1987

Kemp, Warrant-Officer 2 R.A., 49th Battalion, August 1987

Kienzle, Captain H.T., ANGAU., December 1986

Lang, Sergeant E.K., 2/14th Battalion, 29 July 1987

Lockie, Staff Sergeant W.J., 49th Battalion, July 1987

McDermant, Sergeant D.A., 49th Battalion, April 1987

Morris, Corporal A.H., 2/14th Battalion, 1 June 1989

Meredith, Corporal C.C., 53rd Battalion, March 1987

Newman, Private R.D., 2/16th Battalion, 30 July 1987

Peters, Lieutenant W.A.A., 49th Battalion, August 1987

Pascoe, Private R., 55th Battalion, 14 April 1987

Roberts, Lance Corporal J.H., 2/14th Battalion, 21 July 1987

Sheldon, Lieutenant, E.F., 2/14th Battalion, July 1987

Sublet, Lieutenant-Colonel F.H., 2/16th Battalion, 20 July 1987

Spratford, Sergeant J.W., 2/16th Battalion, August 1987

Stephan, Sergeant A., 49th Battalion, March 1987

Sly, Sergeant S.A., 55/53rd Battalion, April 1987

Thompson, Captain R.N., 2/14th Battalion, July 1987

Woodward, Corporal R.F., 2/14th Battalion, July 1987

Watson, Sergeant R., 2/14th Battalion, July 1987

Walker, Private W., 2/14th Battalion, July 1987

Warbrick, Lieutenant D.M., 49th Battalion, 10 March 1987

Wood, Corporal L.W., 49th Battalion, March 1987

21st Brigade Unit Diary, August–December 1942

2/14th Battalion Unit Diary, August–December 1942
2/16th Battalion Unit Diary, August–December 1942
2/27th Battalion Unit Diary, September–December 1942
39th Battalion Unit Diary, March–December 1942
49th Battalion Unit Diary, April–December 1942
53rd Battalion Unit Diary, May–August 1942
55/53rd Battalion Unit Diary, December 1942
Report Into Operations 21st Brigade—Owen Stanley Campaign
Allen Papers. Papers of Major-General A.S. Allen, File No. 419/3/9
Australian Archives
CRS A2673, Advisory War Council Minutes Vol 5, 12

Articles

Honner, R. 'The 39th Battalion at Isurava' *Australian Army Journal*, July 1967
——'This is the 39th' *The Bulletin*, 3rd August 1955
Hansard
Australian Commonwealth Parliament Hansard, Vol. 21

Newspapers

The *Advertiser*
The *Argus*
The *Sydney Morning Herald*

Books

Austin, V. *To Kokoda and Beyond, The Story of the 39th Battalion 1941–43* Melbourne: Melbourne University Press, 1988
Budden, F. *That Mob: The Story of the 55th/53rd Australian Infantry Battalion AIF* Sydney, 1973
Burns, J. *The Brown and Blue Diamond at War* Adelaide: 2/27th Battalion Ex-Servicemen's Association
Carlyon, N.D. *I Remember Blamey* Melbourne: MacMillan, 1980
Cranston, F. *Always Faithful, The History of the 49th Battalion* Brisbane: Boolarong, 1983
Eichelberger, R.L. *Jungle Road to Tokyo* London: Odhams, 1951

Bibliography

Fearnside, G.H. and Clift, K. *Dougherty, A Great Man Among Men* Sydney: Alpha, 1979

Hall, T. *New Guinea 1942–44* Sydney: Methuen, 1981

Hasluck, P. *The Government and the People 1939–1941* Canberra: Australian War Memorial, 1952

Hetherington, J. *Blamey, Controversial Soldier* Canberra: Australian War Memorial, 1973

Horner, D.M. *Crisis of Command, Australian Generalship and the Japanese Threat, 1941–1943* Canberra: Australian War Memorial, 1978

Long, G. *To Benghazi* Canberra: Australian War Memorial, 1953

——*The Six Years' War* Canberra: Australian War Memorial, 1973

McCarthy, D. *South-West Pacific Area First Year* Canberra: Australian War Memorial, 1959

Manchester, W. *American Caesar, Douglas MacArthur 1880–1964* Melbourne, Hutchinson, 1978

Mayo, L. *Bloody Buna* New York: Doubleday, 1974

Paull, R.A. *Retreat from Kokoda* Melbourne: Heinemann, 1958

Robertson, J. and McCarthy, J. *Australian War Strategy 1939–1945; A Documentary History* St Lucia: University of Queensland Press, 1985

Rowell, S.F. *Full Circle* Melbourne: Melbourne University Press, 1974

Russell, W.B. *The History of the Second Fourteenth Battalion* Sydney: Angus and Robertson, 1948

Scott, G. *The Knights of Kokoda* Sydney: Horwitz, 1963

Steward, H.D. *Recollections of a Regimental Medical Officer* Melbourne: Melbourne University Press, 1981

Uren, M. *A Thousand Men at War* Melbourne: 1959

Index

Index

Index